D0991550

LEADING AMERICAN INVENTORS

John Stevens of Hobo...

[From a portrait in the possession of Miss M. B. P. Garnett, Hoboken.]

LEADING AMERICAN INVENTORS

BY

GEORGE ILES

WITH FIFTEEN PORTRAITS AND
MANY ILLUSTRATIONS

Essay Index Reprint Series

277832

MITCHELL MEMORIAL LIBRARY
MISSISSIPPI STATE UNIVERSITY

BOOKS FOR LIBRARIES PRESS
FREEPORT, NEW YORK

First Published 1912
Reprinted 1968

LIBRARY OF CONGRESS CATALOG CARD NUMBER:

68-8472

PRINTED IN THE UNITED STATES OF AMERICA

TO

MY DEAREST FRIEND

GEORGE FREDERICK CUMMING SMILLIE

ARTIST-ENGRAVER

OF WASHINGTON, D. C.

INTRODUCTORY

WITHIN its twelve chapters this book presents a group of leading American inventors of the past. First in time, and, in many respects, first in talent, is Colonel John Stevens, who built a successful screw propeller, and who devised a sectional boiler of a model which, duly modified, is in wide use to-day. Beside him stands his son Robert, who devised the T-rail and much other equipment for railroads and workshops. Fulton comes next with his *Clermont* and his torpedoes, an inventor with a statesman's breadth of mind, with the outlook of an artist no less than that of an engineer. The mastery of land and sea is continued by Ericsson with his *Novelty* locomotive, his *Monitor,* and his caloric engine. These four great engineers are succeeded by four mechanics, each the leader of an industrial revolution. First Whitney, with his cotton-gin; then Blanchard, with his copying lathe; McCormick, with his reaper; Howe, with his sewing-machine. Then, all alone, stands Charles Goodyear, who came to the vulcanization of rubber by dint of a courage unsurpassed in the annals of peace or war. A final quartette are inventors who broadened the empire of the printed word: Morse, who gave electricity a pencil to write its messages a thousand miles away; Tilghman, who derived paper from wood so as to create a new basic industry for mankind; Sholes, who built a typewriter to replace the pen with the legibility and swiftness of printing; and last of all, Mergenthaler, who took a Sholes keyboard, and bade it compose both the columns of newspapers and the pages of a book.

The sketches of these heroes and their exploits include much information never published before. Inventors are apt to be a silent race, more given to experiment than to

vii

recording its results. We can retrace only a few of the,
steps which took such a man as Blanchard, for instance,
from apprenticeship to primacy and triumph. Mergenthaler, fortunately, during months of rest and quiet as an
invalid, wrote his autobiography. His son, Mr. Eugene G.
Mergenthaler, has permitted several of its golden pages to
appear in this volume. They picture the formative years of
one of the great inventors of all time.

Where opportunity has proffered itself, a contrast betwixt old and new, the days of small things and the present
hour, is exhibited. Noteworthy here is the comparison of
modern telegraphy with its puny beginnings, involving a
struggle which all but overwhelmed Morse, the dauntless
pioneer.

In preparing this book I have received much generous aid.
The Stevens chapter owes many facts to President A. C.
Humphreys and Professor F. de R. Furman of Stevens Institute, as well as to Mr. Edwin A. S. Brown of Hoboken. The
pages on Eli Whitney are largely drawn from contributions
by his grandson and namesake of New Haven, Connecticut.
Mr. Edward Lind Morse of Stockbridge, Massachusetts, son
of Professor Samuel F. B. Morse, has given me much in-
formation. Mr. James Cumming Vail of Morristown, New
Jersey, sent me the portrait of his father printed in this volume, and has rendered me constant help. From Mr. S. M.
Williams of the Western Union Telegraph Company, New
York, came the statistics which round off the sketch of
American telegraphy. The chapter on Charles Goodyear is
mainly derived from his notebook, lent by his grandson,
Mr. Nelson Goodyear of New York. Professor William H.
Goodyear, a son of Charles Goodyear, has given me interest-
ing facts hitherto unpublished. I owe an informing survey
of a model rubber factory to Mr. A. D. Thornton, chemical
director of the Canadian Consolidated Rubber Company,
Montreal. In reciting the story of rubber I was favored with

indispensable aid by Mr. Henry C. Pearson, editor of the *India Rubber World*, New York. From the late Mr. Bruce J. Home and his son, Mr. Robert Home, of Edinburgh, Scotland, came the narrative by Patrick Bell of his invention of the reaper. This story has, I believe, never before appeared in America. From Mr. Louis Sholes of Milwaukee, and Mr. Zalmon P. Sholes of New York, I have learned much as to the career of their honored father. My information regarding General Benjamin C. Tilghman was in chief part contributed by his niece, Miss Emily Tilghman of Philadelphia; and by Mr. F. C. Brooksbank and Mr. F. E. Hyslop, long associated with the General. For the Mergenthaler chapter I received cordial aid from Mr. Norman Dodge of the Mergenthaler Linotype Company of New York, Mr. Frank P. Hill, librarian of the Public Library, Brooklyn, Mr. R. C. Jenkinson of Newark, New Jersey, and Mr. W. F. Schuckers of Washington, D. C. From first to last my task in writing this book has been loyally seconded by Mr. William Murdoch Lind of New York.

GEORGE ILES.

NEW YORK, *November, 1912.*

CONTENTS

ILLUSTRATIONS

PORTRAITS

OTHER ILLUSTRATIONS

xiii

ILLUSTRATIONS

LEADING AMERICAN INVENTORS

JOHN AND ROBERT LIVINGSTON STEVENS

A BIRD builds its nest from an impulse which fills its heart. A like instinct, every whit as compelling, urges a Mergenthaler to create a composing machine. He conceives its plan, and, while his wheels and levers unite under his touch, he sees how he can remodel every part from base to crest. This rebuilding is no sooner accomplished than the machine is cast into the melting-pot, to emerge with a new pace and precision. If, incidentally, this man of experiment can earn his bread, well and good, but there may be no gold in the horizon which allures him. It is enough that his new devices glide together with the harmony and economy of his dreams.

But among inventors we meet men of a wholly different stamp. First and last, they are pioneers who descry new worlds for industrial conquest. To plant, till, and water these empires they need new tools, machines, and engines. These they build, not for the joy of building, as might your instinctive inventor, but simply as means to the mastery of a continent, with fibers of gainful service reaching every home in the land. Preëminent in this company of industrial chieftains in America stand John Stevens and his son, Robert Livingston Stevens, who seized a supreme opportunity as they yoked steam as a burden-bearer on land and sea. They were themselves engineers of original talent, and this gave them a fellow-feeling with the engineering fraternity not always found in the councils of great firms and corporations. Of course, such men, however ingenious and skilful, never rise to such a triumph as the steam condenser of James Watt. In their schemes invention is always the servant

3

of enterprise, and not for a moment its master. From the best engineering practice of their day the Stevenses chose this device, or that method, with a judgment cooled and steadied by the responsibilities of large investments. Where original inventions were demanded, these they created, all to rear units for trade and commerce wholly new, units so daring that men of narrow outlook and restricted means would never have called them into being.

Goodyear, Howe, and Mergenthaler, beset by chronic poverty, in building their models were obliged to limit themselves to dimes when they should have laid out dollars. Not so with the Stevens family: their work from the outset drew upon every source of aid and comfort. Before they touched a drawing-board with a pencil, they could fully learn the state of the art in which they meant to take new strides: they could confer with their peers in engineering circles both at home and abroad. Mechanics of the highest skill stood ready to carry their plans into effect with despatch. When their experiments turned out well, as they usually did, there was no weary waiting in the ante-rooms of capital that their ventures might be adopted. The Stevenses were themselves men of wealth, so that when they launched a steamboat, its freight and passengers were ready to go on board. If they built a locomotive, they could also build a railroad to give it profitable traffic. Poverty as a sharpener of wits has had much and frequent praise. Let us sing a new song, this time unto wealth! The race is not always to the impeded, and much sound fruit mellows in the sunshine, and nowhere else. The Stevenses were leaders whom other men were glad to follow, well aware that their path was free from obstacles, so that, in a following, more was to be won and more to be shared than under chieftains of less faculty and fortune. As America grows richer, we are likely to see more of this leadership on the part of wealthy and cultured men who, alive to their responsibilities, repay their debt to the nation by wise and faithful captaincy. There are many perplexities in productive and distributive economy, in governmental reform, largely created by advances in applied science itself. For their solution, trained ability, backed by abundant means, is demanded. Better than a Board for such tasks may be an Individual Man, and no better prototype of him has appeared in this country than John Stevens, or his son, Robert Livingston Stevens, whom we are now to know.

John Stevens was born in the city of New York in 1749. His grandfather came to New York early in the eighteenth century as a law officer of the British Crown, and afterward resided in Perth Amboy, then the principal town in Eastern New Jersey. John Stevens, a son of this Englishman, rose to distinction in public service. At Princeton he was vice-president of the Council convened on August 27, 1776, by the first Legislature of New Jersey. So well did he serve that he was chosen to preside over the Council of Eastern New Jersey proprietors. Next he was elected a Member of Congress for New Jersey, and president of the State Convention, which met on December 11, 1787, to consider the National Constitution, duly adopted eleven days thereafter by New Jersey, as the third commonwealth to do so. He was the delegate from his State to present this ratification to Congress. Here, plainly, was a man cast in a large mold,—an administrator of acknowledged power, the first among equals to lay foundations broad and deep for his State and his country. In the home of this man questions as wide as America were discussed day by day, with hope for happy issues, with courage for whatever might befall. He was, moreover, a man of ample fortune, so that the talents of his children had generous and timely tilth, bringing to their best estate a fiber at once refined and strong.

John Stevens took to wife Mary Alexander, of as good blood as himself. She was a daughter of the Honorable

James Alexander, Surveyor-General of New York and New Jersey. This worthy had gifts as an amateur student of the heavens; for years he corresponded with Edmund Halley, the English astronomer. John Stevens, as son of this pair, was born, as we have said, in New York in 1749. During 1762 and 1763 he attended Kenersly's College in Perth Amboy, New Jersey. Thence he passed to Columbia College, New York, where he was graduated in 1768. Among his classmates were three lifelong friends, who rose to eminence,—Gulian Verplanck, as an author; Gouverneur Morris, in public life; and Benjamin Moore, who became the second bishop of New York. With the best academic training of his day, young Stevens took up the study of law, receiving his license as an attorney on May 1, 1772. Law, however, he never practised; but his legal discipline inured throughout his life to an uncommon clarity of deduction and of statement. He early entered heart and soul into his father's convictions regarding the new-born Union, and the defense it should command. In 1776 he became a Captain in Colonel Beaver's Battalion; he was soon the Colonel of a regiment of his own. Like his father, he was marked for public trusts at an early age. From 1777 to 1782 he was the faithful and honored Treasurer of New Jersey, a post which broadened his knowledge of business while it matured his executive faculty.

Toward the close of his term of office, on October 17, 1782, Colonel Stevens married Miss Rachel Cox of Bloomsbury, New Jersey. Soon afterward the wedded pair removed to New York, establishing their home in the house vacated by the Colonel's father at 7 Broadway, opposite Bowling Green. Here the Colonel and his family resided until 1814, for thirty-one years. In March, 1784, Colonel Stevens bought for ninety thousand dollars the confiscated lands of William Bayard, a Tory, across the Hudson River, comprising what was then the Island of Hoboken. In addition he purchased a large adjoining tract of land in Wee-hawken. Soon after these acquisitions, Colonel Stevens built a homestead on the site of the present Castle. Here he lived every summer until 1814, when this became his residence the year round. He cultivated his grounds with keen and intelligent interest, planting many fruit trees new to the region. His library was one of the best in America for its day. Here philosophy and religion, history and biography, travels and poetry, were not the mere ornaments of handsome shelves, but well-thumbed tomes, furnishing and refreshing a brain of uncommon activity. Then, as now, the windows of the Stevens homestead commanded a full view of the city of New York, distant no more than a mile. Colonel Stevens as early as 1824 proposed that his estate should become a park for the metropolis, for which its easy accessibility and long shore-line fitted it admirably. But his suggestion met with no response. In 1911, however, the Palisades Park, to stretch for fifty miles along the Hudson River, was planned for Greater New York, one of its commissioners being Edwin A. Stevens II., a grandson of Colonel Stevens.

So long as Colonel Stevens maintained a home at 7 Broadway, near the Battery, his sole means of reaching Hoboken was a boat impelled by oars or a sail. In fine weather nothing could be pleasanter. In a fog or a storm, the trip was perilous and uncomfortable. No wonder, then, that he listened with both ears to reports that John Fitch was running a steamboat on the Delaware. Why could not the same feat be accomplished on the Hudson? Steam engines for years had driven the huge pumps of Cornish mines; they were now entering upon the less arduous task of propelling canal barges and excursion boats. One memorable morning in 1787, about a year before Symington's success on the Forth and Clyde Canal, Colonel Stevens saw Fitch's little craft as she sped between Burlington and

Trenton, New Jersey. There and then he was convinced that steam could far outvie sails or the tense muscles of horses or men. Fitch, poor man, had fallen into a cardinal error of design. His mechanism directly imitated manual toil,—his oars swept the water much as if pushed by an oarsman's thews, and this while rotary paddle-wheels had propelled his first models. In 1788 these wheels appeared in Symington's steamer on the Clyde. Fitch's piston was one foot in diameter, with a stroke of three feet. Each turn of his axle-tree moved its oars through five and a half feet. As. six oars came out of the water, the other six entered the water, each having a stroke like that of a canoe-paddle. When all went well, six miles an hour was the pace attained. But the machinery was so roughly made, so badly fitted together, that interruptions were frequent and repairs costly, so that Fitch's backers became disheartened, and his enterprise was abandoned. He stands a pathetic type of the inventor with much initiative and no staying power. But while his steamboat was in itself a failure, it had given Colonel Stevens a golden impulse. With characteristic promptitude he petitioned the Legislature of New Jersey to place a steam engine on board a vessel by way of experiment. He then informed himself as to the difficulties which had thwarted Fitch, that these might be avoided. His plans, carefully drawn, were handed to the official commissioners and a patent was granted to him on September 6, 1791. To grant a patent required a Patent Office, and this was founded at the instance of Colonel Stevens for the express purpose of duly guarding his rights in this invention. At first he used a horizontal wheel. This he soon abandoned for elliptical paddles, which were tested as well as their faulty machinery would allow. His steam engine was copied from a design of James Watt, by an engine-builder who had been long in the service of Boulton & Watt. Colonel Stevens wished to avoid the alternating stroke of this model, so he devised a rotary engine, which he thus describes:

" A cylinder of brass, about eight inches in diameter, and four inches long, was placed horizontally on the bottom of the boat. By the alternate pressure of the steam on two sliding wings, an axis passing through the center was made to revolve. On one end of this axis, which passed through the stern of the boat, wings like those on the arms of a windmill were fixed, adjusted to the angle most advantageous for operating on the water [as a propeller]. This constituted the whole of the machinery. Working with the elasticity of steam merely, no condenser, no air-pump, was necessary. And as there were no valves, no apparatus was required to open and shut valves. This simple little engine was, in the summer of 1802, placed on board a flat-bottomed boat I had built for the purpose. This boat was about twenty-five feet long, and five or six feet wide. She occasionally kept going until cold weather stopped us. When the engine was in the best order, her velocity was about four miles an hour. I found it, however, impracticable on so contracted a scale to preserve due tightness in the packing of the wings in the cylinder for any length of time. This determined me to resort again to the reciprocating engine. But the unsuccessful experiment in which I had been engaged with Chancellor Livingston and Mr. Roosevelt had taught me the indisputable necessity of guarding against the injurious effects of partial pressure, and, accordingly, I constructed an engine, although differing much from those described in my patents, yet so modified as to embrace completely the principle stated therein. During the winter this small engine was set up in a shop I then occupied at the Manhattan Works, and continued occasionally in operation until spring, when it was placed aboard the above-mentioned boat, and by means of bevel cogged wheels it worked the axis and wheels above described, and gave the boat somewhat more velocity than the rotary engine. But after having gone some time in crossing the river, with my son on board, the boiler, which was constructed of small tubes inserted at each end into metal heads, gave way, so as to be incapable of repair.

In 1804, Colonel Stevens planned a ferryboat to be driven by a steam engine of modified design. To bore its two cylinders, each sixteen inches in diameter, he erected a boring machine in Hoboken. Both the furnace and the boiler of this boat proved faulty, and she was dismantled. Her cylinders afterward did duty on the *Phoenix*, to be presently mentioned.

Colonel Stevens, in successful practice, originated many distinctive features for steamboats. He thus set them forth:

1. The cylinder, condenser, and air-pump are all firmly bedded upon a single plate of cast-iron, and the power of the engine exerted without causing strain to any part of the boat.

2. The air-pump has a double stroke, and its piston pumps out the injection water from the bottom of the condenser when the piston rises, and by exhaustion removes the air from the top of the water as the piston descends.

3. A new parallel motion for preserving the vertical position of the piston rod of the air-pump.

4. A new method of fixing the valve-seats with firmness and accuracy.

5. Valves with perforated stems passing through from the upper seat downwards, and from the lower seat upwards.

6. The levers for opening and shutting the valves are worked by a rotary motion, instead of the reciprocating motion of the common plug frame, the working gear of which is liable to get out of order.

7. The guide-posts are triangular, greatly increasing their strength and firmness.

8. By means of a cylinder placed above, between the two main cylinders of which the boiler is built, a supply of water is furnished to the boiler whenever it is necessary to stop the engine. This contrivance, if the stop is not very long, prevents the safety valve from rising and making a loud noise, and thus avoids loss of steam and heat; while the engine is going it furnishes more steam room to the boiler.

" It is very true," he says, " that I now make use of water-

Boiler, Engine, and Propellers of the 1804 Boat

wheels on each side of the boat. It is surely very far from my intention to attempt to invalidate Mr. Fulton's claim to water-wheels thus applied. It is an unquestionable fact that he was the first person who, for any practical useful purpose, applied water-wheels on each side of a steamboat.

" It may not be amiss to mention that in 1807, when the North River steamboat [Fulton's *Clermont*] made her first appearance on the waters of the Hudson, I constructed an engine and boat on a very small scale, namely fifteen feet long, and four-and-a-half feet wide. To this boat, considering her size, I gave the astonishing velocity at times of not less than six miles an hour. To be sure, she had water-wheels on each side. That her extraordinary velocity was not owing to this circumstance is evident from the fact of her going, notwithstanding every disadvantage, much faster than the North River steamboat. . . ."

Concurrently with this small vessel Colonel Stevens built the *Phoenix,* which, but for the monopoly held by Livingston and Fulton, would have plied on the Hudson River. The rivalry between the *Phoenix* and Fulton's *Clermont* was close. To the credit of the *Phoenix* stands the fact that her engines were built in America, whereas those of the *Clermont* were imported from England. The *Phoenix* was excluded from New York, but the port of Philadelphia was open to her. Accordingly, by sea, to Philadelphia Robert L. Stevens took her, embarking one afternoon in June, 1808. A fierce storm was encountered. A schooner in her company was blown out to sea, and was not heard from for nearly a fortnight, but the *Phoenix* made a safe harbor at Barnegat, whence, when the storm abated, she proceeded to Philadelphia, and plied many years between that city and Trenton. Mr. Stevens thus earned the honor of being the first to brave the ocean in a craft propelled by steam.

The next steamer built by John Stevens was the *Juliana,* a ferryboat, launched in 1811. She was an undecked open boat, 62 feet in length and 12 in breadth, drawing from 2½ to 3 feet of water. Her engines were of the model patented by her builder, having a cylinder of 14 inches diameter and 30 inches stroke. Her boilers and flues were of copper. Her steam was used expansively, being cut off in the main valves as in modern practice. Her furnace and flue were suspended on a frame-work of cast-iron, conducing to safety from fire, and superseding much heavy brickwork. The *Juliana* rose to a speed of seven miles an hour. Robert Fulton, having exclusive rights in the Jersey City ferry, would not allow the *Juliana* to run between New York and Hoboken, so she was placed on the route betwixt Middletown and Hartford, on the Connecticut River, being the first steamer to navigate Long Island Sound, as her cousin, the *Phoenix*, had been the first, in 1808, to navigate the ocean from Sandy Hook to the mouth of the Delaware River.

John Stevens, taking a comprehensive survey of steam practice, clearly saw that great economy lay in using high pressures, especially with expansion gear. But an obstacle which had confronted James Watt remained in the path of his American successor. Workmanship in those days was inadequate to the task of tightly riveting a large boiler to resist high pressure. A means of avoiding this difficulty was to revive and improve an old invention,—a boiler which, instead of being formed of one huge cylinder, was built of many long narrow cylinders, or mere tubes, each of which could be produced perfectly tight, while so thin as to have its contained water quickly heated by an impinging flame. The first boiler of this kind on record was devised · in 1766, by William Blakey, an Englishman. He connected together several water-tubes in a furnace, alternately inclined at opposite angles, and united at their contiguous ends by smaller pipes. This design was improved by James Rumsey, an American pioneer in steamboating. He patented, in 1788, several forms of this boiler. One had a firebox with flat water-sides and top, across which were horizontal water-tubes connected with the water-spaces.

Another was a coiled tube within a cylindrical firebox, connected at its two ends with the annular surrounding water-space. This was the first "coil boiler." A third type was the vertical tubular boiler, as built to-day. John Stevens' design was patented in Great Britain in 1805, by his son, John Cox Stevens, who said:

"The principle of this invention consists in forming a boiler by combining a number of small vessels, or tubes, instead of using a single large one. . . . Suppose a plate of brass one foot square, in which a number of holes are perforated, into each of which holes is fixed one end of a copper tube, of about one inch in diameter and two feet in length; the other ends of these tubes being inserted in like manner in a similar piece of brass. In order to insure tightness, these tubes are to be cast in the plates; these plates are to be inclosed at each end of the pipes, and the cast-iron cap at each end; the caps at each end are to be fastened by screw-bolts passing through them into the plates. The water supply is to be injected by a forcing pump into the cap at one end, and through a tube inserted into the cap at the other end the steam is to be conveyed to the steam cylinder of the engine. The whole is then to be inclosed in brickwork or masonry in the usual manner, placed either horizontally or perpendicularly at option."

In adopting and improving the water-tube boiler, Mr. Stevens showed his wonted sagacity. Since his day its advantages have been fully realized in improved designs. Let us remark how it excels a boiler of the fire-tube model: First of all, the flames rush *across* its tubes, so that they are much more thoroughly and quickly heated than if the fire merely glided along their length. A fire-tube accumulates dust, ashes, and soot on its inside surface, with risk of utter choking. These deposits attach themselves, and in much less quantity, to the outside of a water-tube, whence they are easily removed. All the joints of a water-tube boiler may be placed elsewhere than in the hottest parts

cient number of trials the wheel was taken off and the same men were furnished with oars. The result of repeated trials was a few seconds in favor of the wheel. It is unnecessary to observe that the wheel must have worked to much disadvantage. The proper angle of obliquity was not attended to, besides the wings were made with a flat surface, whereas a certain curve was necessary. And in order to give a due immersion to the wheel, its axis was inclined 30 to 40 degrees below the horizontal line. The machinery, too, was put up in a very coarse manner. One important consideration in favor of these wheels is the facility with which they can be defended from all external injury by placing them in the stern. My foreman promises to have the engines going in the boat in about two weeks from this time." *

Colonel Stevens for six years, ending with 1806, sought to establish steam navigation by the screw propeller, endeavoring to introduce (1) the short four-bladed screw, (2) steam at high pressure, (3) multitubular boilers, (4) quick-moving engines directly connected to propeller shafts, (5) twin screws.

*Francis B. Stevens, grand-nephew of Colonel John Stevens, in the *Stevens Indicator*, April, 1893, said:

"Colonel Stevens considered himself the inventor of the screw propeller. He was mistaken. It was proposed by the mathematician, Daniel Bernouilli, in 1752. It is described by David Bushnell in a letter to Thomas Jefferson, in 1787, giving an account of his submarine boat, in which a screw propeller, worked by hand, was used. The same idea was afterward suggested by Franklin, Watt, Paucton, and others. Prior to 1802 the screw propeller was twice distinctly patented in England: first, by William Lyttleton, in 1794; second, by Edward Shorter, in 1800."

John Bourne, in his "Treatise on the Screw Propeller," London, 1867, mentions a prior patent, that of Joseph Bramah, issued May 9, 1785. His propeller was "a wheel with inclined fans or wings, similar to the fly of a smokejack, or the vertical sails of a windmill. This wheel was to be fixed on the spindle of a rotary engine, and might be wholly under water, where it could be turned round either way, causing a ship to be forced forward or backward, as the inclination of the fans or wings might determine."

Forty years had to elapse before these elements of success were adopted in ocean navigation. At the time of Colonel Stevens' experiments there were no competent workmen in America to construct the boilers and engines he planned. He had, therefore, to fall back upon the paddle-wheel as a propeller. with its slow-moving engine, whose boilers carried steam at only two or three pounds above atmospheric pressure.

Speed soon became a prime consideration in steamboating. At first Colonel John Stevens bestowed his attention wholly upon his motive power and machinery, giving little heed to the hulls of his vessels. In improving their lines, his son and associate, Robert, effected a notable advance. At first his father's steamers were little else than boxes with pointed ends. In the *New Philadelphia,* Robert Stevens introduced a false bow, long and sharp, which parted the water with a new facility. At once this vessel bounded forward at thirteen and a half miles an hour, a marvelous speed for that period, and even to-day a goodly pace. When the designer asked his shipbuilders, Brown & Bell, to construct this bow, they declined from fear of public ridicule. Mr. Bell said: " That bow will be called ' Bell's nose,' and I will be a general laughing-stock." So Robert Stevens had to build the bow himself, with anything but laughter at the result. The *New Philadelphia* inaugurated a day line between Albany and New York. No predecessor of hers had ever run fast enough to complete a trip betwixt dawn and dusk. With her, too, began models which, in clipper sailers and steamers, won new records in speed. Of equal importance with the steamboats plying between the metropolis and the capital of New York, were the steam ferries which joined New York City with the shores of New Jersey and Long Island. Until 1810 only comfortless rowboats or pirogues offered a passage across the North and East Rivers. First as an improvement came twin boats, with a central wheel turned, treadmill fashion, by horses. These horses were supplanted by steam, first by Fulton in a ferry to Jersey City, in 1812. Then came single boats with sidewheels, of which the first was the *Hoboken,* built in 1822 by Robert L. Stevens. In that year he introduced at his docks string piles which directed a boat as she entered her pier. One stormy night, Mr. Stevens' attention was called to a pilot as he stood at his wheel, wholly unprotected from beating rain. Mr. Stevens at once planned and built shelters for his pilots, the first to be provided for them.

A thorn in the side of the Stevens family was the monopoly granted by the State of New York to Robert Fulton and his partners, bestowing the exclusive right to steamboat service on the waters of New York. After much preliminary skirmishing, this monopoly was attacked in February, 1824, in the Supreme Court of the United States, by Daniel Webster, in a masterly argument. Mr. Oakley, and Mr. Emmett, who had been a personal friend of Fulton, appeared in defense. Chief Justice John Marshall rendered a decision adverse to the monopoly, holding that the power vested in Congress, to regulate commerce, included power to regulate navigation. Said he: " The power to regulate commerce does not look to the principle by which boats are moved. That power is left to individual discretion. . . . The act demonstrates the opinion that steamboats may be enrolled and licensed in common with vessels having sails. They are, of course, entitled to the same privileges, and can no more be restrained from navigating waters and entering ports, which are free to such vessels, than if they were wafted on their voyage by the winds instead of being propelled by the agency of fire." Thus ended a monopoly which, during seventeen years, held back the progress of steam navigation in America, clearly proving the impolicy of rewarding enterprise by an exclusive privilege.

His success with the *Phoenix* and her sister craft showed Colonel Stevens how mighty a stride steam could effect on waterways. He had long been convinced that a like gain could be reaped by steam as a motive power for travel on land. In 1810 the Legislature of New York appointed commissioners to examine the routes proposed for the Erie Canal, and to report upon the feasibility of that project. When Colonel Stevens read their report, which discussed a continuous inclined plane from Lake Erie to the Hudson River, to be fed by the waters of the lake, he urgently pressed upon the commissioners, as preferable in economy, speed, and rapidity of construction, a system of steam railways. In 1812 he published his argument as a pamphlet, adding the objections of the commissioners, and his rejoinders. He said:

" So many and so important are the advantages which these States would derive from the general adoption of the proposed railways, that they ought, in my humble opinion, to become an object of primary attention to the national government. The insignificant sum of $2,000 to $3,000 would be adequate to give the project a fair trial. On the success of this experiment a plan should be digested, a general system of internal communication and conveyance be adopted, and the necessary surveys be made for the extension of these ways in all directions, so as to embrace and unite every section of this extensive empire. It might then, indeed, be said that these States would then constitute one family, intimately connected and held together in bonds of indissoluble union.

". . . To the rapidity of the motion of a steam carriage on these railways, no definite limit can be set. The flying proas of the islands in the Pacific Ocean are said at times to sail more than twenty miles an hour; but as the resistance of water to the progress of a vessel increases as the square of its velocity, it is obvious that the power required to propel her must also be increased in the same ratio. Not so with a steam carriage; as it moves in a fluid eight hundred times rarer than water, the resistance is proportionately diminished. Indeed, the principal resistance arises from friction, which does not even increase in a direct ratio with the velocity of the carriage. If, then, a proa can be driven by the wind (the propulsive power of which is constantly diminishing as the velocity of the proa increases), through so dense a fluid as water, at twenty miles an hour, I can see nothing to hinder a steam carriage from moving on these ways at one hundred miles an hour. . . . This astonishing velocity is considered here as merely possible. It is probable that it may not, in practice, be convenient to exceed twenty or thirty miles an hour. Actual experience, however, can alone determine this matter, and I should not be surprised at seeing steam carriages propelled at forty to fifty miles an hour."

The Erie Canal was built, notwithstanding the arguments of influential opponents led by Colonel Stevens. Year by year he closely followed the developments in railroad locomotion in England, resolved that he should have a leading part in promoting like projects at home. For this a door stood open before him. Philadelphia and New York, in an airline but ninety miles apart, even at that early day transacted a huge business with one another. Added to this was the trade of intervening towns and villages, steadily growing in population and wealth. The Stevens family, as men of enterprise and capital, had developed the traffic on this highway until almost the whole rested in their hands. As far back as 1795 Colonel Stevens had designed a steam locomotive, which he had hoped to patent during the administration of President Washington. His great difficulty was to provide a track strong enough to support the heavy low-pressure engine of that day. In 1817 he obtained a charter from the State of New Jersey " to build a railroad from the river Delaware, near Trenton, to the river Raritan, near New Brunswick." No action followed the granting of his charter, as its project was deemed visionary. But Colonel Stevens never for a moment relaxed his labors on behalf of steam railroads. In 1823, with Stephen Girard and Horace Binney as his associates, he projected a railroad from Philadelphia to Harrisburg and Pittsburgh, which resulted in the incorporation of the Pennsylvania Railroad Company, twenty-three years before the present corporation was chartered. In 1826 Colonel Stevens built at his own cost the first steam locomotive that ran on rails in America. This engine was furnished with a sectional boiler of high efficiency, and coursed upon a circular track laid within a few hundred yards of the present Stevens Institute. This was three years before Horatio Allen ran the "Stourbridge Lion" at Honesdale, Pennsylvania, and nearly four years before Stephenson won his prize with the "Rocket" at Rainhill in England.

About 1829, Colonel Stevens conceived a bold project, which, duly modified, forty years afterward was developed as the elevated railroad system of New York. He sketched a scheme for a railway starting from the Battery, and proceeding along Greenwich or Washington Street, to a suitable spot opposite Castle Point, Hoboken, and from an elevated structure there to cross the Hudson River upon a high bridge made chiefly of Manila hemp, supported by several piers. The track was to be "supported on pillars of stone, iron, or wood, placed near the curb stones, and elevated about ten or twelve feet above the pavement." After crossing the river, the railway was to proceed over Bergen Hill to the Little Falls of the Passaic River. The real objective point was Philadelphia, and thence to Washington. Stoves were to be erected on the bridge, and a supply of pure water was to cross with it—brought from Little Falls.

It was not in this bold project, but in ordinary railroading, that Colonel Stevens was to engage. Less ambitious than the proposed line from Philadelphia to Pittsburgh was a scheme requiring comparatively small outlay, to provide a short railroad which should complete a steam route between New York and Philadelphia. These cities were at that time joined by the Union Line in three links:—

Steamboat route from Philadelphia to Trenton..   36 miles
Turnpike for stage and wagons, Trenton to New
    Brunswick ....   25· "
Steamboat route, New Brunswick to New York.   40   "

                                101 miles

To build a railroad between Trenton and New Brunswick, twenty-five miles, and capture the traffic carried by horse-drawn vehicles, was a most inviting enterprise for Colonel Stevens, his family, and his wealthy associates. In 1830, accordingly, at their instance, the Camden & Amboy Railroad Company was incorporated. Robert L. Stevens was appointed its president; his brother, Edwin Augustus, was chosen its treasurer and general manager. As a first step toward building the line, Robert L. Stevens posted to England, where, since 1825, the railway between Stockton and Darlington had been successfully operated with locomotives designed by the Stephensons. Before leaving home he resolved to adopt an iron rail as better than a wooden rail, or than the stone stringer thinly plated with iron, which his Company had laid by way of experiment. There was then no mill in America to roll T-rails, and as both iron and labor were scarce and dear in the United States, Mr. Stevens wished to lay a rail which would need no chair to hold it in place. During his voyage across the Atlantic he whittled bits of wood into varied rail contours, at last carving a form in which a broad and firm base was added to a T-rail, so as to give it a continuous foot, or flange, dispensing with chairs. In this he carried forward by an important step the advantages presented in the rail suggested by Thomas Tredgold in 1825, which had a base comparatively narrow.

On landing in Liverpool, he asked for bids on five hundred tons of such a rail as he had whittled, since known by his name the world over. As first designed, the base of this rail was wider at its points of support than elsewhere. Afterward it was rolled throughout with a uniform breadth of three inches. The first shipment, which reached Philadelphia on the ship *Charlemagne* on May 18, 1831, comprised 350 bars, each 18 feet long, weighing 36 pounds to the yard. It was soon found that heavier rails were less

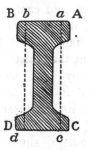

An enlarged section of an Edge-rail to show the disposition of parts which gives greatest strength. If the rectangle *a b d c* contains the same quantity, the strength of the rail A B D C is to the strength in the form of the rectangle as 1¾ is to 1.

[From "A Practical Treatise on Railroads and Carriages." By Thomas Tredgold, New York, 1825.]

yielding, so that weights were increased forthwith to between 40 and 42 pounds to the yard. These new rails were 16 feet long, 3½ inches high, 2⅛ inches wide at the head, and 3½ inches wide at the base. They were rolled by Sir John Guest at Dowlais, in Wales, at eight pounds sterling ($38.93) per ton.

Mr. Stevens added to his rails several auxiliary devices of importance. He designed the iron tongue, or toe-piece, which has become the fish-plate, as well as the bolts and nuts which give unity and rigidity to track construction. When he called upon the Stephensons they showed him their

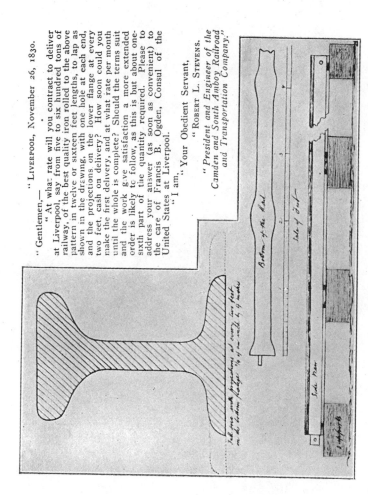

"LIVERPOOL, November 26, 1830.

"Gentlemen,—

"At what rate will you contract to deliver at Liverpool, say from five to six hundred tons of railway, of the best quality iron rolled to the above pattern in twelve or sixteen feet lengths, to lap as shown in the drawing, with one hole at each end, and the projections on the lower flange at every two feet, cash on delivery? How soon could you make the first delivery, and at what rate per month until the whole is complete? Should the terms suit and the work give satisfaction a more extended order is likely to follow, as this is but about one-sixth part of the quantity required. Please to address your answer (as soon as convenient) to the care of Francis B. Ogden, Consul of the United States at Liverpool.

"I am,

"Your Obedient Servant,

"ROBERT L. STEVENS.

"*President and Engineer of the Camden and South Amboy Railroad and Transportation Company.*"

Facsimile of sketch of cross-section, side-elevation, and ground-plan of the first T-rail. Also transcription of letter addressed by Robert L. Stevens to English ironmasters, asking for bids.

[Originals preserved in the United States National Museum, Washington, D. C.]

"Planet," introducing marked improvements on the "Rocket." Mr. Stevens at once ordered a like engine for the Camden & Amboy line. This engine, the "John Bull," was landed in August, 1831. It weighed 10 tons; its boiler was 13 feet long and 3½ feet in diameter. Its cylinders were 9 inches by 20; its firebox had a surface of 36 square feet; its four driving-wheels ran on a gauge of five feet. Water and fuel were borne on a rough four-wheeled flat car; the tank had been a whisky barrel in a Bordentown grocery. The boiler hose of leather had been stitched by a local shoemaker. Liberal supplies of pine generated a steam pressure of thirty pounds to the square inch. The first run of this locomotive took place near Bordentown on a track 1,067 feet long, with rails laid on stone blocks. Here a demonstration was given to the assembled lawmakers of New Jersey, much to their amazement and delight. On October 9, 1831, the line from Bordentown to Hightstown, twelve miles, was opened for traffic. Two months later the road was completed to Amboy, but locomotives were not used until August, 1833, when an adequate number were ready for service.

The early records of this Camden & Amboy line present the trial or adoption of many devices since familiar,—the first pilot, or cowcatcher, was planned and placed by Mr. Stevens in 1832. During that year he began to spike rails directly to his cross-ties. Soon afterward he introduced the bogie-truck, borrowing its vertical axle from a common wagon, greatly easing movement around short curves. He designed a vestibuled car, such as, in a developed model, is now operated by the Pullman Company. He began experiments in the chemical preservation of wood, doubling the life of his ties. Amusing are many incidents of those pioneer times. During the first months of business, a man on a fast horse went ahead of the train to clear its track and warn off trespassers. One of the Stevens brothers

owned a fine stud, so that a quick steed was always ready
to make safe the path for the rival horse of iron. On one of
its first trips, the " John Bull " came upon a curve at undue
speed. As track builders had not yet learned to raise the
outer rail at curves, the engine left its line and slid down
an embankment into an adjoining field, where half a dozen
farmhands were cradling wheat. They fled instanter, nor
did their panic cease until they had placed two hundred
yards between themselves and the pursuing monster.

In America the first business for railroads was to carry
coals, just as with their forerunners in England long before.
As far back as 1602 wooden railways joined collieries at
Newcastle to docks on the Tyne. Nicholas Wood, in his
" Practical Treatise on Railroads," published in 1838, quotes
from a description in 1676: " The manner of carriage is by
laying rails of timber from the colliery to the river, exactly
straight and parallel. Bulky carts are made with four
rollers fitting these rails, whereby the carriage is so easy
that one horse will draw four to five chaldrons of coals,
two-and-a-half times as much as if a load were drawn upon
a common road." First of American railroads worth while
was that built at Mauch Chunk, Pennsylvania, to carry anthracite for the Lehigh Coal & Navigation Company. Its
length was 12¾ miles. Next came the Quincy Railroad,
near Boston, about three miles in extent, completed in 1826
for the conveyance of granite. The South Carolina Railroad, begun in 1829, finished in 1832, came next. Then
followed this Camden & Amboy Railroad: its first division,
from Camden, opposite Philadelphia, to Bordentown, was
34½ miles; its second division, from Bordentown to Amboy, was 26½ miles. This line, a double track, was laid at
a cost of $1,466,376.64. It was profitable from its first day,
under the control of Edwin A. Stevens. His ability was
manifest early in his career: at twenty-five his family
gave him charge of the larger part of their property. Dur-

First Train on the Camden and Amboy Railroad

ing the thirty-five years of his railroad administration he allied himself with the best engineering talent in America. His own faculty in this province made him at once a competent judge and a whole-hearted coöperator.

While still a young man, with the aid of his brother Robert, he invented a cast-iron plow. Its moldboard was so curved as always to scour, and leave no earth sticking to its surface. Ribs were cast on its interior, insuring strength with lightness. On the bottom of the landside a heel-piece was attached: when worn out, it could be replaced by a new one in a few minutes. This plow for years enjoyed a large sale.

Some years after its invention, Robert L. Stevens perfected his air-tight fire-room, patented in April, 1842. He arrived at this fire-room by steps worth retracing. In 1827 he fitted the boilers of the *North America* with closed ash-pits, into which air for combustion was forced by a fan. In 1828, Ericsson in England installed a like fan in the *Victory*, commanded by Sir John Ross in an Arctic cruise. The brothers, Robert and Edwin Stevens, varied thrice their draft production. First, they sent a blast into a closed ashpit; second, they exhausted the base of their smokestack by a fan; third, they forced air into an air-tight stokehold. A nephew of the inventors, Francis B. Stevens, has said that when the closed ashpit was used, the blast pressure would often force the gases of combustion through the rims of the furnace-doors, so as greatly to distress the stokers. This suggested to Robert L. Stevens, in 1836, a horizontal screw ventilator turning on a vertical axis at the base of the smokestack of the *Passaic*. In 1837 and 1838 the brothers tried an exhaust fan on a horizontal spindle in the chimney of one of their shops. This was so effective that they placed a sister fan in their steamboat *Philadelphia*, plying the Delaware River. The final method to which Edwin Stevens came was to drive air above atmospheric pressure into an air-tight fire-room. This is the closed stokehold system of to-day. That system is the latest feat in the long series that began when a primeval Edison first blew a fire with his breath. He had a worthy successor in the son, or daughter, who seized a palm leaf and waved it as a fan. Ages thereafter arose the devisers of leather bellows, such as linger to this day in country forges, or hang on the walls of museums, with carved and studded woodwork. Incomparably better than any bellows are the rotary fans now whirling in every modern boiler-room. They render the engineer independent of fitful winds, so that, in foggy weather, his fires burn as vividly as if a Northern gale were blowing. He is free to use peat, or coal of poor quality, or even the refuse from sugar cane, fuels that refuse to burn with an ordinary natural draft. With all fuels an improved combustion yields him a new economy of one-seventh, so that he may use a smaller boiler than would otherwise be required. Mechanical draft, also, lends itself to mechanical stoking. It prevents smoke. It shortens chimneys, or, indeed, dispenses with chimneys altogether,—to the joy of designers of men-of-war.

Early in 1838, on March 6, while his sons were perfecting their methods of mechanical draft, Colonel John Stevens passed away at the ripe age of eighty-nine. His remains were laid in the graveyard of the Dutch Reformed Church, Bergen, New Jersey. Toward the close of his life he turned with zest to metaphysical speculation. A volume which he planned was to have comprised thirty-six chapters. Of these he completed the first, on the skepticism of Hume, and part of the twenty-second, on " Matter, Body, and Extension." Long before that period he had been warmly interested in combating the epidemics which from time to time assailed New York. He had once been severely attacked by yellow fever, an ailment treated with unusual success by his friend and physician, Dr. David Hosack. On the Colonel's recovery he wrote a descriptive article about yellow fever in the *American Medical and Philosophical Register.*

Let us return to the achievements of his son, Robert, who, at the end of years of experiment, had perfected a system of forced draft. This was but one among many of his exploits as an engineer. His activity as an inventor began as early as 1814, and in the field of gunnery. For service in the war with Great Britain he devised an elongated shell for use with ordinary cannon. At the end of decisive experiments, his patents were bought by the War Department. On one occasion at Governor's Island, near the city of New York, a target of white oak, four feet thick, was destroyed by one of his shells weighing 200 pounds, and carrying 13 pounds of gunpowder. He sealed each shell hermetically, so that no deterioration took place in storage. Some shells, twenty-five years after manufacture, had gunpowder exploded beneath them, others were taken to high towers and dropped to rocks below, all without causing them to explode. They were plunged into water, and placed in a cannon: upon striking their target they burst with devastating effect.

But it was in arts of peace that Robert L. Stevens was to win his chief laurels. He changed for the better every feature of his steamboats as first designed. He suspended their projecting guards from above by iron rods. He strengthened their frames with ties and braces, secured by screwbolts. By a judicious placing of diagonal knees of wood and iron he reduced weight while conferring rigidity on his hulls. In 1815, in the *Philadelphia,* he began to use steam expansively, doubling the value of his fuel. He was the first engineer to burn anthracite in a cupola furnace: he afterward adopted this fuel in his fast steamboats, beginning with the *Passaic.* He placed the boiler on the guards of his steamers, conducing to their steadiness, and facilitating both coaling and stoking.   In the *Trenton* he introduced divided paddle-wheels, with their lessened jar and quickened pace.   Beginning with the *Hoboken,* he replaced the heavy walking-beam of cast-iron with the wrought-iron skeleton now universal,—at once lighter and stronger.   In the *North America* he introduced the hog frame, in which large timbers on each side prevented the vessel from bending or being " hogged."   This boat was so well contoured that she ran at fifteen miles an hour, the utmost speed of her day. In the *New Philadelphia* he placed steel spring bearings under the wheel shaft, and gave the engine, for the first time, valves perfectly balanced.   He then braced the connecting rod, so as to prevent its tremulous motion and add to its strength.   A few months later he built a steamboat which might have been serviceable in Arctic seas, for it easily strode through heavy ice between Camden and Philadelphia.   His next task was to build a tubular boiler of new economy: its flames beat under the boiler and returned through its tubes.   Leaky pistons had bothered him for years, wasting fuel and lowering speeds.   This he overcame by making steam itself press his packing-rings against their pistons, with a tightness denied to steel springs or India rubber.   With the aid of a nephew, Francis B. Stevens, he devised a cut-off by means of main valves worked by two eccentrics.   In the same year, 1841, he invented for his locomotives a double-slide cut-off.   This he afterward applied in large stationary engines.   He greatly promoted the adhesion of his locomotive to their rails by giving them eight wheels instead of four or six, so that short curves were now turned with but slight friction on flanges.

As a recreation amid so much hard work, Robert L. Stevens took up yachting.   Here he exercised, with delight, the ingenuity which had won him fame and fortune in steam

[From a portrait in the possession of Miss M. B. P. Garnett, Hoboken.]

locomotion. In 1844 he built the big sloop *Maria,* with two centerboards and outside lead ballast. She was for years the fastest yacht in the world, and in many respects she was the prototype of the swiftest racing machines of to-day. She vanquished the *America,* which, in her turn, was victorious against every rival in British waters. In 1860, the *Maria,* commanded by her owner, overhauled and sailed around the revenue cutter *Harriet Lane,* carrying the Prince of Wales, afterward King Edward VII. Until she foundered in the Gulf of Mexico in 1869, she remained at the head of her class. She was 110 feet in length; 26 feet wide 8 inches, in beam; with a draft of 6 inches under her forefoot, increasing to a maximum of 5 feet 3 inches, aft. Her bow was long and hollow, and so sharp that where the bowsprit entered the hull the bows had to be widened. Her main boom, 100 feet long and 3 feet in diameter, was built hollow of doweled staves of white pine, bound together by iron hoops like a barrel, and secured by iron trusses. In this feature, and in her outside lead, the *Maria* was many years in advance of her time. Her lead was poured into molds 5 inches deep, fixed outside on her bottom, conforming to the lines of the floor for a distance of 20 feet on each side of the keel. Her mainsail at the foot measured 96 feet, and her jib—the only headsail she carried—70 feet. This was laced to a boom. The forward centerboard was weighted with lead, and, when down, drew 20 feet. Springs fitted to its base enabled it to touch ground without harm. Her speed was marvelous. In a piping breeze, in smooth water, she once scored 17 nautical miles an hour. In rough water her behavior was not so remarkable, so that the Swedish yacht *Coquette* once passed her in bad weather. Nineteen years later, in 1865, she was beaten by the *Magic.* The success of the *Maria* had much to do with founding the New York Yacht Club in the year of her launching. Every contest of this Club, at

home and abroad, for years enlisted the keen interest of
Robert L. Stevens and his brother, John Cox Stevens, one
of the owners of the *America*, the first yacht to cross the
Atlantic. John Cox Stevens was managing owner of the
America at the winning of the *America* cup, retained by
American yachts to the present day. Mr. Stevens was the
first commodore of the New York Yacht Club.

And now, to take up another naval feat of the Stevens
family, we must hark backward to 1814, when, toward the
close of the war with Great Britain, Colonel John Stevens
projected a circular iron fort, to be rotated by steam, for the
defense of the harbor of New York. He directed his son
Edwin, then a youth of nineteen, to experiment with a six-
pounder cannon fired against iron plates. Iron armor for
a warrior's body had been worn from prehistoric times. In
1530 the largest ship of that day, one of the fleet of the
Knights of Saint John, was sheathed with lead so as to
withstand every shot fired at her. Iron armor for vessels
was patented by Thomas Gregg, of Pennsylvania, in 1814.
No exemplification, however, of this armor is on record
until 1841, when the United States was once again on the
verge of war with England. In that year Edwin A. Stevens
reverted to his experiments of 1814. In a formal note to
the War Department on August 13, 1841, he and his
brother John presented a design recommended for a steam
vessel of war. Its motive power should be out of the
reach of shot and shell, and the vessel herself should be
proof against attack. Instead of wood for construction,
iron was to be employed, as much stronger and more resistant, weight for weight. In 1841 stout armor plate
could not be rolled in America, so that comparatively thin
plates were to be riveted in tile fashion on the sides of
this projected ship. She should, moreover, be capable of
high speed, so as to take any desired position with ease and
certainty. To afford power with the minimum of fuel, her

boilers were to be so strong as to resist high pressure, and their steam was to be used expansively. Her propeller was to be a Stevens screw, wholly submerged.

Robert L. Stevens then proceeded to learn the thickness of plate necessary to withstand the various shot then employed. From experiments at Bordentown he found that a target four and a half inches thick would resist a four-pound shot, then the heaviest missile of the United States Navy. He and his brother, John Cox Stevens, laid these results before President Tyler, who forthwith appointed a committee to continue experiments. These fully confirmed the tests by the brothers Stevens. Thereupon Congress authorized the Secretary of the Navy to contract with Robert L. Stevens for an ironclad steamer, to be shot-and-shell-proof. With his brother Edwin, he began at once to plan and construct this vessel. One of their first tasks was to build a dry-dock at Hoboken for their ship. Next they built at Bordentown a steamboat for the purpose of experimenting with screw propellers of various curves, which they compared with sidewheels as to efficiency. While thus engaged they devised a method of turning a vessel on a pivot, as it were, by a cross-propeller near her stern, so that, in case one battery of a warship were disabled, the other might be quickly presented.

At that time there had been but little advance in gun-power since the victory of Nelson at Trafalgar in 1805. But when Commodore Stockton, after the failure of his first gun in 1844, had introduced a wrought-iron gun of British make, whose round shot easily pierced four and a half inches of iron, Robert L. Stevens had to thicken his armor, and this meant enlarging his ship so as to keep afloat her heavier burden. There and then began for the navies of the world their unending duel betwixt gun and armor. As guns of new might were cast, new resisters were imperative on the part of Mr. Stevens. Hence interruptions without number, entailing delay after delay, and asking outlays far beyond those authorized by Congress. Thus it came about that when Robert L. Stevens died in 1856, his warship was still unfinished, although her plating was complete, and her boilers were in place, with their twin-screw engines. Her grates exposed a surface of 876 square feet, an area then extraordinary. As she lay at her basin in Hoboken, she measured 410 feet in length, 45 feet in beam inside her armor shelf, with her deck two feet above the water; being in these features like the Monitor class of vessels built six years later by Ericsson, but differing from them in having a turret square and immovable instead of circular and rotating.

At the outbreak of the Civil War in 1861, twenty years after his proof at Sandy Hook that a ship could be protected by iron armor, Edwin Stevens presented to the government of the United States a plan for completing the Stevens Battery, bequeathed to him by his brother Robert, together with the *Naugatuck*, a small vessel, to demonstrate his schemes as practicable. The *Naugatuck* was accepted by the government, and was one of the first fleet which attacked the *Merrimac*. She was a twin-screw vessel, immersible by water ballast to three feet below her load-line, so as to be nearly invisible, with pumps which could lift her to a normal plane in eight minutes. She could turn end for end, on her center, in seventy-five seconds. As Mr. Stevens' plans for the modification of his battery were wholly novel, his offer was declined. The country was then in desperate need of armored craft, and the Navy Department was patiently hearing, day by day, designers of new types of armored ships. Yet it meant nothing to these naval officials that the Stevens family were eminent as engineers, and of the highest financial responsibility. Their plans included much novel mechanism, and bore many marks of forge and foundry, all profoundly distasteful to men whose tradi-

The Stevens Battery in her Dry Dock

tions were of sails and tackle. Since that day every iota of the Stevens plans has proved not merely feasible, but indispensable. It was a sad sight to her owner to see his battery through all the recurrent crises of the Civil War, untouched in her basin. In 1868, three years after Lee's surrender at Appomattox, Edwin Stevens died, bequeathing the vessel to the State of New Jersey, with a million dollars for her completion. This sum was expended in 1869 and 1870. Much additional outlay was necessary, and, as this was withheld by Congress, she was taken apart in 1881 and reduced to junk.

While Robert L. Stevens was busy constructing this battery, every incident bearing on his work was eagerly wrought into his plans. One day a North River steamer, the *Thomas Powell,* through derangement of her rudder, ran into a crib dock, smashing its heavy timbers and displacing fifteen feet of its stone filling. The vessel then backed out of the wound she had inflicted, but little harmed by her onslaught. Argued Mr. Stevens, if a frail wooden hull can do all this damage with scarcely any hurt to herself, an iron steamer with a steel prow could deliver with impunity a mortal blow to an ordinary ship. His conviction so impressed Congress that it authorized him, in 1843, to build a warship equipped with an immense iron ram, axlike in shape, and so braced and supported as to be part and parcel of the hull behind it.

Edwin Augustus Stevens was a man to whom wealth brought a keen sense of responsibility. Toward the close of his life he resolved that the name of his family should be borne by " an institution for the benefit of the youth residing from time to time in New Jersey." Accordingly, with leaders in education he had long and earnest conferences, that his foundation might be wisely laid and firmly built upon. His death took place in 1868, and his will provided for the projected Stevens Institute of Technology at

Hoboken, land valued at $100,000, a building fund of $150,000, and $500,000 for endowment, in all three-quarters of a million dollars. In June, 1911, the assets of the Institute stood at $1,550,000, including gifts from Dr. Henry Morton, its first president, of $145,000; and from Andrew Carnegie, chiefly for endowment, $340,000. It was largely through one of its first trustees, Samuel B. Dod, that a school of mechanical engineering was formed. On May 27, 1911, Edwin Augustus Stevens, II., son and namesake of the founder, conveyed a part of his father's estate, the Castle and its grounds, to the Institute, to serve as its social rallying center. The present Castle was built in 1853, on the site of the original residence of Colonel John Stevens. The plans of President Humphreys for the development of Stevens Institute center in the acquisition of twenty-two acres of the Stevens Castle estate. This would provide a site for an engineering college unsurpassed in America, while within two miles of the City Hall of New York. President Humphreys says: " Stevens Institute stands for thoroughness in engineering education and well-balanced coördination between theory and practice. Some emphasis is placed on the mechanical side of engineering, but not such an emphasis as to make it a narrow course in education."

Stevens Institute, including the class of 1912, has graduated 1,686 students. Among these are many engineers of note, both at home and abroad. In the class of 1883 appeared Frederick Winslow Taylor, of Philadelphia, and, had Stevens no other student of whom to boast, his name would amply justify its existence. Mr. Taylor, in pursuing methods begun in the laboratory and workshops at Hoboken, has worked out scientific management from practice to rule. In many cases his methods have multiplied fourfold the output of a factory or mill, and bid fair to bring to an end antagonisms of capital and labor by creating

[From a portrait in the possession of Miss M. B. P. Garnett, Hoboken.]

for them both a new and large profit as they work shoulder to shoulder.

While Stevens Institute was taking form in the mind of its founder, his constant adviser was the late Abram S. Hewitt, of New York, the famous ironmaster. His services as a Member of Congress and as Mayor of New York have earned for him grateful remembrance in the Empire State. He was often wont to recall his friendship with the successive generations of the Stevens family, and never were his reminiscences so full and so interesting as when he addressed the alumni on February 18, 1897, the twenty-fifth anniversary of the founding of Stevens Institute:

" I suppose that I am one of the very few persons living who can say that they have seen and known the entire Stevens family, from its founder, John Stevens, who was born in 1749, before the Revolution, as well as his children, grandchildren, and great-grandchildren, who have gathered around the old ancestral home on the other side of the Hudson River. When I was about six years of age I was taken by my father to Hoboken to be introduced to John Stevens, because I had a few days before seen from the Jay Street Wharf a magnificent steamer, with four ponderous smokestacks, passingly rapidly up the Hudson River, and had asked whose steamer it was, and where it was going.

" My father told me that there were two of these boats, the finest in the world, and that they had been built by the Stevens family of Hoboken. I said: 'Do you know the Stevens family?' To which he replied: 'Yes. I will take you to Hoboken and present you to the greatest engineer of his time.'

" And so some time between 1828 and 1830, I was taken to Hoboken and introduced to John Stevens, who was then eighty-three years of age, but in possession of all his faculties, and manifesting the greatest possible interest in this visit from an old friend and a young boy. Familiarly he called my father ' John,' for both bore the same name, and my father said: ' This is my son. I want him to see and know you.' And then they began to talk of old times, and particularly of this remarkable story, which was so often repeated to me by my father, or else I should not remember it so well.

"My father was the draftsman and pattern-maker who had come out from England, with a party of machinists, to erect the first stationary double-acting condensing engine which was put at work in America. It was built by Boulton & Watt at the Soho Works, near Birmingham in England, and was brought out and erected at Centre Square, in Philadelphia, to supply that city with water before the Fairmount Works, on the Schuylkill River, were erected. Thus John Stevens had built for himself the first Watt engine ever constructed in America. His corps of workers, whose chief was an engineer named Smalman, included Rhode, an ironfounder, the predecessor and instructor of James P. Allaire, who founded the Allaire Works in New York. These men, with my father as draftsman and pattern-maker, erected a new Soho Works at Belleville, near Newark, New Jersey. There John Stevens built the first low-pressure engine ever constructed in America.

"Of course, this interview with John Stevens made a profound impression upon my mind, and on my way home my father said: 'Yes, that engine was put in a boat in which I traversed the route from Belleville to New York and back again, John Stevens being the owner, builder, and captain of the boat, and Mr. Smalman, Mr. Rhode, and myself being the passengers; and we came to New York in that boat nine years before Fulton put the *Clermont* on the Hudson.'

"Portions of the engine thus constructed were for a time preserved in the Stevens Institute, and must be there still, unless transferred to the National Museum at Washington. But the boat in which the engine was placed must not be confounded with the one whose model I see here upon the table, built later, in 1804, with a double screw, and which preceded Fulton's boat by four or five years. I only remember the Belleville boat had a stern wheel, and my father said that Mr. Stevens, during the trip, remarked that wheels should have been placed at the side, and not at the stern.

". . . Robert L. Stevens, as you all know, was the designer of what is known as the flange rail. He had it made

in Wales at the works of Sir John Guest, and with such expedition that within two years from the time of undertak-
ing the practical scheme of building the Camden and Amboy
Railroad, that road was constructed and carrying passengers between New York and Philadelphia. Robert L.
Stevens and his brother Edwin, who was the business manager of the enterprise, thus performed in two years a feat
which at that time, if you will consider the development of
the mechanical arts, the state of the finances of the world,
and the unknown elements which entered into the problem,
was a greater performance than if a man were now to
build a road from New York to San Francisco in two
years.

" John C., Robert, and Edwin Stevens had tried and
trusted assistants, but the superintendence of the work to
the minutest part was carried out by themselves personally.
Together they built railroads, ferries, steamboats, yachts,
and ironclad batteries; indeed, these three brothers worked
as though they were one man. No one ever heard of any
quarrel or dissension in the Stevens family. They were
workmen themselves, and they were superior to their sub-
ordinates only because they were better engineers and better
men of business than any other folk who up to that time
had undertaken the business of transportation in the United
States.

". . . These men were the pioneers and founders who
have made this country what it is. . . . No one who cannot go back as I can to the time when there were no railways, no ocean steamers, no telegraphs, no telephones, no
armored navies, when the great West was yet unsettled,
when this great empire was a wilderness,—cannot recall the
primitive condition of things, and did not see it, can realize
what the Stevens family has done for America.

" I have said enough of the achievements of this remarkable family, but I have not said enough of the other
side of their personality,—the lovely, gentle, sweet, and
human character which belonged to the father and the
three brothers of whom I have spoken. I told you that I
was a poor and diffident boy, yet when I was brought into
contact with them I never was made to feel that there was
any difference in social standing, in wealth, in years, or even
ability. I was welcomed to Castle Point in my early youth

just as I would be to-day by the honored mistress of that mansion. They did not believe that the acquisition of wealth was sufficient for the development of human nature. They knew that the emotional side of man's nature controls in the long run, and that the reason is always the servant of the imagination. Hence, when they ran stage-coaches, they had fine horses; when they ran boats for profit to Albany, they adorned them with pictures and beautiful objects. The sense for beauty was manifest in all that they did. Their leisure hours were regaled by the charms of art and music. I believe that no connoisseur who ever lived in New York was superior to Robert Stevens in knowledge of music, and no man ever lived who enjoyed it more.

"The Stevens Institute was created by Mr. E. A. Stevens' will, which was signed on April 15, 1867, on the night before he embarked on the *Great Eastern* for that trip from which he was never to return. It was my good fortune to accompany him. He was very anxious to understand the *Great Eastern*. . . . During the voyage I had many conversations with Mr. Stevens on the subject of the Stevens Institute. Mr. Peter Cooper, my father-in-law, had founded the Cooper Union in New York, and it had been in operation for eight years at that time. I explained to Mr. Stevens that Mr. Cooper was a mechanic, and that his foundation was for mechanics; that, as the Stevens family were engineers, it was fitting in every way that the Stevens Institute should be devoted to the education of engineers. I explained to him that all the resources of the Cooper Union were giving the education which mechanics needed, and that what was wanted in this country was a higher institution which could start where the mechanic ended, and produce the engineers who were to become the leaders of modern enterprise and the captains of industry.

"Mr. Stevens entered heartily into this view of the subject, so that I have reason to know that, while the will provides for 'an institution of learning,' President Morton, with the approval of the trustees, carried into effect the views which Mr. Stevens entertained as to the objects of the institution and the place it should fill in the domain of education.

"But I referred to the voyage which we took together for the purpose mainly of showing some of the traits of Mr.

Stevens, which made him so interesting and lovable to his friends. The *Great Eastern*, for want of funds, had but a scanty supply of bituminous coal, which was supplemented by a stock of anthracite, which not a stoker on board had ever used or even seen before. The Captain, Sir James Anderson, came to us and asked what he should do. So Mr. Stevens, seventy-two though he was, and I, crawled down through many devious passages until we reached the boiler-room, and there found a very discouraged lot of people who were trying to burn anthracite as they would burn bituminous coal. Of course, their fire went out, and you will be astonished to learn that he and I, mostly he, spent nearly two days in the boiler-room, teaching those stokers how to burn anthracite coal, which we succeeded in doing so that we duly arrived at Brest. This is a simple illustration of the character of Mr. Stevens.

" The Stevens family in the last generation were creators as well as founders. You gentlemen who have profited by the beneficence, and foresight, of Edwin A. Stevens, are reaping the fruits of the seed which his family sowed abundantly in their day and generation. They were men not only of great sagacity and untiring energy, but of a high order of courage. When Robert L. Stevens found that Fulton had preceded him by a few weeks in placing the *Clermont* on the Hudson, thus securing the monopoly of the navigation of that river, he boldly took the *Phoenix* by sea from New York to Philadelphia, thus gaining the imperishable glory of being the first man to traverse the ocean with a boat propelled by steam. The honor is heightened by the fact that, while Fulton had imported his engine from England, Stevens used one which he had constructed in America, and which I believe to have been in part identical with the one I have referred to, as used in propelling the boat which ran from Belleville to New York in 1799." *

*The "Abram S. Hewitt Memorial" was erected in 1912 beside Cooper Union. It will eventually comprise six stories accommodating the technical and scientific departments of the Union.

ROBERT FULTON

RICH harvests, we are often told, await explorers who
will but pass beyond the horizons now limiting our studies
of atom and molecule, body and mind. All this is true:
every word said on behalf of original research is just and
worth heeding. It is also true that much golden knowledge, won long ago, is less honored by use than it deserves
to be. We inherit, and neglect our inheritance, while we
laboriously seek possessions of much less worth. It is well
that discovery should steadily advance; it would be well also
to bring plow and seed to vast areas that have for many
years lain fallow. This was what Robert Fulton thought
more than a century ago. He is commonly supposed to
have invented the steamboat. He did nothing of the kind.
The steamboat was launched and plied long before he trod
its deck. Its supreme value, ignored by heedless eyes, he
distinctly saw. With enterprise and perseverance he put
the steamboat at work in earnest: soon his example was
followed on both sides of the Atlantic by scores of acute
men of business. And Fulton had shrewd common sense
as well as a keen prophetic gaze. His boats on the Hudson, from their first trip, earned a good dividend, so punc-
tual was their carriage of passengers and freight.

Why was it left to Fulton, and so recently as 1807, to
accomplish a feat so simple? Because civilized nations had
not fully awakened to what the steam engine stood ready
to do for them. Watt, in trebling its efficiency, had ushered in the mechanical age. Before his day, a Newcomen
engine, here and there, turned a winch or pumped a mine.
But the usual prime-mover was a water-wheel, a windmill,

[From the "Portrait of Himself" owned by the late Col. Henry T. Chapman, of Brooklyn, exhibited at the Museum of the Brooklyn Institute of Arts and Sciences.]

or an inclined plane gliding under the patient tread of horses. Watt's engine, with its new economy, created new fields for itself: it was soon applied to spinning-jennies and looms, as well as to hoisting and pumping. Could it be taken aboard ship as an aid to sails? This question occurred independently to many engineers at the same time, and why not? On every sea, boats and ships were often becalmed for days together; as frequently they faced adverse gales and currents. It needed no more ingenuity to yoke a steam engine to a paddle-wheel, or to a screw propeller, than to link it to a pair of millstones or to the derrick of a shipyard. The steamboat was, accordingly, invented, and in several places far apart, a task which proved much less difficult than to secure its adoption. Who was the man who accomplished this feat?

Robert Fulton was born in Little Britain, Lancaster County, Pennsylvania, on November 14, 1765. His father, of the same name, of Scottish-Irish blood, had immigrated from Kilkenny about thirty years before. The farmhouse in which Fulton was born is still standing: it remains, in part, as it met his gaze as an infant. When he was a year old, his parents removed to the town of Lancaster, where they had formerly lived. In 1768, when Robert was only three years of age, his father died, leaving a widow and five children, with but a small estate for their maintenance. Under these circumstances, Robert could receive but scant education. Like many another boy of original powers, he did not excel at his printed lessons. When but ten years old he told his schoolmaster that his " head was so full of his own ideas that there was no room for the storage of dusty books." Even at that early age his natural gifts began to appear. He hammered out pencils from stray bits of sheet-lead that came in his way, and these he employed to draw with an ease and accuracy that steadily increased. He could soon sketch a friend's likeness, a neighboring landscape, or a new machine. Benjamin West, the artist, lived in the adjoining county of Chester. He had been a warm friend of Fulton's father, whose home was adorned by family portraits from the brush of West. These and other of his canvasses, at home and in neighboring houses, young Robert ardently admired. He had enough artistic judgment to feel that West was a master: he earnestly longed that he himself might some day be a painter, too.

There was a streak of adventure in this boy. Reigate, whose biography of Fulton appeared in 1856, tells us:

" On July 1, 1778, the following notice was published in Lancaster:

" ' The excessive heat of the weather, the present scarcity of candles, and other considerations, induce the Council to recommend to the inhabitants to forbear illuminating the city on Saturday evening next, July 4th.

" ' By order,

" ' TIMOTHY MATLACK, Secretary.'

" Robert had candles prepared and went to John Fisher, brushmaker, living near the jail, who kept powder and shot for sale. Fisher was astonished at Robert's desire to part with the candles, which were then scarce articles: and he asked why he wished to part with them? Robert replied that ' our rulers have requested the citizens to forbear illuminating their windows and streets; as good citizens we should respect their request; and I prefer illuminating the heavens with skyrockets.' Having procured the powder, he left Fisher's store, and entered a small variety store kept by Theophilus Cossart, where he asked the price of the largest pasteboard. Having bought several sheets, he said that he meant to make rockets with them. ' Tut, tut!', said Cossart, ' that's an impossibility.' ' No, sir,' said Robert, ' there is nothing impossible.' "

Young Fulton had not only artistic faculty, which made him an admirer of West, he had the constructiveness of a born mechanic. The best gunsmiths in the State were Isch

& Messersmith, whose premises were near his home. Robert had free access to their workshop, and there, without formal engagement or apprenticeship, he learned the art of a gunsmith. While still a boy, he made capital stocks, locks, barrels, and other parts of pistols and guns. Here his skill with the pencil stood him in good stead; he drew new patterns skilfully and well; their outlines were as clear in his imagination as were the finished arms to his eye. Yet more: he computed the best proportions for a firearm, and his figures proved true when tested with powder and ball.

But Robert was not always at work: sometimes he took a holiday. When he was about fourteen he went with a chum, Christopher Gumpf, on a fishing excursion, taking his turn at poling the boat. Robert found the exercise more severe than he liked. Soon thereafter he built a boat driven by paddle-wheels; it demanded less muscular exertion than poling, so the boys used it for several seasons as they fished on the Conestoga Creek, near Rockford. This service of paddle-wheels clung to the young sportsman's memory, to be fruitfully revived, as we shall duly see. But at that time there was more in the air of Pennsylvania than an interest in the mechanics of navigation. While peace prevailed, there was a threat of war, and a threat to be soon fulfilled. Fulton was eleven years old when the Declaration of Independence was signed in Philadelphia. As a boy and a youth he saw all that led to the War of the Revolution; and later he beheld the founding of the Union, with the nomination of George Washington as President. Naturally he imbibed the convictions of his kith and kin, and joined in their whole-souled hatred of the Tories. This feeling was intensified by the quartering in the neighborhood of a troop of Hessians, sent out by King George III. Robert made fun of these mercenaries in more than one spirited caricature. All this atmosphere of conflict, together with his learning the trade of a gunsmith, told deeply upon his mind and heart, as we shall presently note.

But as Fulton grew from youth to manhood, art drew him more strongly than arms. So well did he draw and paint, so much pleasure did he feel in wielding pencil and brush, that, when seventeen, he went to Philadelphia, there to earn his bread at the easel. He did that and more. On his twenty-first birthday he came home with money enough to buy his mother a small farm in Washington County. While in Philadelphia, then the capital of the country, his talents and address, his good nature and good will, gained him attached friends. He was presented one day to Benjamin Franklin, then in his seventy-sixth year, who was about to embark for France, there to represent his country with distinction. It was during his stay in Philadelphia that Fulton acquired the tact and courtesy which marked him ever afterward, and so notably smoothed his difficulties as an inventor and a pioneer.

At home in Lancaster, it was plain that his health was impaired. His lungs showed weakness; he had worked too long and too hard in an ill-ventilated studio. He resolved to go abroad, where he could study art and enjoy a holiday at the same time. His friend, Benjamin West, had risen to fame and fortune in London; from him he might reasonably look for aid and counsel. After a refreshing sojourn at the Warm Sulphur Springs of Virginia, he sailed for England late in 1786. Mr. West received him most hospitably, and this kindness Fulton endeavored to requite. West's pictures were then to be had at prices comparatively low. Fulton sought to secure a series of them for Philadelphia, but he failed to collect the fund required, moderate though it was. To-day the Academy of Fine Arts in that city has West's "Death on a Pale Horse," "Paul and Barnabas," and "Christ Rejected," three characteristic compositions.

Fulton, while traveling as an artist in Devonshire, became acquainted with the Duke of Bridgewater and Earl Stanhope. Both noblemen were warmly interested in engineering as well as in fine art; there was much to win their regard in the young American, who was as much at home at the lathe as at the easel. The vast estate of the Duke of Bridgewater held minerals of great value, if they could only be brought to market. Manchester nearby, already an important center for manufactures, needed coal such as abounded in the lands of the Duke, who at length engaged Brindley, the engineer, to build him canals on a comprehensive scale. Fulton discussed with the Duke every detail of these projected waterways, with the effect that, in his own brain, art became eclipsed by engineering, and permanently. Earl Stanhope was of a wholly different type from the Duke of Bridgewater; he was a man of paper projects rather than a practical inventor. He was fully alive to the benefits which canals would confer on England; indeed, it was his pamphlet on this subject that first directed Fulton's mind to canal-building. Lord Stanhope one day told Fulton that he meant to equip a boat with a steam engine, using a propeller modeled on the web foot of a waterfowl, opening as thrust backward in the water, and closing when driven forward. Fulton told the Earl that such a propeller was not feasible. It would meet so much resistance as to be unendurably slow.

In 1794, Fulton, freed from the toil of his brush, was prolific in new devices. He invented and patented double inclined planes to carry a ship overland from one canal or stream to another. Planes of this kind were duly adopted on the Morris and Essex Canal in New Jersey. Captain James B. Eads' scheme of a trans-isthmian railroad, to unite the Atlantic and Pacific Oceans, was developed from these designs. Fulton took a broad, statesmanlike view of transportation as a national unifier. Said he: " I contemplate a time when canals shall pass through every vale, winding around each hill, and bind the whole country together in bonds of social intercourse." His forecast of national unification is fulfilled, but chiefly by railroads, which have reduced canals to a subordinate place. Let us pursue Fulton's interest in these waterways until we reach 1807, when he returned to America, and pleaded with the National Government for a comprehensive canal policy. In 1810 he wrote the Legislature of New York on the same subject. His advocacy in mind, he was afterward appointed a commissioner to investigate the feasibility of connecting the Great Lakes with the Hudson River. This project fired his imagination; a year before his death he urged it with force and eloquence. His persuasions finally blossomed in the building of the Erie Canal, an enterprise which gave a golden impulse to the fortunes of New York City.

To return to 1794, when Fulton was living in Birmingham, not far from Boulton & Watt's manufactory of steam engines. During this year, in quick succession, he devised a marble-sawing machine, a machine to spin flax, and a rope-making apparatus. He also designed a mechanical dredger, or power-shovel, for canals. This was long used in England; it foreran the excavator, since familiar in surface mining and railroad construction on both sides of the Atlantic. In 1795 he invented an iron aqueduct, whose parts could be cast in open sand, and erected with simple staging. This aqueduct could be rendered water-tight much more easily than stonework. A structure on this plan was built over the Dee, at Pont-y-Cysyllte, twenty miles from Chester; its spans, each of 52 feet, were supported on pillars, the highest standing 126 feet from the ground. He applied similar principles to bridges, several of which were built for the Surrey Iron Railway. Some of these bridges were provided with endless ropes for haulage, using water-power, so as to dispense with horses and their towpaths. Another of Fulton's plans, greatly extended since its alliance with steam, was to discharge loads from cars or wagons into slides leading to wharves. These inventions were described and illustrated in papers which were lost at sea in 1804, aboard a ship bound for New York. No such mishap befell his treatise on " Canal Navigation," published in 1795, presenting original designs for locks and other accessories of canals. This work displays Fulton's excellence as a draughtsman: every line from his pencil is clear and neat. As a modeler he was equally skilful. These gifts were partnered with uncommon practical ability. His computations of cost were exact and cautious, giving all dimensions, the load for each horse or wagon, the speed of projected machinery, with careful estimates of revenue and net profits.

In 1797, France and England were temporarily at peace. A new chapter in Fulton's life opened when, in that year, he went to Paris to patent his inventions, and offer them to the French people. He took credentials to Joel Barlow, an eminent American publicist, who received him most cordially. In Mr. Barlow's house Fulton resided for seven years, a cherished friend. During this period Fulton illustrated his host's ambitious poem, " The Columbiad," which was dedicated to Fulton, who, in 1807, published it at a cost of $5,000. Another task in art was his huge panorama, produced in 1800, " The Burning of Moscow." This canvas, delineating an early conflagration in the Russian capital, was a singular forecast of the tragedy in 1812, which cost Napoleon the flower of his army, and drove him from Russia.* But it was not to illustrate poetry or to

*In the memorable retreat from Moscow, Barlow, then minister to France from the United States, fell a victim. He was to lay the draft of a treaty before Napoleon, and proceeded to Russia with that purpose. Barlow, traveling in a carriage, through extreme cold

paint panoramas that Fulton came to Paris. David Bush-nell, of Connecticut, during the War of the Revolution, had applied clockwork to magazines of gunpowder, sunk with intent to destroy the invader's warships. This apparatus, from crudity of design and faulty workmanship, had failed, but Fulton saw in it the germ of a weapon so deadly that it might prove fatal to war itself.

Late in 1797, with aid from Barlow, Fulton began experiments with cylinders of gunpowder exploded under water. These he called torpedoes, from the cramp-fish of that name, which paralyzes or kills its victims by an electric shock. Fulton's first torpedoes failed: their failure taught him how to improve his plans. His amended designs were offered to the Dutch Government through Mr. Schimmel-penninck, ambassador from Holland to France. A commissioner was appointed by the Batavian Republic to examine Fulton's scheme; he gave the inventor no encouragement. At this juncture a Dutchman, Mr. Vanstaphast, furnished Fulton with means for the construction of an improved machine. This he offered to the Batavian Government, eliciting no response. · By 1800, partly with profits from his panorama, Fulton built his first diving-boat, the *Nautilus*. It embodied original features which survive in all the submersible craft of to-day, and which stamp Fulton as an inventor of the first rank. She was launched on the Seine, near Rouen, on July 30, 1800, and submerged for three hours, the river at that point being about twenty-five feet deep. Next day Fulton took his boat down the Seine to Havre, where he carried out further experiments. Soon afterward he built at Paris a second and improved *Nautilus*.

and privation, was attacked by pneumonia on his way to Wilna, where he was to meet the Emperor. At Zarnaweic, a village near Cracow, Barlow could proceed no further; and there, on December 24, 1812, he died. His biography, by Charles Burr Todd, appeared in 1886.

She had iron ribs and was sheathed with copper; her shape was that of a long narrow egg. On her deck in a groove lay a small mast, which could be erected from a hinge. In the interior, about six feet in diameter, were the handles of the oars, arranged screw fashion. A reservoir for water, controlled by a lever, enabled the vessel to descend at will. She rose in obedience to a force-pump. This *Nautilus* was finished in June, 1801, and was tested on the Seine above the Hôtel des Invalides. Fulton and a sailor shut themselves in, with a single candle, and remained under water twenty minutes, emerging after a voyage of several hundred yards. He again descended and returned to his first point of departure, amid the applause of thousands of spectators.

No picture of the first *Nautilus* is known to exist. It is said to have had a superstructure which gave it the look of an ordinary boat when on the water. At the top forward rose a dome-like conning tower with glass scuttles; just abaft was a mast built of light spars framed together so as to stow snugly along the top of the boat when submerged. The keel was a heavy metal bar which formed a counterpoise and steadied the boat. The anchors and hoisting apparatus were in a compartment right forward, while amidships was the handworked mechanism that revolved the propeller. Whether this propeller was a screw, or a wheel fitted with elliptical buckets, is uncertain. The torpedo appliance was like that of Bushnell's " turtle," the wood screw coming through the dome of the conning tower. The torpedo itself was fitted with a gun-lock fired by a lanyard instead of Bushnell's clockwork.

Through his friend, the secretary of the port of Brest, Fulton received from Napoleon an order to direct his torpedo-boat against the British fleet, then blockading the French coast. If he destroyed a warship of ten guns he was to receive 60,000 francs; with rewards rising to 400,000 francs if he blew up a vessel of more than thirty guns. Three leading members of the National Institute, Monge, Laplace, and Volney, were appointed by Napoleon to examine and report upon the performance of this *Nautilus*. In a note to them Fulton said: " On the third of Thermidor (the eleventh month of the French Republican calendar) I commenced my experiments by plunging to a depth of 5 feet, then 10 feet, then 15 feet, and so on to 25 feet. I went no further, as the machine could bear no greater pressure of superincumbent water. My boat had 212 cubic feet capacity, containing enough oxygen to support four men and two small candles for three hours."

This *Nautilus* plunged and rose while perpendicular; it turned to the right or left at pleasure. Its compass was unaffected by submersion. In later experiments air was compressed in a brass globe to a pressure of two hundred atmospheres, affording a supply for a lengthened voyage. The bombs to be fired from this boat were of copper, and varied from a capacity of twenty pounds of gunpowder to ten times as much. They were provided with a trigger, so as to explode when they struck their target. This mechanism was tested by the destruction of a sloop during August, 1801, in the harbor of Brest, a bomb containing twenty pounds of powder being used. For a whole summer Fulton pursued one British vessel after another with this *Nautilus*. Once he came near a seventy-four gun frigate, but she managed to escape. Fulton, therefore, received no reward from France. This failure chilled the ardor of his friends in the French army and navy, but it had no effect on his own sanguine spirit.

He now proved himself a man of decided political inconstancy. Earl Stanhope had, all along, kept himself informed regarding Fulton's boats and torpedoes, as successively improved. In the House of Lords he warned the British nation that Fulton's weapons boded ruin to the

British fleet. Negotiations were accordingly opened with Fulton, and in September, 1803, he was invited to exhibit his inventions to officials of the British Government. He reached London on May 19, 1804, and soon laid his plans before Mr. Pitt, the prime minister, who remarked that these weapons might annihilate every fleet in the world. It was proposed to pay Fulton a salary of two hundred pounds, about one thousand dollars, per month, and one-half the value of all the vessels that he destroyed within fourteen years, the period of his patent. An expedition, including a torpedo boat of Fulton's, set sail against the French fleet in the harbor of Boulogne, but without success. Fulton's torpedoes were in perfect order, but they were handled by gunners without experience in their control. Shortly afterward, on October 15, 1805, Fulton blew up with torpedoes a heavy brig at Walmer Roads, near Mr. Pitt's castle. Seventy pounds of powder sufficed, and Fulton recorded: " Exactly in fifteen minutes from the time of drawing the peg and throwing the carcass (torpedo) into the water, the explosion took place. It lifted the brig almost bodily, and broke her in two. The ends sank immediately, and nothing was seen but floating fragments." On January 23, 1806, Mr. Pitt died, at the early age of forty-seven, and in the ensuing change of ministry, Fulton's friends were dispersed. The succeeding government, under Lord Granville, asked the inventor if they might suppress his weapons if they wished, in case of purchase. His refusal concluded:

" At all events, whatever may be your reward, I will never consent to let these inventions lie dormant, should my country at any time have need of them. Were you to grant me an annuity of twenty thousand pounds a year, I would sacrifice all to the safety and independence of my country. But I hope that England and America will understand their mutual interest too well to war with each other, and I have no desire to introduce my engines into practice for the benefit of any other nation."

Fulton, taking a far look ahead, believed that his promotion of canals would do much to insure peace, while his plunging boats and torpedoes, after a single decisive battle, would abolish war. In his " Thoughts on Free Trade " he declared:

"After this (laying his views before the Directory of France) I was convinced that society must pass through ages of progressive improvement, before the freedom of the seas could be established by an agreement of nations that it was for the good of the whole. I saw that the growing wealth and commerce of the United States, and their increasing population, would compel them to look for a protection by sea, and, perhaps, drive them to the necessity of resorting to European measures by establishing a navy. Seeing this, I turned my whole attention to finding out means of destroying such engines of oppression by some method which would put it out of the power of any nation to maintain such a system, and would compel every government to adopt the simple principles of education, industry, and a free circulation of its produce."

Fulton far excelled his predecessors in the construction and control of torpedoes; and his devices were the precursors of the Lay and Howell torpedoes, the Whitehead and other models. He lived, however, before it was possible to bring submarine warfare beyond a moderate degree of effectiveness. In his day electricity was unmastered, and its igniting, propelling, and directive services were unimagined. Steels, and other strong and tough alloys, existed only in qualities which, to-day, are deemed weak and inferior. And the explosion engine, uniting high energy with a lightness which to-day gives it the freedom of the skies, had not been born. Fulton, of course, could not foresee these and other modern resources of invention, or the seesaw which they create betwixt the arts of attacks and of defense. First, an armor is rolled of steel so stout and tough as to arrest the heaviest shot. At once projectiles are improved in contour, are increased in weight, are built of stronger alloys, and they pierce the armor easily. The armor is now reinforced to a doubled resistance, only within a few months to face shot of new penetrating power. Torpedoes are devised which threaten to send every warship of an enemy to the ocean floor. Very soon a torpedo destroyer is built, which, for a little while, lets designers of warships catch their breath; and so proceeds an unending conflict, as successive strides are taken in the production of alloys, in the chemistry of explosives, in the speed and dirigibility of submarine or aerial craft.

A word from Fulton himself should be heard at this point. In his " Torpedo War," published in New York, in 1810, he said :

" Although cannon, firearms, and the whole detail of ammunition, now appear extremely simple, yet we here see the very slow advances to their present state of perfection; and they are still improving. Hence I conclude that it is now impossible to foresee to what degree torpedoes may be improved and rendered useful. When Schwartz invented powder, it may be presumed that his mind did not embrace all its consequences, or perceive that his discovery would supersede the use of catapults, armor, bows and arrows, and totally change the whole art of war. He certainly could have no conception of such a combination of art as we now see in ships of the line; those movable fortifications, armed with 32-pounders, and furnished with wings, to spread oppression over every part of the ocean, and carry destruction to every harbor of the earth. In consequence of the invention of gunpowder, ships of war have been contrived, and increased to their present enormous size and number: then may not science, in her progress, point out a means by which the application of the violent explosive force of gunpowder shall destroy ships of war, and give to the seas the liberty which shall secure perpetual peace between nations that are separated by the ocean? My conviction is that the means are here developed, and require only to be organized and practised, to produce that liberty so dear to every rational and reflecting man; and there is a grandeur in persevering to success in so immense an enterprise—so well calculated to excite the most vigorous exertions of the highest order of intellect, that I hope to interest the patriotic feelings of every friend to America, to justice, and to humanity, in so good a cause."

While Fulton had been devising and improving his plunging boat and torpedoes, he had kept in view the building of a steamboat. Peaceful commerce had as large a place in his mind as the enginery of destruction. As a boy, steam navigation had been brought to his notice by a neighbor, William Henry. This inventor, who deserves more praise than has fallen to his lot, in 1763 built and successfully worked a steamboat. Soon after its launching, it was wrecked by accident. Henry seems to have thought the time unripe for his enterprise, so he went no further than to construct a model which embodied improvements on his first design. Henry owned several of Benjamin West's pictures, and these attracted Fulton, as a visitor, in his boyhood and youth. It is altogether probable that Henry often discussed with Fulton the topic uppermost in his own mind, that of steamboats. Henry died on December 15, 1786, just about the time that Fulton embarked for England.

William Henry had, among the frequent callers at his house, John Fitch, a skilful mechanic from Connecticut, who in 1785 presented to the American Philosophical Society of Philadelphia a model of a machine for propelling a boat by steam. He tried in vain to secure aid from the Legislatures of Pennsylvania, Maryland, and Virginia. He was more fortunate in New Jersey, whose Legislature granted him the exclusive right to build and use any kind of boat propelled by steam in the waters of the State for four-teen years from March 18, 1786. He formed a joint-stock company, and proceeded with experiments. On July 27, 1786, he placed a small boat or skiff on the Delaware River propelled by oars moved by a steam engine. In 1790 he built another and improved steamer, which ran at seven miles an hour. In June of that year it began to ply as a passenger boat between Philadelphia and Trenton. It ran more than two thousand miles, and never met with an accident. In 1796 or 1797 Fitch launched a small steamer, propelled by a screw, on the Collect, a pond which occupied the present site of the Tombs in Centre Street, New York.

James Rumsey, also in 1786, drove a boat at four miles an hour, employing a steam engine to force water abaft in an impelling stream. His feat was witnessed, with marked approval, by General Washington, on the Potomac at Shepherdstown, Virginia. But the most memorable success attained by any early inventor of steamboats in America, stands, as we have already seen, to the credit of John Stevens, of Hoboken, New Jersey. One day, driving along the bank of the Delaware River, he saw the little steamboat of John Fitch, on its way to Bordentown. He resolved to outdo what Fitch had done. After a long course of experiment, he launched in 1804 and 1805 two steamboats, incorporating original features of great value. His boilers were of sectional design, his engines were at once compact and strong, he employed steam at a pressure of fifty pounds to the square inch, and he adopted screws as his propellers. One of his steamboats, which attained a speed of eight miles an hour, had two of these propellers, prophetic, indeed, of a modern ocean greyhound.

But all this advance in engineering, all this enterprise in commercial adoption, seems to have remained unknown to Fulton. Ever since 1786, he had resided abroad, and even the striking experiments with steamboats in Europe appear to have long escaped his attention. In Paris he had often discussed steamboat projects with Chancellor Livingston, then Minister of the United States, who, years before in America, had built steamboats of disappointing slowness, although he was aided by Mark Isambard Brunel, one of the most eminent engineers of his day. At that time the United States had not established its patent system, and each State could reward an inventor, or an introducer of inventions, with a monopoly duly defined as to period and territory. Livingston was offered by the Legislature of New York a monopoly of the steam navigation of the Hudson River, on his accomplishing a successful voyage upon its waters. Fulton, while residing at Plombieres, after prolonged study, drew plans for his first steamboat, with a view to navigation in America. It occurred to him that the best form of propellers might be chaplets, small, square floats, fastened to an endless belt, and kept in motion by a steam engine. Tests with models proved that paddle-wheels, such as he had turned by hand as a boy on the Conestoga, were more efficient. He had once used a primitive kind of screw propeller, and for some unknown reason abandoned it. On February 16, 1796, he wrote to Dr. Edmund Cartwright: " I have just proved an experiment on moving boats, with a fly of four parts, very similar to that of a smoke-jack. I find it applies the power to great advantage, and it is extremely simple." *

Chancellor Robert R. Livingston, who now became Fulton's equal partner, was one of the leading publicists of his time, so that he brought to their joint interests wide influence and high prestige. He had been a member of the Continental Congress, had taken part in drafting the Declaration of Independence, was one of the framers of the Constitution of the State of New York, and, as its first

* Proceedings Institute of Civil Engineers, London, 1844.

Chancellor, had administered to George Washington his oath of office at his inauguration in New York. Chancellor Livingston, while Minister to France, negotiated the purchase of Louisiana from Napoleon. With pecuniary aid from Livingston, Fulton completed his steamboat, and launched it on the Seine early in the spring of 1803. Its length of hull was 66 feet, its beam 8 feet, its draught 3 feet. Unfortunately, its construction was flimsy; no sooner did the machinery come on board, than the hull broke in

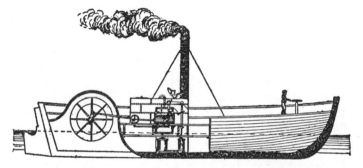

WILLIAM SYMINGTON'S STEAMBOAT "CHARLOTTE DUNDAS"

In March, 1802, ran through the long reach of the Forth and Clyde Canal, against a quick breeze, tugging two vessels, each of more than 70 tons' burden, completing 19½ miles in six hours. When she went by herself, she ran six miles an hour.

Her cylinder was 22 inches in diameter with a stroke of four feet.

two and sank. The machinery was little harmed by its drenching; the hull had to be rebuilt. In that reconstruction a lesson was taught which American builders of steam craft have never forgotten; their hulls, while light, are always abundantly strong. In July, Fulton floated his vessel once more; on August 9 a trial trip took place, at a speed of four and a half miles an hour. This experiment, although really epoch-making, was regarded with indifference by the people of Paris. The steamer remained for months on the Seine, near the palace, without calling forth any remark. One feature of its equipment was noteworthy, —a water-tube boiler, patented by Barlow in France, and affording so extended a surface to the fire that steam was raised with a new rapidity.

In May, 1804, when Fulton was in England, on behalf of his plunging boat and torpedoes, news came to him of the steamboats of William Symington. The first of these boats had demonstrated its success in 1788; in the following year a better designed steamer had attained a still quicker pace. A third steamboat, the *Charlotte Dundas,* had, in 1802, reached a speed of six miles an hour on the Forth and Clyde Canal. This crowning feat aroused interest throughout Great Britain, and Symington was asked by the Duke of Bridgewater to design steam vessels to ply on his canal. Fulton saw at once that Symington had surpassed his own achievements, so he called on the Scottish inventor in quest of information. Symington's account of the visit appears in J. Scott Russel's " Steam and Steam Navigation ":

" I caused the engine fire to be lighted up, and in a short time thereafter put the steamboat in motion, and carried him from Lock No. 16 (of the Forth and Clyde Canal), where the boat then lay, four miles west of the canal, and returned to the place of starting, in eighty minutes, to the great astonishment of Mr. Fulton and several gentlemen who at the outset chanced to come on board.

" During the trip Mr. Fulton asked if I had any objections to his taking notes respecting the steamboat, to which question I said—none; as I considered the more publicity that was given to any discovery intended for the general good, so much the better; and having the privilege secured by letters-patent, I was not afraid of his making any encroachment upon my right in the British Dominions, though in the United States, I was well aware, I had no power of control. In consequence, he pulled out a memorandum-book, and, after putting several pointed questions respecting the general construction and effect of the machine, which I answered in a most explicit manner, he jotted down particularly everything then described, with his own remarks upon the boat, while moving with him on board, along the canal; but he seems to have been altogether forgetful of this, as, notwithstanding his fair promises, I never heard anything more of him till reading in a newspaper an account of his death."

Fulton must have been chagrined to discover that, through sheer ignorance of what Symington had accomplished years before, his own plans for a steamboat had been misdirected and were, indeed, wholly forestalled. Even in those days of slow mails, of belated publication, it seems inexplicable that Fulton, until his return to England, did not know of experiments so decisive as those of Symington. Fulton, we must remember, lived in the chief city of continental Europe, where he was constantly meeting many of the best informed men of his time. His later services, on behalf of steam navigation, did much toward making impossible a repetition of so costly an ignorance. As Fulton's negotiations with the British Government for submarine warfare gradually drifted into failure, he saw that his future career lay in launching steamboats on American waters. With characteristic promptness he proceeded to his drawing-board, to complete a design at the earliest feasible moment. For motive power he ordered a steam engine from Boulton & Watt, of Birmingham, its price being £548 ($2,670). Soon afterward, in October, 1806, he sailed from Falmouth, reaching New York two months later. His drawings were forthwith placed in the hands of Charles Brown, a shipbuilder at Corlears Hook, on the East River side of New York. While the hull was still unfinished, Fulton and Livingston ran out of funds. To John Stevens, of Hoboken, a brother-in-law of Livingston's, who had operated steamboats with success, they offered a third interest in their venture if he would come to their aid. He said no, as he disapproved Fulton's design. On another occasion Fulton was so hard pressed for cash that he spent a whole evening trying to persuade a friend to advance him $1,000. All in vain. Next day he resumed his plea; his friend proffered $100 as a loan, provided that the remaining $900 could be borrowed without delay. These loans were at length effected, but all the lenders stipulated that their names be withheld, dreading the ridicule which would attach to so foolhardy an experiment as steamboating. Fulton narrated to a friend the continuing disfavor of the New York public: "When I was building my first steamboat, the project was viewed by the public either

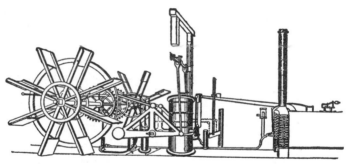

MACHINERY OF FULTON'S STEAMBOAT "CLERMONT," 1807

with indifference, or with contempt, as a visionary scheme. My friends, indeed, were civil, but they were shy. They listened with patience to my explanations, but with a settled cast of incredulity on their countenances. As I had occasion daily to pass to and from the shipyard while my boat was in progress, I have often loitered unknown near the idle groups of strangers, gathering in little circles, and heard various inquiries as to the object of this new vehicle. The language was uniformly that of scorn, sneer, or ridicule. The loud laugh often rose at my expense; the dry jest; the wise calculation of losses and expenditures; the dull but endless repetition of 'Fulton's Folly.' Never did a single encouraging remark, a bright hope, a warm wish, cross my path. Silence itself was but politeness, veiling its doubts, or hiding its reproaches."

Chancellor Livingston's estate on the Hudson was called Clermont, and its name was bestowed on Fulton's steamboat. The *Clermont,* duly launched and equipped, started from New York on August 17, 1807, for her first trip to Albany. Fulton thus narrated the journey:

" To the Editor of the *American Citizen.*

" SIR—I arrived this afternoon at four o'clock, in the steamboat from Albany. As the success of my experiment gives me great hopes that such boats may be of great importance to my country, to prevent erroneous opinions, and give some satisfaction to the friends of useful improvements, you will have the goodness to publish the following statement of facts.

" I left New York on Monday, at one o'clock, and arrived at Clermont, the seat of Chancellor Livingston, at one o'clock on Tuesday—time, twenty-four hours—distance 110 miles. On Wednesday I departed from the Chancellor's, at nine in the morning, and arrived at Albany at five in the afternoon—distance forty miles, time eight hours. The sum is 150 miles in 32 hours, equal to nearly five miles an hour. On Thursday at nine o'clock in the morning I left Albany and arrived at the Chancellor's at six in the evening. I started thence at seven, and arrived in New York at four in the afternoon, time thirty hours, equal to five miles an hour. Throughout my whole way, going and returning, the wind was ahead: no advantage could be derived from my sails: the whole has, therefore, been performed by the power of the steam engine."

The *Clermont* was 150 feet long, 13 feet beam, and 7 feet in depth of hold. Her tonnage was about 100. The engine cylinder was of 24-inch diameter, and 4 feet stroke. The boiler was 20 feet long, 7 feet high, and 8 feet wide. After her first season, encouraged by financial success, the *Clermont* was strengthened throughout and widened to 18

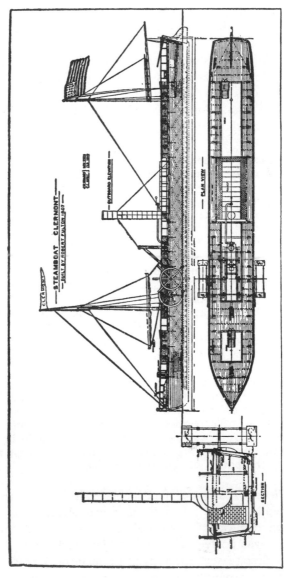

PLAN OF THE "CLERMONT," AS REPRODUCED BY THE HUDSON-FULTON CELEBRATION COMMISSION, 1907

feet, while her engine was improved from plans furnished by Fulton. Two more boats, the *Raritan* and the *Car of Neptune*, were added to the *Clermont*, establishing the first regular line of steamboats in the world, some years in advance of similar lines in Europe. The Legislature of New York extended its monopoly to Fulton and Livingston, adding five years for each new boat of their line, up to a limit of thirty years.

A ferry service from New York to Jersey City followed, after considerable delay. In March, 1811, Elisha Boudinot and other citizens of Newark subscribed $50,000 for a steam ferry between Jersey City and New York, and Fulton was requested to design the required boats, two in number. They were constructed by Charles Brown, the builder of the *Clermont*, and on July 2, 1812, one of them, the *Jersey*, crossed the North River, beginning her regular trips fifteen days later. Fulton thus described her: " She is built of two boats, each of 10 feet beam, and 5 feet deep in the hold: which boats are distant from each other 10 feet, confined by strong transverse beam knees and diagonal braces, forming a deck 30 feet wide and 80 feet long. The propelling water-wheel is placed between the boats to prevent it from injury from ice and shock on entering and approaching the dock. The whole of the machinery being placed between the two boats, leaves 10 feet on the deck of one boat for carriages, horses, and cattle; the other, having neat benches, covered with an awning, is for passengers, and there is also a passage and stairway to a neat cabin, which is 50 feet long and 5 feet clear from the floor to the beams, furnished with benches and provided with a stove in winter. Although the two boats and the space between them give 30 feet beam, yet they present sharp bows to the water, and have only the resistance in the water of one boat twenty feet beam. Both ends being alike, and each having a rudder, she never puts about."

In 1813, the *York*, a sister-vessel to the *Jersey*, was launched and placed in service. These boats ran every half hour during the day, accomplishing their trip of a mile and a half in fifteen minutes. This was the first permanent steam ferry ever established. Brooklyn, during 1813, was joined to New York by a similar service.

Fulton was well aware of the golden harvest that steamboats would reap in America, especially in the Western States, then fast coming under the plow. To his old and faithful ally, Joel Barlow, residing near Washington, he wrote:

" My steamboat voyage to Albany and back turned out rather more favorably than I had calculated. The distance from New York to Albany is 150 miles. I ran it up in thirty-two hours, and down in thirty. I had a light breeze against me the whole way, both going and coming, and the voyage has been performed wholly by the power of the steam engine. I overtook many sloops and schooners, beating to the windward, and parted with them as if they had been at anchor. The power of propelling boats by steam is now fully proved. The morning I left New York, there were not, perhaps, thirty persons in the city who believed that the boat would ever move one mile an hour, or be of the least utility, and, while we were putting off from the wharf, which was crowded with spectators, I heard a number of sarcastic remarks. This is the way ignorant men compliment what they call philosophers and projectors. Having employed much time, money, and zeal in accomplishing this work, it gives me, as it will you, great pleasure to see it fully answer my expectations. It will give a cheap and quick conveyance to the merchandise on the Mississippi, Missouri, and other great rivers, which are now laying open their treasures to the enterprise of our countrymen; and although the prospect of personal emolument has been some inducement to me, yet I feel infinitely more pleasure in reflecting on the immense advantage that my country will derive from the invention."

During the winter of 1807-08, the *Clermont*, as virtually rebuilt, was named the *North River*; she made regular trips on the Hudson for several years. Fulton wrote to Charles Wilson Peale, the portrait painter, regarding the enlarged boat:

"CLERMONT, N. Y., June 11, 1808.
"My steamboat is now in complete operation and works much to my satisfaction, making the voyages from New York to Albany, 150 miles, on an average of 35 hours. She has three excellent cabins, or, rather, rooms, contained 54 berths, with kitchen, larder, pantry, bar, and steward's room. Passengers have been encouraging. Last Saturday she started from New York with seventy, which is doing very well for these times, when trade has not its usual activity."

Some of the regulations posted on this steamboat quaintly tell of manners and customs a century ago in America:

"Way-passengers, who are not out for more than half the night, are not entitled to lie down in a berth.
"As the comfort of all passengers must be considered, cleanliness, neatness, and order are necessary. It is, therefore, not permitted that any persons shall smoke in the ladies' cabin, or in the great cabin, under a penalty, first of $1.50, and 50 cents for each half hour they offend against this rule; the money to be spent in wine for the company.
"It is not permitted for any person to lie down in a berth with their boots or shoes on, under penalty of $1.50 and 50 cents for every half hour they may offend against this rule.
"In the ladies' cabin, in the great cabin, cards and all games are to cease at ten o'clock in the evening, that those persons who wish to sleep might not be disturbed."

Before the death of Fulton, in 1815, he had built seventeen boats, which included the first steam war frigate, the first torpedo-boat, and the first steam ferry-boats, the latter equipped with rounded ends for approach at either shore, and floating docks to receive them. At the time of Fulton's death, the steamboat *The Emperor of Russia* was under construction for the Russian Government. The enterprise was postponed, and was afterward taken up by other contractors.

Fulton's steamboat project had not wholly allured him from his long cherished plans of submarine warfare. Shortly after his return to America he offered his torpedoes to the Federal Government at Washington, maintaining that "in the hands of a righteous nation, they would insure universal peace." Fulton had a warm friend in President Jefferson, whose interest in applied science was second only to his devotion to the duties of government. Largely at the instance of the President, Fulton was given an opportunity to prove the value of his torpedoes. Governor's Island, a mile from the Battery at the foot of Manhattan Island, was granted him for his tests. He invited the magistracy of New York and a party of citizens to witness his torpedoes at work. While he was explaining their mechanism, his auditors crowded round him with a discommoding effect. He pointed to a copper case, standing under the gateway close by, to which was attached a clockwork lock. This he set in motion with the remark: "Gentlemen, this is a charged torpedo, with which, precisely in its present state, I mean to blow up a vessel. It contains 170 pounds of powder, and if I would let the clockwork run fifteen minutes, I doubt not that this fortification would be blown to atoms." The circle around Fulton was enlarged in a twinkling, and before five of his fifteen minutes had elapsed, there were not more than two spectators within sight of the speaker. Much more striking than any feat of that afternoon was his destruction, by a torpedo, on July 20, 1807, of a large hulk brig in the harbor of New York. He was ever a severe critic of his own plans, and this success only led him to imagine improvements in construction and control, which he did not live to complete.

He had derived his idea of torpedoes from David Bushnell: another weapon of attack was original with himself. This was ordnance used under water instead of, as usual, through the air. Ericsson, in his *Destroyer,* developed Fulton's scheme much further than was possible with the scant resources at his predecessor's command. To ex-President Jefferson, Fulton sent a long letter describing his experiments in submarine gunnery, with penciled sketches, concluding:

" Instead of having the cannon and portholes of a warship, as usual, above the surface of the water, I place my cannon so low in the vessel that their portholes will be below the surface of the water, from six inches to ten feet or more. Thus the cannon, being fired with its muzzle under water, the bullets will pass through the water instead of the air, and through the sides of the enemy, from one to ten feet below the waterline, which, letting in the water in quantity, will sink the vessel attacked."

All this may be found, with much else, in his book, " Torpedo War." In the course of a letter to the Hon. Paul Hamilton, Secretary of the United States Navy, Fulton said on February 1, 1811:

" It is proved and admitted, first, that the waterproof locks will ignite gunpowder under water; secondly, it is proved that seventy pounds of powder, exploded under the bottom of a vessel of two hundred tons, will blow her up; hence it is admitted, that if a sufficient quantity of powder, which, I believe, need not be more than two hundred pounds, be ignited beneath the bottom of a first-rate man-of-war, it would instantly destroy her; thirdly, it is proved and admitted that a gun can be fired under water, and that a cable of any size can be cut by that means, at any required depth. With these immediately important principles approved and admitted, the question naturally occurs, whether there be, within the genius of inventive faculties of man, the means of placing a torpedo under a ship in defiance of her powers of resistance. He who says there is not, and that consequently torpedoes can never be made useful, must, of course, believe that he has penetrated to the limits of man's inventive powers, and that he has contemplated all the combinations and arrangements which present or future ingenuity can devise to place a torpedo under a ship. . . .

" Of the anchored torpedoes, I have had the pleasure to show you the improvements I have made on these since the meeting of the committee in New York last fall, to give them stability under water, or to take them up or put them down when necessary. There is a very simple mode to convince any unbeliever of the advantage which this kind of engine will present, and the respect for our harbors which it will create in the mind of an enemy: let me put one under water, and they who do not believe in its effect may put their confidence to the proof by sailing over it.

" A compound engine of this kind will cost from $800 to $1,000: 320 of them could be made for the first cost of one ship of 54 guns; of these, say, 100 should protect New York; 100, Boston; 100, Charleston; 20 to be placed in the Delaware between its forts or batteries. Thus four ports could be guarded so as to render it impossible for an enemy's ships to enter any of them, unless first they had strength to take possession of the land and forts, and then time deliberately to search for the torpedoes. Yet one ship of 54 guns cannot guard one port against one 74-gun ship, although the first cost of that vessel in anchored torpedoes would guard at least three ports against ten ships of 74 guns. In commission a 54-gun ship costs to maintain $100,000 a year; this, at five per cent., represents two million dollars in capital. . . . I do not mean to object to ships to protect our coast; but when considered for harbor defense, or for aiding forts or batteries to defend harbors, the money can be better expended in torpedoes."

Commodore Rodgers was an unsparing critic of Fulton's torpedoes and submarine boats. He said, referring to a figure of one of these boats:

" I leave the reader to make his own conclusions, and to judge whether such torpid, unwieldy, six-feet-sided, six-inch-decked, fifteen-sixteenth-sunk-water dungeons, are calculated to supersede the necessity of a navy, particularly when the men who manage them are confined to the limits of their holds, which will be under water, and in as perfect darkness as if shut up in the Black Hole of Calcutta."

No opposition, however severe, could for a moment check Fulton in his endeavor to bring submarine warfare to success. Colden, his biographer, thus describes a submarine boat which was projected during the closing days of Fulton's life:

" He contrived a vessel which was to have a capacity, by means of an air-chamber like that on board the *Nautilus*, to be kept at a greater or less depth in the water, but so that her deck should not be submerged. That chamber communicated with the water, and was shaped like a diving-bell; but it could at pleasure, by an air-pump, be exhausted of air, and then would fill with water; or, any required quantity of air could be forced into it, so as to expel the water from it entirely. The sides of the vessel were to be of ordinary thickness, but her deck was to be stout and plated with iron, so as to render it ball-proof, which would not require so much strength as might at first be imagined, because, as no shot could strike it from a vessel but at a very great angle, the ball would ricochet on a slight resistance from a hard substance. She was of a size to shelter a hundred men under her deck, and was to be moved by a wheel placed in another air-chamber near the stern, so that when the vessel was to be propelled only a part of the under-paddles should be in the water; at least, the upper half, or more, moving in the air. The wheel was to be turned by a crank attached to a shaft, that should penetrate the stern to the air-chamber through a stuffing-box, and run along the middle of the boat until it approached her bows. Through this shaft rungs were to be passed, of which the crew were to take hold as they were seated upon each side of it on benches. By merely pushing the shaft forward and backward the water-wheel would be turned, and the boat propelled. By means of the air-chamber, she was to be kept, when not in hostile action, upon the surface, as common boats are; but when in reach of an enemy, she was to sink, so that nothing but her deck would be exposed to his view or to his fire. Her motion in this situation would be perfectly silent, and therefore he called this contrivance a mute. His design was that she should approach an enemy, which he supposed she might do in fogs or in the night, without being heard or discovered, and do execution by means of his torpedoes or submarine guns. He presented a model of this vessel to the Government, by which it was approved. Under authority of the Executive he commenced building one in the port of New York. Before the hull was finished, his country had to lament his death, and the mechanics he had employed were incapable of proceeding without him."

Reigate, a later biographer than Colden, says that Fulton derived from nature a hint for his submersible, being thoroughly acquainted with the pneumatic machinery by which fishes rise to the surface or lie at the bottom of the sea. This he imitated in the expansions and contractions of a large reservoir of air.

Fulton was an engineer in his every fiber. In 1802 he examined the patent of M. Des Blancs for a steamboat; in his notebook he jotted down a criticism:

" This imperfection of plan makes me believe that M. Des Blancs has not found the proportion which his paddles should bear to the bow of the boat, or the velocity which they should run in proportion to the velocity which the boat is intended to go. Consequently, if he has not known the proportions and the velocities he has not mounted or deposited a description by which an artist could construct a boat to go any given number of miles an hour, nor, in fact, has he shown the means of constructing a boat which can be of use. He has left the proportions and velocities to be discovered. He has not given any rule to make a boat of any given dimensions, go any given distance in a given time, and he has not as yet mounted a boat to navigate by steam in such manner as to be of use to society; for this invention to be rendered useful does not consist in putting oars, paddles, wheels, or resisting chains in motion by a steam engine—but it consists in showing in a clear and distinct manner that it is desired to drive a boat precisely any given number of miles an hour—what must be the size of the cylinder and the velocity of the piston? What must be the size and velocity of the resisting chains? All these things being governed by the laws of Nature, the real Invention is to find them. Till the artist knows the necessary proportions to this and all other sized boats, he must work in the dark and to great uncertainty, and can not be said to have made any clear and distinct discovery or useful invention."

Fulton's mind was crystal clear in seeing that a plan should proceed on trustworthy weighing and measuring, on the precise adaptation of means to ends. In minor matters, too, his perceptions were unusually keen, and he backed them with a courage that made him a terror to humbugs. In 1813 a German immigrant, Wilhelm Redheffer, exhibited in New York a machine which he boasted as a "perpetual motion." Fulton went to see this marvel; he no sooner heard the throb of the apparatus than he exclaimed, "Why, this is a crank motion." Had the rotation been due to a real "perpetual motion," this inequality of throb would not have been heard. Fulton called the showman an impostor; knocking away some thin laths which joined the frame of the machine to the wall, he exposed a strip of moving catgut which turned the "perpetual motion." Following up the catgut, he reached a back-loft. There sat the explanation of the mystery in the person of a poor old wretch gnawing a crust the while he turned a crank. The proprietor of the show disappeared, as a mob of defrauded patrons smashed his machinery in pieces.

In 1812, when the United States declared war with Great Britain, the mind of Fulton at once reverted to his long-pondered plans for naval offense and defense. In March, 1814, Congress authorized him to supervise the building of the first steam vessel of war ever constructed.

This vessel, the *Demologos,* or *Fulton the First,* was launched, without her equipment, on October 29, 1814, from the yard of Adam & Noah Brown on the East River, New York. She had two hulls, 66 feet in length, with a channel between, 15 feet in width, for a paddle-wheel. Her parapet was 4 feet 10 inches wide; she had portholes for thirty 32-pounder guns; two bowsprits and jibs; two masts; and four rudders, one at each end of both hulls. On February 17, 1815, six days before Fulton's death, peace with Great Britain was declared. Three months afterward the engine of *Fulton the First* was reared, and on the fourth of July following, the vessel made a passage to the ocean and back, a distance of 53 miles, in 8 hours and 20 minutes. For many years Fulton's heirs sought payment from Congress for his services as engineer of this ship, for fees as a patentee, and for outlays. In 1846, thirty-one years after his death, this debt, $76,300, was paid.

It was in the very prime of his activity that the career of this great man came to a close. In January, 1815, he testified at Trenton, in a suit which sought to repeal laws which interfered with the plying of ferryboats between the New Jersey shore and New York City. The weather was stormy, and Fulton, whose lungs had for years been weak, took a severe cold. He returned home, and gradually sank until February 23, when he breathed his last. He left a wife, Harriet Livingston, a son, and three daughters. His burial took place next day, from his residence, 2 Marketfield Street, now Battery Place, in the rear of 1 Broadway, to Trinity Church. His remains were interred in the adjoining churchyard, in a vault belonging to the Livingston family. Above that vault a handsome memorial, with a medallion portrait, was, in 1901, reared by the American Society of Mechanical Engineers.

Fulton's biographer, Cadwallader B. Colden, who knew him well, thus describes him:

"Fulton was about six feet high. His person was slender, but well proportioned and well formed. Nature had made him a gentleman and bestowed upon him ease and gracefulness. He had too much good sense for the least affectation. A modest confidence in his own worth and talents gave him an unembarrassed deportment in all companies. His features were strong and of manly beauty. He had large dark eyes, and a projecting brow expressive of intelligence and thought. His temper was mild, his disposition lively. He was fond of society, which he always enlivened by cheerful, cordial manners, and instructed or pleased by his sensible conversation. He expressed himself with energy, fluency, and correctness, and, as he owed more to his own experience and reflections than to books, his sentiments were often interesting from their originality."

Fulton won his laurels chiefly by his introduction of the steamboat—invented, as we have seen, by engineers in Scotland and America long before his experiments. His alliance with Livingston, who held a monopoly from the State of New York, gave him an advantage as a pioneer of which he availed himself ably and boldly. As an inventor and improver of weapons of war, Fulton rose to the front rank, and here he borrowed only to restore a hundredfold. The torpedo, devised by David Bushnell, in Fulton's designs became an instrument wholly new. He improved plunging boats in every detail of their construction and equipment, so that they bear the marks of his hands to this day. Of submarine gunnery, with possibilities yet to be determined, he was the undisputed creator. Whether promoting arts of peace or of war, he took views as wide as the world, always rejoicing in the boons to mankind which were enfolded in his plans for steamboats and canals, his submarine boats and torpedoes. As he sketched new engines of battle, he believed that he was making war so terrible that soon it should wholly cease. He was a many-sided man, and, as he took up tasks widely diverse, each of his talents lent aid to every other.   He was a capital draftsman and painter, a mechanic and an engineer, an inventor and a researcher.   With all this variety of accomplishment he was a shrewd man of business and a warm friend.   Now that fields of human action are divided and subdivided, minds of his inclusive horizon no longer appear, and, indeed, may no longer be possible.

Eli Whitney

ELI WHITNEY

ELI WHITNEY, famous as the inventor of the cotton gin, was born on December 8, 1765, in Westboro, a pleasant little village of Massachusetts, sixteen miles east of Worcester. The house of his nativity was destroyed long ago; its site, on Johnson Road, bears a bronze tablet as a memorial. Whitney's father, who bore the name he gave his son, was of English blood, and so was his wife. In good Yankee fashion he was both a farmer and a mechanic. When he had nothing to do on his land, he made chairs for his neighbors, and wheels for their wagons and carts. Beside a complete kit of tools for cabinet-making, he had a lathe to turn his chair posts and rails. All this came under the eye of his son as a child, and under his fingers, as he grew big enough to handle a jackplane or a gimlet. Eli soon preferred tasks in the shop to tasks on the farm; his handiness with hammers, chisels, and saws proved him right. At school he stood high in arithmetic, and in nothing else; it was at his workbench that he excelled. When he was twelve he made a fiddle, having learned what woods and strings were to be chosen; his dexterity was rewarded with an instrument of fairly good tone. He now began to repair fiddles for Westboro musicians, and to execute other work requiring a nice touch. His father had a watch that had cost him a round sum. Eli thought it the most wonderful piece of mechanism he had ever seen. One Sunday, while the family were absent at church, Eli, who had feigned illness and stayed at home, took the watch to pieces and reassembled its parts. No mishap befell the exploit, but Eli's father was an austere man, so that years elapsed before his son divulged this daring feat.

75

Eli's mother died when he was a child: when he was thirteen his father married a second time. His stepmother, as part of her dowry, brought home a fine set of table-knives for occasions of state. Eli examined them with the remark: " I could make knives just as good with the right tools." Not long afterward one of these knives was accidentally broken, when Eli kept his word to the letter. Further additions to his tool chest enabled him to earn a decent profit at making nails, then in active demand, owing to the Revolutionary War. He was quick, too, at other tasks: he sharpened knives and axes, replaced old knife-blades with new, and gave every job so good a finish that, boy though he was, no mechanic in town surpassed him. His business grew large enough to demand a helper. His quest for this helper took Eli forty miles from home through a succession of workshops, where he saw many a tool and device to be copied on his return to Westboro. When peace with England was declared, nailmaking was no longer worth while, but fashion smiled on our young mechanic, and gave him as good a market as had war. Just then ladies fastened their bonnets with long metal pins, and in their manufacture Whitney built up a lucrative business. Not only ladies, but men, now became his customers: at odd times his lathe was a-whirl to turn out walking-canes. Plainly enough here stood a born mechanic, and a young fellow of energy and enterprise withal.

As Whitney passed into youth he felt within him a pulse of power which called for the best training: at nineteen he resolved to enter Yale College. This project his stepmother warmly opposed, and Eli was twenty-three before his father said yes, decisively. In the meantime he taught school at intervals, finding, as many another teacher has found, that teaching is a capital mode of learning. At Yale he paid his expenses partly by a loan from his father, whom he repaid within three years of graduation. At college he wrote essays like those of his classmates, ambitious of topic, and rather flowery in diction. In discussions he acquitted himself with credit. Meanwhile his mechanical aptitudes were not gathering rust. One day a tutor found a piece of experimental apparatus out of order. Said he: " It must go abroad for repair to the shop it came from." " I think I can mend it," promised Whitney. Within a week he mended it so thoroughly that it worked as well as ever. Not long afterward he espied a carpenter busy in a house near the college, plying tools of a new kind, which Whitney asked to borrow. " No," said the carpenter, " students always spoil good tools. The owner of this house is your landlord, get him to go bail for you, and then I'll lend you these tools." Bail was given, and Whitney began work. At once the carpenter exclaimed: " There was a good mechanic spoiled when you came to college."

In 1792, in his twenty-seventh year, Whitney was graduated. In those days of short and simple courses, he was about seven years older than most of his classmates. There was gain in this lateness of his education, as knowledge, unstaled by premature familiarity, dawned upon the mind of a man. To-day students of the Whitney stamp take up engineering as a profession, and soon make their mark. At the close of the eighteenth century there was no profession of engineering to attract and develop Whitney's unmistakable talent, so he chose teaching as his field, for a time at least, remembering his success in earlier years with his pupils. He secured an engagement with a school in South Carolina, and took passage on a ship from New York to Savannah. On board was the widow of General Nathanael Greene with her family, on their way to Mulberry Park, their home, twelve miles from Savannah. Mrs. Greene saw at once that the young New Englander was a man of brains and character. Furthermore, he was an alumnus of Yale, the college of Phineas Miller, the manager of her husband's estate, and who afterward became her husband. When Whitney reached Savannah he found that the salary offered him was not a hundred guineas, as he had expected, but only fifty, which he declined. Mrs. Greene then hospitably invited him to her mansion, where he would be at liberty to study law, the course upon which he had now determined. Whitney availed himself of this kind offer, took up his abode at Mulberry Park, and began to read law. In her ungrudging hospitality Mrs. Greene soon discovered that she was entertaining not an angel, but an inventor of the first rank.

One evening, as his hostess sat embroidering, she complained that her tambour frame tore the delicate silk of her pattern. Whitney saw at a glance how he could make a better frame, and this he accomplished next day to her delight. Early next year Mrs. Greene received a visit from three comrades of General Greene, who resided on plantations near Augusta, and who often talked about sowing and reaping, with their vital bearing on profit or loss. They agreed that much of the up-country land belonging to themselves and their neighbors yielded good cotton, but that cotton had little or no value owing to the high cost of dividing lint from seed. At that time, to part a pound of lint from its three pounds of seed, was ten hours' work for a quick hand. Usually this task was taken up when regular work was over for the day. Then the slaves, men, women, and children, sat around a taskmaster, who shook the dozing and nudged the slow. One evening, as her visitors deplored the lack of a machine to supplant this tedious and costly process, Mrs. Greene said: " Gentlemen, apply to my friend, Mr. Whitney; he can make anything," showing them her tambour frame with an array of her children's toys which he had made or mended. Whitney, thus appealed to, said that his home had lain so far north that he had never seen cotton as plucked from the bolls, with its seed firmly attached to its lint, so that the task of separation had never occurred to him.

So deeply did the conversation impress Whitney, that next day he went to Savannah, and obtained a small packet of seed-cotton. As he pulled the seeds one by one from their lint, he felt that it was high time that fingers of iron did this simple work, instead of fingers of flesh and blood. In the basement of the Greene mansion he forthwith set up a workshop with a bench and a few common tools. These assembled, he began to consider his problem. The roller gin, of immemorial form, was then used on Sea Island cotton with its long staple. Such a gin consisted mainly of two rollers, grooved lengthwise, and kept about one-sixteenth of an inch apart; their rotation drew the lint inward to a box, while the seeds, too large to pass between the rollers, were torn off and fell into another box. Occasionally a small seed was caught and crushed by the rollers, and became mixed with the lint, greatly to its damage. Upland cotton, such as Whitney had to treat, was shorter than the Sea Island variety, and its seeds were smaller and more firmly attached, so that the roller gin, either as it stood or as it might be modified, was out of the question. He thought that a good plan would be to thrust the lint through slits a little narrower than the space between the cylinders of a roller gin, so that the seeds would be broken off and remain behind.

First, then, how was he to thrust the lint through these narrow slits? Diverse plans suggested themselves. Teeth cut in circular iron plates, " ratchet wheels," as he called them, would have answered, but he was not able to try these wheels until later, when he found iron plates thin and strong enough for the purpose. Iron in another form was at hand, and this he adopted for his first experiments. One of Mrs. Greene's daughters had a pet bird, and a coil of iron wire to make its cage had just been unpacked. This prompted the notion that wire needles or prongs would serve to thrust lint through narrow openings. But the wire was too thick. Nothing, then, but to draw it to a suitable thinness by appliances which the untiring mechanic made there and then. Day by day he tried various lengths

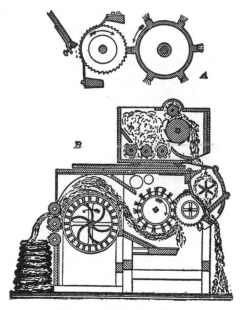

WHITNEY'S COTTON GIN

of wire, and disposed them in various angles and curves. He discovered that the prongs worked best when protruding about an inch from their cylinder. He found, also, that the wire should have a gentle curve opposed to the direction in which the cylinder rotated. Week by week this armed cylinder was tested, and for a few minutes the lint would be duly thrust between the slits in a breastwork, and the seeds forced off with gratifying thoroughness. But soon the wire teeth became clogged with lint, so that work had to stop. Whitney was puzzled by this difficulty, when, one morning, Mrs. Greene picked up the hearthbrush and asked: " Why don't you use this? " The very thing! Behind his breastwork Whitney set up a second wooden cylinder, armed with bristles to form a rotary brush; when this ran four times as fast as the wired cylinder, it swept the lint from its prongs into a box, and trouble was at an end.

Toward the close of the winter, Whitney completed a model so easily turned by hand as to ask no more exertion than a grindstone. Mrs. Greene now invited her friends from near and far to view its hundreds of tiny fingers, each doing as much work as a human hand. The planters in her assembled company were enthusiastic in praise of the inventor's ingenuity, and they clearly saw what his gin meant for the South. They urged him to patent at once his amazing invention, which was certain to bring him wealth and honor. Whitney declared that he was loth to bid farewell to law, the profession for which his studies had prepared him, and embark on the troublous sea which surrounds every inventor. At last he yielded to the entreaties of his friend, Phineas Miller, who proposed that Whitney and himself should become equal partners in patenting the cotton gin and setting it at work throughout the South. Miller agreed to provide the necessary capital, and, as the event proved, unfortunately he did not foresee how much would be needed. On May 27, 1793, the two friends entered into partnership as Miller & Whitney, a firm to be long remembered in the industrial history of America.

Whitney now posted to Connecticut to execute the model required by the Patent Office, and arrange for the manufacture of his machines. His model was soon beautifully constructed by his own hands, and on June 20 he petitioned for a patent to Thomas Jefferson, the Secretary of State. Philadelphia, then the capital of the Union, was that year devastated by yellow fever. This delayed the issue of a patent until March 14, 1794. In the meantime Mr. Jefferson examined Whitney's model with a thorough comprehension of its extraordinary merit and promise. He addressed a cordial inquiry to the inventor, asking how the gin was built and used, and requesting that a machine be sent to him. This good news Whitney repeated to his classmate and lifelong friend, Josiah Stebbins, adding, with characteristic restraint: " I hope to make something of the gin yet."

Miller, whose services included supplying cash for preliminary outlays, soon came to the end of his resources. It then became necessary to borrow $2,000; for this loan, besides legal interest, a premium of five per cent. was exacted. Miller's credit slowly sank from bad to worse; a few years later he had to pay five per cent. a month, then six, and at last seven per cent. This lowness of exchequer, which constantly harassed Miller & Whitney, meant that their cotton gin, while mechanically a success, was an utter failure in yielding them a revenue. In the very year of its invention it had prompted the planting of a crop which yielded about five million pounds of cotton, every pound of which passed through Whitney's gin. And every year thereafter saw more and more cotton planted, until soon this became the main product of the South. Why, then, was Whitney denied any share whatever in the vast wealth he had created?

At the outset Miller & Whitney fell into a cardinal error: they sought to own all the gins in Georgia themselves, and take as their toll one pound in three of their product. This levy was exorbitant, and it aroused the planters to anger and resistance. Their provocation was increased when, in March, 1795, the gin factory established by Whit-

WHITNEY COTTON GIN

ney at New Haven was destroyed by fire, cutting off for many months the supply of new machines. These machines were simple enough to be easily imitated by local blacksmiths and carpenters, and serviceable copies were set going by the hundred throughout the South. Miller & Whitney soon found that their tolls were too high, or certainly higher than planters would pay, so they agreed to accept a royalty for the use of their gins, gradually lowering the fee until it stood at $200. Even this moderate toll was withheld, partly in downright dishonesty, and partly through an omission in Whitney's patent, which opened the door to a vexatious infringement.

On May 12, 1796, Hodgen Holmes, of Georgia, patented a gin which, instead of wire prongs or needles, employed circular saws of the kind now universal. The teeth of these saws were kept slightly dull, so as to tear the lint less than did needles, and the Holmes machine, therefore, was a formidable competitor. Miller & Whitney sued Holmes for infringement, and secured a judgment against him. He acknowledged the justice of this decision by paying Miller & Whitney $200 as royalty on one of their gins. It had been clearly proved in court that Holmes' machine was essentially the Whitney gin, using a saw of the kind which Whitney had openly employed in early experiments, and discarded in favor of his wires. In the first rough draft of his claims as a patentee, Whitney had included saws as alternative devices with these wires. It was the chief misfortune of his life that in his patent only wires were mentioned, without inclusion of saws either in his claims or his drawings.* But the contest with Holmes was by no

---

*In 1804, Miller & Whitney sued Arthur Fort and John Powell for infringement in the United States District Court in Savannah, winning an injunction. As part of their evidence they adduced a certified copy of Whitney's patent, which copy remains on file to this day, with its drawings, in the Court House. In 1836, the Patent Office in Washington was destroyed by fire, and Whitney's original

means at an end when judgment was rendered against him. His further course was narrated by Whitney in a letter to Josiah Stebbins:

".... Several patents have been issued for machines on my principle. One of the patentees [Holmes] claims as his invention the making the rows [as] teeth of sheet iron instead of wire. The fact is, he was told that was my original idea, and my machine was perfectly described to him, even by drawings of every part. It is also plain that the principle is the same in whatever way the teeth are made, and that they may be made in a variety of ways. We commenced a suit against this man to have his patent vacated. After a tedious course of litigation and delay, we obtained a judgment on the ground that the principle was the same, and that his patent was surreptitious. His patent was vacated and declared to be void. He came forward and paid up the costs and purchased a license of us to use the machine for which he pretended to get a patent, and we now hold his note given for that license. By some neglect of the judge, or mistake of the clerk in entering the judgment, upon a new Democratic District Judge being

patent, with its drawings and model, was reduced to ashes. In 1841, thirty-three years after the patent had expired, and sixteen years after Whitney's death, alleged copies of his patent and drawings were placed in the Patent Office by some one whose name cannot now be ascertained. Mr. D. A. Tompkins, in "Cotton," published by him in Charlotte, North Carolina, in 1901, reprints these alleged copies side by side with their originals, disclosing a singular falsification. The specifications of 1841, abridged from those of 1793, close with a paragraph not in the original patent:—"There are several modes of making the various parts of this machine, which, together with their particular shape and formation, are pointed out and explained in a description with drawings attached, as the [Patent] Act directs, and lodged in the office of the Secretary of State." These drawings differ widely from the originals: they include saws as alternative devices with prongs or needles: saws had no place in the drawings of 1793. Nor did the draftsman of 1841 take the trouble to watch a cotton gin at work. He applies its rotating handle to the brush cylinder instead of to the thrusting cylinder. The machine he drew, if executed in oak and iron, would refuse to work.

appointed he found means to revive the cause. After another series of delays, and when his own judge was obliged to give judgment against him, still these designing rascals pretend to uphold his claim and make a handle of it to our disadvantage, and although I have no idea that any court can be so abandoned as to take any serious notice of it, yet I should like to obtain such testimony as will show it [the circular saw] to be my invention, and thereby put a complete stopper on that business. We have already one positive witness of the fact, the first person to whom the machine was shown, besides Miller's family, which was in the spring of 1793. . . ." *

From Whitney let us return to Governor James Jackson, of Georgia, who led the fight against him. In the course of his message of November 3, 1800, he thus refers to the Patent Act of 1793, and to Whitney's cotton gin as protected by that Act:

" The operation of this [patent] law is the prevention and cramping of genius as it respects cotton machines, a mani-

* Professor Denison Olmsted, in his "Biography of Whitney," first published in the *American Journal of Science*, 1832, says:
" In one of his trials, Mr. Whitney adopted the following plan, in order to show how nugatory were the methods of evasion practised by his adversaries. They were endeavoring to have his claim to the invention set aside, on the ground that the teeth in his machine were made of wire, inserted into the cylinder of wood, while in the machine of Holmes, the teeth were cut in plates, or iron surrounding the cylinder, forming a circular saw. Mr. Whitney, by an ingenious device, consisting chiefly of sinking the plate below the surface of the cylinder, and suffering the teeth to project, contrived to give the saw teeth the appearance of wires, while he prepared another cylinder in which the wire teeth were made to look like saw teeth. The two cylinders were produced in court, and the witnesses were called on to testify which was the invention of Whitney, and which that of Holmes. They accordingly swore the saw teeth upon Whitney, and the wire teeth upon Holmes; upon which the Judge declared that it was unnecessary to proceed any farther, the principle of both being manifestly the same."

fest injury to the community, and in many respects a cruel extortion on the gin holders. The two important States of Georgia and South Carolina, where this article [cotton] appears to be becoming the principal staple, are made tributary to two persons who have obtained the patent, and who demand, as I am informed, $200.00 for the mere liberty of using a ginning machine, in the erection of which the patentees do not expend one farthing, and which sum, as they now think their right secured, it is in their power to raise to treble that amount. . . . I am informed from other sources that gins have been erected by other persons who have not taken Miller & Whitney's machine for a model, but which, in some small degree, resemble it, for it has been asserted that Miller & Whitney's gin did not, on trial, answer the intended purpose. The rights of these improvements, however, it appears by the present [Patent] Act, are merged in the rights of the patentees [Miller & Whitney], who, it is supposed, on the lowest calculation, will make by it in the two States [Georgia and South Carolina] $100,000. Monopolies are odious in all countries, but more particularly in a government like ours. . . . Their tendency is certainly to raise the price of the [produced] article from the exclusive privilege—to render the machine or article worse from the prevention of competition or improvement—and to impoverish poor artificers and planters who are forbidden from making, vending, or using it without license from the patentees, or, in case of doing so, are made liable to penalties in a court of law. The Federal Court docket, it is said, is filled with these actions. I do not doubt the power of Congress to grant these exclusive privileges, for the Constitution has vested them with it, but in all cases where they may become injurious to the community, they ought to be suppressed, or the parties be paid a moderate compensation for the discoveries from the government granting the patent. . . ."

Whitney, on behalf of his firm, replied to Governor Jackson:

". . . It has always appeared to us that the private pursuits of individual industry are entitled to the most sacred and inviolable protection of the laws, and that a good

cause, where private right alone was concerned, must suffer
trivial injuries without acquiring the claim to be presented
before the solemn tribunal of public opinion. But when
the title to our property is slandered, and political persecution openly commenced against us, under pretense of official duty by our chief magistrate, silence on our part might
be supposed to sanction the abuse. The urgency of the
case must, therefore, be our apology for meeting Your
Excellency on this ground, and, in making a defense of our
property right, we shall draw a veil over the passions
which have brought it into question, and, passing over the
degraded condition to which the State has been reduced,
shall only notice the measure in which we are immediately
implicated, and shall consult the genius of our government
rather than the acts of your administration, to enable us
to preserve towards you that respect to which your office is
entitled.

" In the first place, Your Excellency will permit us to
remove the deception which is palmed on the public to our
disadvantage in the opprobrious term ' monopoly.' The respectable authors [Edward Coke and Adam Smith], whose
names were brought forward to sanction your opinion on
this subject, speak of the exclusive right to carry on a
trade or manufacture as a ' monopoly,' and not of the protection which government chooses to give the arts. The
principle of the patent law, Your Excellency will please to
observe, consists of a fair compromise between the Government and the author of the invention. There can be no
doubt but that an invention in the arts must remain the exclusive right of the inventor under the most oppressive
laws, while the secret is confined to him, and many instances have occurred of the preservation of the secret
for years, and even of its final loss to the public on the
death of its inventor.

" To remedy which evil and to stimulate ingenious men
to vie with each other, governments, by enacting patent
laws, substantially agree that they will afford to the author
of the invention the most ample protection in the use of
his discovery for a certain term of years, on condition that,
after that period, it shall become public property. And in
carrying into effect all such discoveries, it is well known
that every inventor must incur the whole expense and take

on himself the entire risk of the success of his invention, in which, if he fails, his loss of time and money does not always constitute his greatest mortification, and, if he succeeds, the public advantage must of necessity go hand in hand with his acquirements [acquisitions], since the inventor cannot expect his invention to be employed, or paid for, unless it excels all others in point of utility. In the present case, we believe the utility of our invention well known and candidly admitted by all rational men. At the time it was brought forward, there were millions of pounds of cotton in the seed, which awaited some improvement in the mode of ginning, and wealth, honor, and gratitude were promised to the fortunate exertions of genius which would insure the culture of green-seed cotton to the up-country.

" Under such flattering auspices and under protection of the law, the invention was perfected, and, at great expense in money, which has never been repaid, and of time and labor which is unrewarded, and now Your Excellency would direct your influence to blast the harvest so hardly earned, and which for many years has waved in distant view and buoyed up our hopes under adversity and oppression, which would have better suited the perpetrators of vice than the industrious and successful improvers of so useful an art.

" The idle stories which Your Excellency condescends to repeat, with a view to dividing with some other person the credit of the invention, are not new to us, we have always considered them as harmless, while they only served to amuse some ingenious mechanic, but the place they hold in the executive message requires us to observe that we know of no pretensions of this kind which can stand the smallest examination, and we shall challenge the most distant parts of Europe and Asia to produce a model, or a well attested account of a machine for cleaning cotton upon the principle of ours, which was known previous to our invention. We have not even ascertained that a single improvement has been made upon the machine, of which we have not complete evidence of our previous knowledge, and experimental use. But whether the form that we have adopted [the needle gin] is the best and deserves the preference to that in common use in the up-country [the saw gin], experience must determine. At present public opinion, we acknowledge, in this respect, to be against us.

" The alternative which Your Excellency suggests of paying a moderate compensation to the patentees, or suppressing the patent, appears to us to be injudiciously chosen, for in the first of these cases, if the bargain is to be all on one side, and the persons who would defraud us of our right are to be the sole judges of the compensation to be made, the oppression would be too manifest. The proposition of suppressing the patent is so bold a thing that we forbear giving it comment. . . ." *

Spurred by this appeal, Governor Jackson appointed a committee to examine the cotton gin question, and report with all despatch. This committee recommended that the Senators and Representatives of Georgia in Congress endeavor to obtain a modification of the Patent Act in so far as it affected the cotton gin, " as well as to limit the price of obtaining a right to using it, the price being at present unbounded." In case this modification did not prove feasible, then Congress was to be induced to compensate Miller & Whitney for their invention, their patent was to be cancelled, and the Southern States relieved from a burdensome grievance. And now entered anticipation of the House of Governors established by President Roosevelt in 1908, as suggested by William George Jordan of New York. The Governor of Georgia, in conclusion, was to be asked to transmit copies of this report and its recommendations to the Executives of South Carolina, North Carolina, and Tennessee, to be laid before their Legislatures, with a request for the coöperation in Congress of their Senators and Representatives.

South Carolina, as the chief cotton-growing State, was the first to respond. Her planters, in thousands, petitioned

*These communications are given in full in "Cotton," by D. A. Tompkins, published in Charlotte, North Carolina, 1901. This book contains other data of prime interest.

their Legislature to buy the Whitney patent, and on terms which seemed liberal, to the petitioners at least. In September, 1801, this news came to Whitney in New Haven, from his friend and agent, Russell Goodrich. It was now the eighth year of his patent, and the unfortunate inventor had received from it little or nothing. With hope rekindled, he started in an open sulky, as was his wont, from New Haven for Columbia, the capital of South Carolina, pausing in Washington for a few days' rest. From President Jefferson, and from James Madison, Secretary of State, he received letters so cordial that they rendered him good service in his later negotiations. Whitney duly reached Columbia, and pleaded his case with tact and skill. By this time the yearly cotton crop was more than thirty-five million pounds, many cotton planters had grown rich, and the whole broad belt of cotton country was thriving as never before. Whitney maintained that South Carolina should pay not less than $100,000 for his patent. After prolonged discussion, a vote of $50,000 was passed on December 16, and this vote Whitney with reluctance accepted, $20,000 being paid to him on account. To reimburse itself, the State levied a special tax on cotton gins, requiring Miller & Whitney to refund such license fees as they had collected in the State, and to furnish the State with two model machines.

On November 15, 1802, North Carolina followed suit, enacting a tax of two shillings and sixpence a year for five years on every saw within her borders. This tax, less six per cent. for collection, was to go to Miller & Whitney. It netted them about $20,000. Next year Tennessee fell into line, imposing an annual tax of one shilling and sixpence per saw for each of four years. Tennessee paid about $10,000 to the patentees. From other States, Mr. D. A. Tompkins estimates that $10,000 was received by Miller & Whitney; so that their gross revenue was $90,000, of course greatly diminished by their legal and other expenses. This was their sole reward for having created for the South its principal crop, and added incalculably to the value of Southern plantations.

Within a year of its vote to Miller & Whitney, the enmity against them in South Carolina, frankly declared from the first, had grown strong enough to control the Legislature. Its contract with the patentees was annulled, the promise to pay them was rescinded, and suit was entered to recover the $20,000 paid them a few months before. To gross dishonesty was added sheer brutality. In a bitter remonstrance the inventor cried:

" I was seized and dragged to prison without being allowed to be heard in answer to the charge alleged against me, and, indeed, without the exhibition of any specific charge, in direct violation of the common right of every citizen of a free government. . . . I have manifested no other disposition than to fulfil all the stipulations entered into with the State of South Carolina, with punctuality and good faith; and I beg to observe farther, that I have industriously, laboriously, and exclusively devoted many years of the prime of my life to the invention and improvement of a machine from which the citizens of South Carolina have already realized immense profits,—which is worth to them millions, and from which their posterity, to the latest generations, must continue to derive the most important benefits, and, in return, to be treated as a felon, a swindler, and a villain, has stung me to the very soul. And when I consider that this cruel persecution is inflicted by the very persons who are enjoying these great benefits and expressly for the purpose of preventing my ever deriving the least advantage from my own labors, the acuteness of my feelings is altogether inexpressible."

It is a heart, not a voice, that speaks to us here! Ostensibly the action against Whitney proceeded on the ground that a Swiss inventor had anticipated him in devising a machine which was, in effect, a cotton gin. It was further charged that his firm had not refunded license fees as agreed, and had not delivered the two models as promised. Whitney showed that the licenses not yet refunded amounted to only $580; and pleaded that his delay of a few months in furnishing his models was due to a wish to embody improvements, and execute the construction with his own hands. Incomparably more important was the question, Who invented the cotton gin? At the instance of General Charles Cotesworth Pinckney, and other steadfast friends of Whitney, this question was referred to a committee of the Legislature. This committee took evidence with fulness and impartiality: it concluded that Whitney's claim as inventor of the cotton gin was unquestionable: and that, therefore, the State should reënact the agreement with his firm. When this report came up in the Senate, its adoption was defeated by a tie vote. But the House of Representatives voted favorably, whereupon the Senate took a second vote, recording 14 Yeas to 12 Nays. If a single Senator who voted Yea had changed sides, Miller & Whitney would have lost their case, and, in all probability, have been forced into bankruptcy. We may be sure that they rejoiced greatly when at last they received their $30,000, completing the $50,000 voted them by South Carolina. As this sovereign State had been copied by her sister commonwealths in recognizing the rights of Miller & Whitney, so also was South Carolina followed in her attempt at repudiation. Twice the lawmakers of North Carolina sought to abolish the tax imposed for the benefit of the patentees of the cotton gin, and twice the attempt was a failure. Tennessee, halfway in the four years of her agreement, suspended its tax. Little wonder that Phineas Miller, worn and worried by unending contests with plunderers, fell into bad health and died on December 7, 1803, leaving Whitney to combat his foes single-handed.

His foes prevailed. When Whitney applied to Congress for a renewal of his patent, it was refused. A few Representatives from the cotton districts favored his petition; they were overborne by a multitude of opponents. Thus ended, as far as Whitney was concerned, one of the most remarkable chapters in the annals of industry. In vain did Whitney recount that his gin multiplied a thousandfold the efficiency of labor, so as to confer stupendous benefits upon the Southern States, by enabling them to supply the civilized world at a low price with its chief clothing. From no State had he received as much as half a cent a pound on the cotton separated by his machines in a single twelve-month. Whitney, in the course of a letter to Robert Fulton, reviewed the forces which withstood him:

" The difficulties with which I have to contend have originated, principally, in the want of a disposition in mankind to do justice. My invention was new and distinct from every other; it stood alone. It was not interwoven with anything before known; and it can seldom happen that an invention or improvement is so strongly marked, and can be so specifically and clearly identified; and I have always believed that I should have no difficulty in causing my rights to be respected if my invention had been less valuable, and been used only by a small portion of the community. But the use of the machine being immensely profitable to almost every planter in the cotton districts, all were interested in trespassing upon the patent right, and each kept the other in countenance. Demagogues made themselves popular by misrepresentation and unfounded clamors, both against the right and against the law made for its protection. Hence there arose associations and combinations to oppose both. At one time but few men in Georgia dared to come into court and testify to the most simple facts within their knowledge relative to the use of the machine. In one instance I had great difficulty in proving that the machine had been used in Georgia, although, at the same moment, there were separate sets of this machinery in motion within fifty yards of the building in which the court sat, and all so near that the rattling of the wheels was distinctly heard on the steps of the Court House."

Whitney, indeed, created the keystone for which the arch of textile industry stood agape. Hargreaves invented his spinning-jenny in 1767; two years later Arkwright devised his spinning-frame for warp; in 1774, Compton effectively united both machines: then came Cartwright's power-loom. All these were cheaply driven by the steam engine of Watt. And yet, for lack of cotton at a low price, its manufacture had but limited scope. Cotton came to Great Britain mainly from Asia and the West Indies, where slaves or coolies plucked lint from seed with their fingers, or turned the slow and faulty roller gin. Here and there in the Southern States of the Union a little cotton was sown in gardens, chiefly because of its handsome flowers. In 1784, an American vessel arrived at Liverpool, says Denison Olmsted, Whitney's biographer, with eight bags of cotton on board. It was seized by the Custom House, under the conviction that cotton could not be grown in America. In 1785, five bags were landed at Liverpool; in 1786, six bags; in 1787, 108; in 1788, 282. In 1793, the year in which Whitney devised his gin, at least 5,000,000 pounds of cotton were harvested in the Southern States. This huge figure was soon utterly eclipsed; in 1825, the year of Whitney's death, the cotton exported from the United States was valued at $36,846,000; and all other exports at $30,094,000, considerably less. Let us leap now to 1912, with a crop estimated at 7,000,000,000 pounds, worth about $770,000,000.

For seventy years after its birth the cotton gin exerted as striking an influence in the field of politics as in the markets of the world. Whitney's wheels undoubtedly served to rivet the shackles of the negro slave. When cotton planting was still unknown in America, the tasks for

field hands were few and not especially gainful. No sooner
were Whitney's machines set up, than planters entered upon
a new and immense profit. To plow the ground for cotton,
to sow and weed and till its fields, to pluck the bolls in
their successive harvests, and then to gin and press the
lint, gave all hands lucrative work the year round. The
wealth and power thus won played a leading part in Se-
cession, so that, during four years of Civil War, the fate
of the Union trembled in the balance. Thus entangled in
the skein of invention are its threads of bane and blessing.

Whitney's saw gin, little changed from the form he gave
it, separates most of the cotton grown in America. Fans
have been added to its brushes, and steels, much more flexible and lasting than those of 1790, appear to-day in the
machines descended from his model. Since his time, the
roller gin has been much improved, so as to gain a little
upon the saw gin, as less liable to damage the staple. These
are times when cotton culture, like every other industry, is
being overhauled in the light of scientific management. In
this work the Bureau of Plant Industry at Washington is
playing a leading part. Its assistant director, Mr. Nathan
A. Cobb, has divided cotton into eighteen grades, each of a
specific length and strength of staple. He places a fiber betwixt two glass plates, and throws its enlarged image
upon a screen; the length of that fiber is at once measured
and recorded as he runs a small toothed wheel along its
devious line. It is probable that all the Cotton Exchanges
of the Union will adopt this simple apparatus and the standard grades suggested by the Bureau, so as to abolish disputes
as to the lengths and qualities of specific fibers. Experiments, also, are afoot with a view to ascertaining the speed
at which a given grade of cotton should be ginned. Tests
of length and strength of staple, before and after ginning,
will settle this question, and will further decide upon the
claims regarding new models of gins.

To come back to Whitney and his defeat. When he became convinced that he must abandon all hope of an income from his invention, he cast about for a field of enterprise suited to his talents. He chose the manufacture
of firearms. Here he introduced economies which have so
greatly inured to the benefit of industry as to parallel the
revolution he wrought in cotton production. All this began quietly enough, and in distant France. There, about
1765, General Gribeauval reduced the gun-carriages of the
French artillery to classes, and so designed many of their
parts that they could be applied to any carriage of their
class. This was the beginning of standardization in manufacture, which took a vast stride under the guidance of
Whitney. The methods which he originated in the production of arms we shall presently observe. Those methods
passed long ago, with inestimable gain, to the production of
tools, machines, and engines, from plows to divide furrows
to the steam turbines which impel ocean greyhounds.

Manifold, indeed, are the gifts of war to peace, and many
a tool of industry is but an old weapon in a new guise. A
flint, as an arrowhead, has cleft skulls by the myriad: to-
day not one man in a thousand is deft enough to shape an
arrowhead such as were common in prehistoric days. It
was probably in smiting one flint against another for battle,
that sparks were struck for the first fire-kindler, with all that
that has meant for art and comfort. From ruder stones
have plainly descended the hammers of our shops and
factories. Battle-axes, strong and sharp, told early for-
esters how to fell oaks and cedars with a new ease. Swords,
keen and elastic, are the dignified parents of knives and
planes, of the chisels of carpenters and masons. To-day
at Toledo a steel-worker offers a visitor as a memento not
a sword or a scimetar, but a pair of scissors. Prodigal experiments, such as governments alone conduct, were in
hand for years by the chief War Departments of Europe

to produce steel armor of the utmost resistance, and steel projectiles of surpassing might. Alloys thus created, which otherwise would never have seen the light of day, were then calmly appropriated by builders of turret lathes, steam turbines, motor-cars, and even scoops for dredges.

Gunpowder, when first handed to soldiers, changed the face of war, by making a steady aim and a clear eye count for more than prowess. Let us note what industry does with this compound of saltpeter. During the years of the Civil War, which broke out in 1861 at Fort Sumter, the Northern States burned more gunpowder in their mines, tunnels, and quarries than on their battlefields. It is gunpowder that carries across sea and fog the lines of every life-saving station in the world. That Napoleon might transport his powder carts and heavy artillery, he gave Europe the best roads since those of Rome. To-day these highways bear burdens greater than Napoleon ever laid on them, as they carry the freight and passengers of Italy, France, and Switzerland.

And throughout its vast and expanding breadths, what is the organization of modern industry, under such a captain as Whitney, but military rule over again, with due modification? Instead of a commander in uniform, we have a chief at his desk, who, like Grant or Kitchener, is at the head of his army because he deserves to be. His duty is to plan the cutting of a canal, the building of automobiles, or the construction of a railroad. Every man in the ranks, whether endowed chiefly with brains or with hands, is well aware that most will be done and most divided when orders are faithfully obeyed. A worthy successor to Eli Whitney is Frederick W. Taylor, of Philadelphia,* who has quadrupled the output of metal-cutting machines by an elaborate study of how they are best designed, fed, and operated.

* His methods are set forth in "The Principles of Scientific Management," and "Shop Management": New York, 1911.

Under such a leader the rule of thumb gives place to the much more gainful rule of science. No machine-tender of intelligence demurs to an instruction-card drawn up for him by such a chief. The best way to exert himself is sketched before his eyes, and to do anything else would be to produce distinctly less. For ages have brigades, shoulder to shoulder, fought opposed brigades. Incidentally, all learned self-control, courage, discipline, loyalty to a competent leader. These lessons have been inherited by free men who employ their knowledge and skill to build, not to destroy. They turn their steel not upon other men, but upon the obstacles of nature, that nature may let fall its arms and become their friend.

To return to Eli Whitney, a standard-bearer in this transition from weapon to tool, from war to peace. In 1797, when he was in the thick of his law suits in Georgia, with the stream steadily against him, he despaired of winning any reward whatever from his cotton gin. So he cast about for a field where his ingenuity and organizing faculty would yield him a competence. This field, wherever found, must be safe from depredators. His choice fell upon the production of muskets for the United States Army. Through the influence of Oliver Wolcott, Secretary of the Treasury, Whitney on January 14, 1793, received a contract for 10,000 stands of arms at $13.40, amounting to $134,000, a good deal of money in those days. Of these arms, 4,000 were to be delivered by the end of September, 1794, and the remaining 6,000 within the twelvemonth thereafter. Bonds for $30,000, signed by Whitney's friends, were given for the due fulfilment of his contract.

He began work without a day's delay. He had not only to build, he was obliged to design, many of the tools and machines he needed. He must gather and test unfamiliar woods, metals, and alloys. His workmen had to be trained to tasks never before attempted in America or elsewhere.

He had hardly any capital, but his credit was high. Solid men of New Haven knew his ability, and were proud to become his sureties when he borrowed $10,000 from the Bank of New Haven. Secretary Wolcott, on behalf of the Government, advanced $5,000 when the contract was signed, and stood ready to grant more as soon as manufacturing was fairly under way.

Whitney chose, as the site of his factory, a stretch of land at the foot of East Rock, two miles from New Haven, where a waterfall gave him the motive-power he required. When once work proceeded in earnest, he found his main difficulty to lie in the poor quality of his raw recruits. He wrote to Mr. Wolcott:

" I find my personal attention and oversight are more constantly and essentially necessary to every branch of the work, than I apprehended. Mankind, generally, are not to be depended upon, and the best workmen I can find are incapable of directing. Indeed, there is no branch of the work that can proceed well, scarcely for a single hour, unless I am present."

The slow pace of his work-people perturbed his calculations. At the end of a year, instead of 4,000 muskets, he could deliver only 500. It was eight years instead of two before his contract was out of hand. His factory was planned as a single huge machine, of a type wholly new. In an armory, before Whitney's day, one man made locks, another made barrels, another carved stocks, and so on. Each man, highly skilled, produced by himself a distinct part of a musket. This division of labor Whitney supplanted by so apportioning work that little or no skill was demanded. He separated the various tasks necessary to produce a musket,—planing, filing, drilling, and the like. Then, at each of these operations, simplified to the utmost degree, he kept a group busy. For their assistance he introduced three aids, since indispensable in manufacure—

drilling by templets or patterns, filing by jigs or guides, and milling irregular forms. From first to last a model musket was copied with precision, so that every lock, for example, was exactly like every other among thousands. When all the parts needed to form a weapon were assembled, they united as a musket much superior to an arm produced on any other plan. In case of repair, a new part exactly filled the place of an old part, and at trifling cost. Year by year Whitney invented many tools, machines, and improvements as need arose. None of these did he patent: he had patented the cotton gin, and that was enough. It is a great achievement to contrive a new and useful machine. It is a much greater feat to confer a new efficiency on all the machines in a broad field of manufacture.

Whitney's methods were duly adopted by the Government Armories at Springfield, Massachusetts, and Harper's Ferry, Virginia, where their economies soon exceeded $25,000 a year. In 1856 the British War Office installed similar plans, and in 1871 and 1872 the example spread to Russia and France, Germany and Italy. Every advance of design in engines and machines gives standardization a new field and a new gain. Engine-lathes, automatic planers, modern milling machines, and the Blanchard lathe for carving irregular forms in wood, are but new fingers for the hands of the men who to-day follow the footsteps of the musket-maker of New Haven.

A striking contrast appears between the Springfield Armory of Whitney's day and that Armory as now operated. Colonel Stephen English Blunt, in command, says under date of May 16, 1911:

" With the Springfield plant equipped as it is, with sufficient machines so that each of the 1,004 machine operations on the rifle has its particular machine, thus avoiding the necessity of changing fixtures and adjusting of tools and machines, it requires 24 working hours to make a complete rifle. To make 10,000 rifles would, therefore, require 240,000 working hours, or 30,000 working days of eight hours each. On account of the size of the present Armory it would, of course, not be economical to work as few as 100 men. The smallest economical working force for this plant would be 600 men; they would make 10,000 rifles in 50 working days. It would take 100 men at least two years to make 10,000 rifles. The Springfield Armory has a plant capable of manufacturing 10,000 rifles in less than seven days, working double shifts if the necessity should arise.

"The musket manufactured by Whitney under his contract of January, 1798, was a flint-lock, 59½ inches long, .69-inch caliber, had about 45 component parts, and fired a round bullet of one ounce, at a muzzle velocity of 800 feet per second; while the latest Springfield rifle is a magazine rifle 43.2 inches long, .30-inch caliber, has 105 component parts, fires an elongated and sharp-pointed jacketed bullet weighing 150 grains, less than one-third of an ounce, at a muzzle velocity of 2,700 feet per second."

In 1812, Whitney was awarded a further contract by the War Department, this time for 15,000 stands of arms. Then followed contracts with the State of New York, and with leading firms throughout the Union. His system was constantly extended and improved, so that he earned an ample competence, as he had hoped at the outset. He was now sure that he could safely incur the responsibilities of matrimony. In 1816, he became engaged to Miss Henrietta Edwards, a daughter of Judge Pierpont Edwards. They were married in the following January, a son and three daughters being born to their union. But the happiness of the great inventor was to be brief. His repeated journeys between North and South, taken, as they were, in an open vehicle, and often at inclement seasons, had impaired a frame naturally rugged. In the course of 1824 he developed a distressing malady, which ended his life on January 8, 1825, shortly after he had completed his fifty-ninth year. His conduct as a patient was in line with his career as an inventor. He inquired minutely into the causes and progress of his disease, examining charts of anatomy by the hour. In the intervals between his paroxysms of agony, he devised surgical instruments for the relief of himself and of others in like extremity. Eli Whitney, in his years of vigor, had created for his fellowmen benefits beyond computation: under the shadow of death he sought to subtract from their pain. He had planned a new mansion for himself and his family: he requested that it be duly reared after his death.

What manner of man was Eli Whitney, as in health and strength he strode across the Green in New Haven? Like George Stephenson, he was cast in a large mold, and stood head and shoulders above ordinary folk. He was a kindly man, whose friendships were warm and clinging: his hand never relaxed its grasp of the chums of his youth. Many a man is honest: this man was scrupulously honorable: it was his fate often to be scurvily treated, and then his resentment made him terrible. His chief faculty, of course, was invention, his ability to strike a new path out of an old difficulty. This talent was not confined within the walls of his factory. Every building he reared, and these included dwellings for his work people, bore the marks of his original brain. He used cement liberally for foundations and walls, with prophecy of its wider applications to-day. The drawers of his desk were fastened by a single lock, in a fashion now usual. Even the mangers for his cattle were improved at his hands. He placed a small weight at the end of each halter, so that its wearer could move its head with ease, and yet could neither entangle itself in its rope, nor waste its hay.

His judgments were slowly matured: they were never expressed before they were ripe. In experiment, in his quest for materials, in his choice of lieutenants, he was patience itself. He could plant to-day, and for ten years calmly await his harvest. Unlike most inventors, whatever he began he finished. New projects beckoned to him in vain, so long as unfinished work remained on his hands. The unflinching will of the man revealed itself in the hour of death, as his tremulous fingers were lifted to close his eyes.

THOMAS BLANCHARD

SEVENTY years ago a great triumvirate, Clay, Calhoun, and Webster, were the idols of America. Their portraits adorned parlors and offices, courtrooms and capitols, from one end of the Union to the other. Here and there an admirer, more prosperous than his neighbors, had a bust of one of these worthies on his mantelpiece. The continuing remembrance of these great leaders is due in no small measure to the thousands of pictures and effigies thus set up throughout the country, and still to be found in many a farmhouse and mansion of South Carolina, Kentucky, and New Hampshire. We may feel certain that all three statesmen grew at last thoroughly tired of posing to artists, so that they rejoiced at a reprieve, at least so far as sculptors were concerned. This was promised one morning in 1840, as Clay, Calhoun, and Webster were invited to view busts of themselves copied in wood by a cheap and simple process. These figures, beautifully executed, awaited them on a table in the rotunda of the Capitol. Beside them stood Thomas Blanchard, who seemed truth incarnate, so transparent was his eye, so straightforward his speech. Yet he said that these admirable busts had been carved on a lathe of his invention almost as readily as so many gunstocks. This machine he had invented and patented long ago, but only that year had he built it on lines delicate enough to reproduce statuary. Its chief business, indeed, had been to shape stocks for guns, handles for tools, lasts for shoes, and tackle for ships. Pirates had been so numerous and active a band, that this wonderful machine had brought its inventor but little reward. He had, therefore, come to Washington to ask from Congress a favor without precedent,—

[From a portrait in the possession of F. S. Blanchard, Worcester, Mass.]

a second renewal of his patent. In the Capitol, beneath the table where he displayed his busts, was a basement room where the inventor showed his lathe as it repeated in oak the classical features of Washington. As the principle of the machine came clearly into view, Webster exclaimed: "How simple it is, after all!" Blanchard, thanks chiefly to Webster, was accorded a third term for his patent, on the ground of the high utility and singular originality of his invention, and in view of the inadequate return he had derived from it. Rufus Choate, the eminent jurist of Boston, who opposed the inventor's petition, could only say: "Blanchard has 'turned the heads' of these Congressmen, so we need not wonder at his victory." Sculptors, day after day, came to view the Blanchard machine. In their own reproduction of a bust they were obliged, from moment to moment, to take precise measurements, repeating each dimension with anxious care. That such a task should be performed by a self-acting cutter was simply amazing.

Blanchard's lathe, as it first left his hands, remains the core of its successor to-day. Its principle flashed into his brain because among the prime resources of his workshop were revolving cutters. Let us retrace a few of the steps which led to these marvelous tools. Knives or chisels were doubtless in their first estate mere flints, or bits of shell, to divide a fish or a bird into morsels, to hack a root or a tree, to sever a hide into thongs. Much more recent than the knife is the wheel, which probably began work as a round log turning beneath a burden dragged on the ground. When knives were joined with wheels, their union at once conquered a vast field forever denied to simple knives, or mere wheels, by themselves. This union was prophesied as soon as a stone was rounded into a wheel, mounted on an axle, and bidden to grind blades of iron or bronze. From that contrivance are descended all the grindstones of to-day, and the wheels of emery, corundum, and carborundum, ablaze in ten thousand machine shops at this hour. But every such wheel has its appointed limits: it removes iron or steel, copper or brass, particle by particle. In a much wider province of shaping, the tasks are bolder and the pace swifter. A wheel armed on its rim with steel cutters, as in modern milling machines, sweeps off a thick shaving or even a goodly slice. Revolving cutters, much simpler than these, were used to plane iron by Bramah as early as 1811. Cutters quite as keen and strong were in daily use by Blanchard for years. In his lathe he broadened their scope by nothing less than a leap.

Let us look at his machine as it produces a gunstock. On an axle slowly revolved are placed a stock to be copied and a wooden block in every way larger. Parallel to this axle is hinged a rectangular carriage, sliding gradually from one end of the lathe to the other. A spindle forming the outer boundary of this carriage may freely swing through a wide arc: it carries two wheels of like diameter, about three feet apart. One of them, pressed by a weight or a spring against the rotating stock to be copied, is small enough to touch its every point. The second wheel has at its rim a score of sharp cutters. As the first wheel feels its way along every contour of the original stock from end to end, its path is duplicated by the cutting wheel, which removes wood enough from its block to leave behind a copy of the model stock. When once the lathe is duly set and started, its work proceeds to a finish without a touch from its attendant. His task, therefore, is much easier than when he copies a simple diagram with a pantograph, for then he has to trace with his fingers the whole course of every copied line. Strange that to reproduce a figure of three dimensions should be less trouble than to copy a figure of but two!

Thomas Blanchard, the inventor of this wonderful machine, was born in Sutton, Worcester County, Massa-

ORIGINAL BLANCHARD LATHE, 1822

[Museum, U. S. Armory, Springfield, Mass.]

chusetts, on June 24, 1788. His ancestors, of mingled
French and English blood, were among the first settlers in
that vicinity. His father, Samuel Blanchard, was a hard-
working, thrifty farmer. How large a family he had we
do not know, but of his six sons, Thomas was the fifth.
This boy's talent for building and contriving was manifest
almost from his cradle. At ten years of age he whittled
from cedar shingles a tiny mill, to be impelled by a breeze
or a brook. The poor fellow stammered badly, and this
brought him much thoughtless ridicule. At school he was
shy and seemed backward: it was ever with joy that he
dropped his slate and copybook to take up a penknife and
chisel. His father, though a Yankee, cared little about
tools and machinery, and he glanced without interest at the
handicraft of his ingenious boy. Nor was there much else
in the neighborhood to nourish the budding powers of this
young mechanic. The nearest blacksmith's shop was six
miles off, and it was but seldom that his father went there.
Thither Thomas was taken one day to see a horse shod.
This feat, new to the boy, he watched with both eyes.
What most amazed him was to see the smith weld two
pieces of iron as if mere dough on a baking-board. Why
not repeat this marvel at home?

Near his father's house was a shed, once used for weav-
ing, and now encumbered with hoes and harrows, plows and
spades, old and new. In one corner of its attic lay a heap
of scrap iron, from which the lad chose pieces likely to be
serviceable. With stones and bricks gathered from the
farmyard, he built a forge, like the blacksmith's, only much
smaller. Fuel was needed next: where was he to get it?
When his mother's back was turned he took coals from her
kitchen grate; these, thoroughly drenched, he quietly conveyed to his forge. A big iron wedge, firmly driven into
a log, would do for his anvil. When these preparations
were well under way, Thomas heard joyful news. His

father and mother next morning were to visit a friend twenty miles away. Their absence would give him a chance to weld a dozen bits of iron together if he liked. When his parents drove off, he was soon plying a bellows at his little forge. In a few minutes its blaze was fierce enough to soften his metal, so that it took any shape he pleased. But to weld any of his iron scraps proved impossible, for the reason, then unknown to the boy, that his fire was not hot enough. He saw with dismay that he must call a second time on the blacksmith, so as fully to learn an art not so easy as it seemed to be. As the lad stood surveying his darkened lumps of metal, in strode his father, wondering what all this smoke and fire were about. His scolding was qualified by paternal admiration of the spunk and gumption so plainly in view. But it was a good while before Thomas Blanchard undertook his second task at a forge. His father had hoped to make a farmer of him, and when with reluctance, he saw that his son was resolved to be a mechanic, he said: " Well, my boy, learn blacksmithing if you like. Only learn it thoroughly, and never let a job leave your hands unless it is the best you can do."

While yet a schoolboy, he took his first step as an inventor, holding fast to his father's injunction of thoroughness. A schoolmate one day told him of an apple-paring machine of lightning pace that he had seen in Boston. Without so much as a hint regarding its construction, Blanchard said: " I will make one." Within a week he built a parer of wood and iron, its spindle swiftly rotating an apple as the crank was turned; but its knife at once slid toward the core of the fruit, instead of removing its rind. To remedy this fault, our young inventor took occasion to observe that a hand-parer, by way of gage, always kept his thumb close to the rind he was slicing off. Accordingly he added a gage of wire to his blade, which now pared its fruit just as it should. From that day forward

Thomas Blanchard was in high favor at paring bees near and far: he could easily peel more fruit than any six rivals together, no matter how quick their fingers and thumbs. His apple-parer taught him a lesson he never forgot: that if a machine is to supplant the human hand, it must faithfully imitate every successive act of that hand.

Blanchard's parer was a hit both social and mechanical, and it gave him confidence to attack devices for work much more serious than apple-paring. At West Milbury, a few miles from Sutton, Stephen, an elder brother, kept twenty boys and men busy at tack-making. He gave Thomas work at a vise, where, hammer in hand, he headed tacks one by one. It was so tedious a task that the lad became disgusted, especially when Saturday night brought him a mere pittance as wages. One of the hands in the factory was employed to count tacks, that they might go into packets of a hundred each. Blanchard devised a self-acting counter, arranging a clockwheel so that it advanced one tooth every time a heading blow fell on a tack. At every hundreth blow, a bell was rung, announcing that it was time to fold up a packet. Blanchard's brother looked askance at this contrivance, but its inventor was not to be chilled by lack of sympathy. He determined to pass from counting blows to dealing blows, so timed and directed as to produce tacks better and faster than human hands ever did. Machines for this purpose had been brought out long before, but without practical success. A machine that would avoid their faults would be profitable, and this young Blanchard believed he could design. He mentioned his project to his brother, who said: "It takes a knack to make a tack: no machine can do it."

Blanchard was about eighteen when he began to build a tack-making machine. For the next six years he kept at work upon it at odd times, taking it with him as he went from place to place in a round of factories and shops.

Whenever he saw how to simplify the action of a knife or hammer, an earlier plan was discarded that very day. When he had reached twenty-four, he felt that he could bestow no further improvement on the thoroughly built model he now showed his family. His machine steadily poured out two hundred tacks a minute, all with better heads and points than those of hand production. His brother Stephen had been sure that tacks of ordinary size, such as fasten carpets, were too small to be shaped by machinery. He was silent when a machine-made tack weighing the one-thousandth part of an ounce was placed on his palm. Blanchard sold his patent for this machine for $5,000. This seemed to him a goodly price: it was a mere trifle for so valuable a property. The purchasers shrewdly marketed their tacks without disclosing that they were made by machinery. As they charged the prices then paid for hand-made goods, their profits were encouraging.

This tack-machine was so well designed that it remains to this day much the same as when it left its modeler's shop. In Blanchard's time it was fed by hand: in its modern forms it feeds itself. A single tacker and a quick boy can now mind as many as twelve machines, while keeping their dies well ground and in good order. Blanchard carefully studied the successive operations of making a tack by hand: he then so disposed his levers and wheels, his knives and hammers, that these operations were duly copied, with a force and at a speed far surpassing the possibilities of fingers and fists. First of all, thin plates of steel were divided into strips, each strip as broad as a tack is long. Just enough steel for a blank was then cut off by the contact of two upper knives with a lower bed knife below. In this cut, both upper knives worked as one. As soon as the steel for a tack was cut off, the left-hand knife stopped, and the right-hand knife held the blank by the aid of a steel finger. This finger brought down the blank into the gripping dies

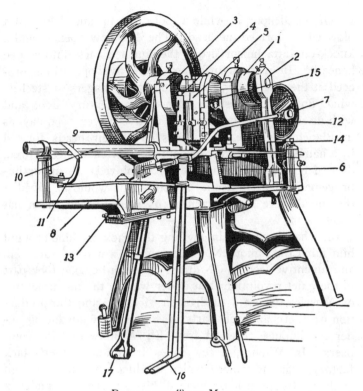

BLANCHARD TACK MACHINE

1, Spindle.   2, Connecting-rod to operate heading lever.   3, Gripping lever.   4, Logy jaw for cutting plates.   5, Carrier jaw, carrying tack to gripping dies.   6, Heading lever.   7, Feed gear. 8, Boom.   9, Clearer.   10, Barrel.   11, Fiddle-bow.   12, Feed-rod. 13, Elbow or feed arm.   14, Spring to hold tack while carried to the die.   15, Haul-off lever.   16, Nippers for holding plate.   17, Rest for nipper rods.

In operating this machine the plate, of a width and thickness suited to making the required tacks, is held in the nippers and fed through the barrel (10) by means of a weight. The barrel is set at such an angle that the two jaws (4 and 5), actuated by cams on the spindle, cut off a wedge-shaped blank with the thick part of the wedge toward the header (6). The bearer (14) is under that portion of the wedge which is to form the head, and after the two jaws have together cut off the blank, the logy jaw (4) comes to a stop, and the blank or wedge is carried down between the leader-tool and the bearer to the proper point to be taken by the gripper (3), which holds it to be headed by the header (6). As soon as the header recedes and the dies open, the tack is ejected by the clearer (9) operated by a cam on the hub of the balance wheel. The plate is turned over every half-revolution by the fiddle-bow operated by the elbow and feed-rod from the gear (7).

[Courtesy of Henry Perkins Foundry Co., Bridgewater, Mass.]

which closed upon it, while a tool came up and delivered a blow which formed the head. The dies now opened, and a knock-out attachment drove the finished tack into a pan beneath. In modern machines these five operations proceed at the rate of 275 tacks a minute. Fingers of steel do what fingers of flesh had to do a century ago, and with no waste of either metal or motive-power. To-day, as in Blanchard's time, most tacks have their heads formed by a hammer. If heads of round or other shape are desired, dies of corresponding outline are employed. A minor improvement suggests itself. A little labor would be saved if the metal were fed in continuous rolls instead of in flat sheets.

Blanchard's success in devising this tack machine brought him fame throughout New England as a man of rare skill and inventive faculty. Naturally enough he soon took part in the quiet revolution then under way in the manufactures of America, where a subdivision of labor, and the production of interchangeable parts, was constantly advancing under the impulse received from Eli Whitney and his compeers. In Milbury, a few miles from his brother's tack factory, was an armory which produced muskets of high quality. Its proprietor welded his gun barrels under a hammer, and then turned them for almost their whole length on a lathe, leaving about three inches at the breech to be chipped and filed along two flat and oval sides. This task of finishing cost one dollar per weapon, a sum which the gunmaker was anxious to reduce. He sent for Blanchard, and asked him to devise, if he could, an appliance which would mechanically finish his muskets. Blanchard carefully inspected a completed weapon, looked critically at its lathe, and began a monotonous whistle, as was his wont when in deep study. Before the end of that week he had added to the gun lathe a simple cam motion, controlled by a lever, which executed the flats and ovals of a butt with ease and at trifling cost. One afternoon, while a journeyman was watching this cam at work, he said to a shopmate: " Well, Blanchard can't take my job away from me, for I turn gunstocks." Blanchard overheard this remark, and muttered to himself: " I am not so sure of that. I'll think it over."

There and then the desire to build a self-acting lathe to turn gunstocks took possession of him, and refused dismissal from his mind. Day by day he felt more and more convinced that such a lathe was feasible, and that he was the man to invent it. While manifold schemes for this machine were afloat just below the level of his conscious thought, he was driving homeward through Brimfield, thirty miles from Sutton. In an instant there emerged to his imagination a hinged carriage to hold a feeling wheel, and beside it, a twin cutting and copying wheel. He cried: " I have got it! " Two passers-by heard this exclamation. One of them said to his comrade: " I guess that man's crazy." Within a month Blanchard built a lathe which carved so neat a gunstock that it hardly asked a touch from sandpaper. While at Washington securing his patent for this lathe, Blanchard exhibited his machine at the War Department. One of the company was an admiral who inquired jocosely: " Can you turn a seventy-four frigate? " " Yes," replied the inventor, " if you will furnish a block."

Blanchard next entered the service of the United States Armory at Springfield, Massachusetts, where he erected, in 1822, a large copying lathe, still on view in the Museum of the Armory. It carved two gunstocks per hour. Its successor, much smaller and neater, works nearly six times as fast. In addition to setting up his lathe, Blanchard created or improved at least a dozen machines for the manufacture of firearms. One of these appliances cut square mortises to receive the lock, barrel, butt-plates, and other mountings of a musket. His absorption in all this arduous toil diverted his attention from his chief item of property, the copying lathe. This gave a horde of pirates a welcome opportunity; soon more than fifty of their machines were running throughout the country, passing out of Vermont and Maine northward into Canada. To hunt down and punish these thieves was both costly and baffling. The United States Armories at Springfield and Harper's Ferry paid him a royalty of nine cents for each gunstock turned on his lathes. Apart from these payments, his invention for years scarcely netted him any income whatever. His troubles with rogues began, indeed, before the issue of his original patent. While he was building his first model, he was watched by a machinist who copied his work day by day. When Blanchard reached Washington and applied for his patent, he found that a caveat had been filed on the previous day. But the would-be pirate was foiled. Blanchard, on the morning when he had first tested his model, had called in two witnesses, who noted the date. This precaution secured a just title to the inventor. Of course, his patent did not extend to Canada, so that his lathes taken across the border made lasts by the million, to be exported to the United States free of duty. Blanchard appealed to Congress to have a high tariff imposed upon these wares; after years of delay this was enacted and the importations from Canada came to an end. In its latest form a Blanchard lathe cuts six to ten pairs of lasts per hour, depending upon their size and the finish desired. The five cutters of a last machine are so shaped as to take cuts successively deeper and deeper.

It was in developing the manufacture of shoe-lasts that Blanchard first showed the wide scope of his copying carriage as duly modified. To form a left-foot last from a right-foot last, he caused his pattern and his wooden block to revolve in opposite directions. With equal simplicity he produced from a single pattern a wide variety of lasts, proportionately larger and smaller. He employed copying wheels differing in size from the feeling wheel, and differing proportionately, also, in their lengths of path. A Blanchard lathe thus equipped attracted much attention at the Universal Exposition of 1857 in Paris, as it executed in miniature exquisite reproductions of life-size busts of Napoleon III. and the Empress Eugénie. The French admirers of Blanchard recalled, with pride, his descent from a Huguenot of Rochelle, who, with many another refugee, brought rare skill to his new home in America.

Blanchard did not always stay indoors at his work. He was a pioneer in adapting steam to transportation by land and water. In 1825 he built in Springfield a steam vehicle which sped along its highways at a rattling pace, a forerunner of the motor-cars of to-day. It was controlled with ease, turned sharp corners without strain, went forward or backward as readily as a horse, and its power could be doubled when a hill was to be climbed. Blanchard clearly foresaw a great future for railways, with their tracks so much less resistant than roadways. He exerted himself to form a joint-stock company to build a railroad across Massachusetts, submitting his plans, with a model steam carriage, to the State Legislature. On January 23, 1826, its committee reported favorably, but when Blanchard sought to enlist capital, none was forthcoming. He then proceeded to Albany, where he explained his project to Governor Clinton, suggesting that the Empire State should build a comprehensive railroad system, with a line from Albany to Schenectady as its first link. Governor Clinton heard Blanchard with his accustomed courtesy, and told him that his proposal came too soon after the exhausting demands for the Erie Canal. For that great artery the Governor had wrought valiantly for many years. Blanchard was now convinced that the time was not ripe for railroads, and he left their advocacy to other promoters, whose success was not long delayed. While railroading had been in his thoughts, he sketched a variety of switches and the like, which were duly adopted when locomotives began their transformation of America.

While railroads had remained merely in the stage of discussion, steamboats had for years been plying with profit the Hudson, the St. Lawrence, and the Mississippi. Blanchard did all that lay in his power to confer a like boon on the Connecticut River. In 1826, the principal business men of Hartford decided to improve the navigation of that stream flowing by their city. Accordingly a canal was built to overcome Enfield Falls, a few miles distant, so that a free channel was opened all the way to Springfield. For the traffic thus offered, Blanchard built the *Vermont,* the *Massachusetts,* and other steamers. Of course, he bestowed original features upon them all. In the *Massachusetts* he employed two steam engines, so coupled as to avoid dead centers at the crank pin. He boldly employed steam at a pressure of 500 pounds to the square inch, aware of the economy attending its use. Of course, to withstand a pressure so extreme he was restricted to boilers of small size. But he found leaks to be unavoidable, and lubrication so difficult at the great heat involved that his experiment was abandoned. Even to-day it would be repeated with hesitation. In 1830, Blanchard designed the steamer *Allegheny,* to ply between Pittsburgh and Olean Point, 300 miles apart. In this stretch of water there were falls and rapids having a total extent of 600 feet.

In building the hulls of his steamers, Blanchard found the knee timbers, for which he paid a high price, to be sometimes weak and faulty. This led him to examine processes for steaming timbers, and then bending them into forms needed in shipbuilding. He noticed that usually these products were badly cracked and splintered on their outer curves. As the result of many experiments, he designed a machine which bent steamed timbers quite free from frac-

ture. Its curved links grasped a stick, while a stout screw
firmly pressed the wood against its container. To stretch
the fibers of wood, as Blanchard's predecessors had done,
was to weaken them; he employed only compression, which

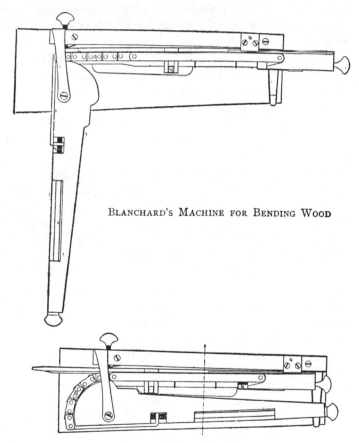

BLANCHARD'S MACHINE FOR BENDING WOOD

does little harm or none at all. His machine proved to
be by far the most lucrative of Blanchard's inventions.
For its applications to ship timbers he received $150,000. It
also profitably turned out handles for plows and other farm

tools, it curved felloes for wheels, it provided slates and pictures with frames much stronger than those made of straight and jointed wood. In this last-mentioned field, small as it seemed, the inventor reaped a harvest which astonished him. A manufacturer of school slates came from Philadelphia one day, and, showing Blanchard an old-fashioned square slate, asked him if he could furnish a frame that would not break apart when let fall to the ground. Blanchard took the slate, chipped off the corners so as to leave it an oval, and then steamed and bent around it an oak strip fastened by an iron loop. The slatemaker let this frame fall to the floor repeatedly, and, finding it none the worse, asked Blanchard his terms for the right to manufacture such a frame for slates. " Two thousand dollars," said the inventor. " Five hundred is enough," replied the Pennsylvanian. " Give me five per cent. royalty on your sales," said Blanchard. His visitor consented, with the result that he paid Blanchard more than two thousand dollars during the first year of their contract.

Blanchard's income from his patents was now ample, and he removed to Boston. Here, during the remainder of his life, a considerable part of his time was devoted to acting as an expert in patent cases. His intuitive perceptions as a mechanic, his wide and varied experience in machine shops, and his sterling honesty gave unimpeachable value to his judgments. He died in Boston April 16, 1864, at the age of seventy-six.

Saml F. B. Morse,,

[From a painting by himself, using a mirror. By permission of the owner, G. William Rasch, of Brooklyn. This portrait is exhibited at the Museum of the Brooklyn Institute of Arts and Sciences.]

SAMUEL F. B. MORSE

OF all the services of electricity the chief is its carriage of our words with the speed of light. Seventy years ago so few could see that this great boon lay within easy grasp, that the pioneers of telegraphy had to fight many a hard battle before they came to victory. And, quite without knowing it, they were breaking ground for other conquests as decisive as their own. Morse and his lieutenants sought to convey an electric current forty, seventy, or a hundred miles, with so little loss by the way that, at its journey's end, it should excite an electro-magnet, and attract an armature of an ounce or two. They had to find out what wire to use, how to place it, how to keep its current from leaking away. They had to learn what electrical intensities are best for long or for short lines; and how properly to enwrap the tell-tale cores of their electro-magnets. They accomplished nothing less, therefore, than the long-distance transmission of electricity, and of the motive-power into which it may be instantly converted. They dealt, to be sure, with only trifling volumes of current, but all the while they were making straight the paths for the modern engineers who send millions of horse-power from Niagara, and from other cataracts the world over, to chains of motors, lamps, and furnaces which may be as far off as three hundred miles. These inestimable services had their unregarded beginning as an aid to telegraphy almost at its birth. Professor Charles Grafton Page in 1838 designed a simple dynamo as a rival to voltaic batteries: on Christmas Day, 1844, it operated a Morse circuit of eighty miles.

In American telegraphy, Morse is the commanding figure. Artist that he was, first and always, he placed pencils in

electric fingers in such wise that, instead of waving idly in
the air, they might record their signals simply and indelibly.
With a tenacity never for a moment relaxed, with the address and tact of a born diplomatist, he sought information
from investigators, enlisted inventive skill superior to his
own, secured votes from lawmakers, and borrowed capital
with nothing in pledge but his own fervid hopes. He owed
much, nearly everything, indeed, to a succession of discov-
erers all the way from Galvani to Henry. But, however
large his debt to these devisers, and to their interpreter,
Professor Leonard D. Gale; however much his first instruments were transmuted by his partner, Alfred Vail; it was
Morse who was captain of the ship, who planned its voyage,
engaged its crew, filled its treasury, and, after many a
storm, anchored in port at last. For this mastery of men
and events he was equipped by nature and nurture. To
begin with, he was well born. His father, the Rev. Jedidiah
Morse, was a man of force and initiative, who counted
Daniel Webster among his admiring friends, and with good
reason. Before he was licensed as a clergyman, and while
a teacher in New Haven, he began writing his " American
Geography," which, duly completed, won wide acceptance
throughout the Union. He was settled as pastor of the
First Congregational Church in Charlestown, Massachusetts, on April 30, 1789, the day of Washington's inauguration in New York as President of the United States.
Rev. Dr. Morse served his parish all the more fruitfully
because he looked beyond its bounds. He took part in
founding the Theological Seminary at Andover, the American Board of Foreign Missions, the American Bible Society, and the American Tract Society. A fortnight after
his installation he married Elizabeth Ann Breese, a grand-
daughter of the Rev. Dr. Samuel Finley, who became
president of the College of New Jersey, now Princeton
University.

On April 27, 1791, in a house at the foot of Breed's Hill, in Charlestown, was born his famous son, who, to recall eminent forbears, was baptized Samuel Finley Breese. Rev. Dr. Morse, like the shepherd whom Chaucer praised, recommended the narrow way by walking therein himself. Thanks to his example and loving discipline, his son was ever a man of profound religious convictions. As one reads his intimate letters, it is plain that a slight jolt in his kaleidoscope would have patterned him as a minister of the Gospel, and not as a painter and an inventor. His bent toward art declared itself early. When four years of age, he attended a school kept by Old Ma'am Rand, a cripple unable to leave her chair. Young Samuel outlined her features in a style so unflattering that he received more than one rebuke from her long rattan. When seven years old, he was sent to a preparatory school in Andover, where he was fitted for Phillips Academy, near by. Thence, after a brief sojourn at home, he proceeded to Yale College, entering at sixteen. Thither, within a year or two, he was followed by his brothers, Sidney and Richard. Thus generously did their father, with a comparatively small income, provide his children with thorough education at his own *alma mater.* At that time the president of Yale College was Timothy Dwight, a teacher of national fame. When failing sight obliged him to have assistants at his desk, he chose the three young Morses. His molding influence, strong upon every student under his care, was all the stronger with the trio for an intimacy which became paternal.

Samuel Morse's knack in seizing a portrait was meantime improving by constant practice. To eke out his modest expenses, he painted miniatures at five dollars, and drew profiles at a dollar. He began to feel that his skill and joy at the easel were pointing to his career, and he earnestly toiled for a proficiency which might win his father's concurrence in his desire to become an artist. And meanwhile, day by day, term by term, he received the best scientific instruction that any American college could then bestow. As part of his course, he learned all that was then known about electricity; and just because he filled and connected voltaic cells, charged and discharged Leyden jars, noted the vibration of compass needles, his brain was planted with seeds which more than twenty years afterward germinated in his recording telegraph. Much, evidently, may turn upon an all-round appeal to a student's intelligence, upon bringing to his view the whole circle of human activity. In a golden hour a latent and unsuspected faculty may be thus awakened, and nourished, before the brief springtime of responsiveness has passed forever. Morse, let us bear in mind, was not a probable man to be the Columbus of American telegraphy. His natural bent was strongly toward art; he had but moderate skill as a mechanic; his inventive powers were not remarkable; he was no chemist; neither had he the talent nor the ambition of a researcher. Yet, in the mind of this man, and in the mind of nobody else, was kindled the spark which, all in good time, gave the telegraph to America. Who was the teacher at Yale, who, by experiment and interpretation, so fruitfully impressed this young student? Jeremiah Day, then professor of physics, who, a few years later, rose to the presidency of his university, a post which he filled with distinction. How he sowed the good seed in Morse's mind is told in a note from Morse to his father, written on March 8, 1809:

" Mr. Day's lectures are very interesting, they are upon electricity. He has given us some very fine experiments, the whole class, taking hold of hands, formed the circuit of communication, and we all received the shock at the same moment. I never took the electric shock before; it felt as if some person had struck me a slight blow across the arms.

Mr. Day has given us two lectures on this subject, and I believe there are two more remaining. I will give you some account of them as soon as they are delivered, which will probably be in the course of this week."

Morse was also much indebted to Professor Benjamin Silliman, who then taught chemistry at Yale, and who employed in his experiments Volta's pile and crown of cups, and a Cruikshanks' battery. Experiments other than electrical at times exercised the ingenuity of Morse, and of his brothers as well. One day they built a fire-balloon, and sent it skyward. On its second voyage it lurched against the middle college building, took fire, and was soon reduced to ashes. But this sort of thing was to Morse play rather than work. He felt an impulse ever growing stronger toward art. On July 22, 1810, he wrote to his parents:

"I am now released from college, and am attending to painting. As to my choice of a profession, I still think that I was made for a painter, and I would be obliged to you to make such arrangements with Mr. Allston, for my studying with him, as you shall think expedient. I would desire to study with him during the winter, and, as he expects to return to England in the spring, I should admire to be able to go with him, but of this we will talk when we meet at home."

His father and mother already had had proof of his ability with the brush. He had depicted them both, in a family group, and with decided skill, some time before this at college. Just before his graduation, in 1810, he painted *The Landing of the Pilgrims at Plymouth*, with so assured a touch that his father was convinced that there was in his son the making of an artist. Dr. Morse now consented that Samuel should adopt painting as his vocation. It was speedily arranged that, as he had suggested, he should study with Washington Allston. That famous artist was soon to cross from his native America to his studio in London. He and Morse sailed on July 13, 1811, on the *Lydia,* from New York for Liverpool. On arriving in London, Morse engaged a lodging at 67 Great Titchfield Street, and began work at his easel with diligence. One morning Allston presented him to Benjamin West, the leading American artist of his time, then in the zenith of his renown. Morse intended to offer for exhibition at the Academy a drawing from a small cast of the Farnese Hercules. This he submitted to West. After strict scrutiny for some minutes, and much commendation, West handed the drawing back to Morse, saying, " Very well, sir, very well; go on and finish it." " It is finished," replied Morse. " Oh, no," said West; " look here, and here, and here," pointing to many unfinished places which had escaped the untutored eye of the young student. No sooner were they pointed out, however, than they were felt, and a week was devoted to a more careful finishing of the drawing, until, full of confidence, Morse again presented it to West. Praise was warmly accorded, but once again West said, " Very well, indeed, sir; go and finish it."

" Is it not finished? " asked Morse, deeply chagrined.

" Not yet," replied West; " see you have not marked that muscle, nor the articulations of the finger-joints."

Morse now spent three or four days retouching and improving his work, resolved, if possible, to have his critic say that the drawing was really finished at last. West acknowledged the drawing to be exceedingly good, " Very clever, indeed;" but he ended up with, " Well, sir, go and finish it."

" I cannot finish it," said Morse almost in despair.

" Well," said West, " I have tried you long enough. Now, sir, you have learned more by this drawing than you would have accomplished in double the time by a dozen half-finished beginnings. It is not numerous drawings, but the *character of one,* which makes a thorough draughtsman. Finish one picture, sir, and you are a painter."

How well he laid to heart the severe lessons from West appears in a letter to his parents, written on September 20, 1812:

"I have just finished a model in clay of a figure (*The Dying Hercules*), my first attempt at sculpture. Mr. Allston is extremely pleased with it; he says it is better than all the things I have done since I have been in England put together, and says that I must send a cast of it home to you, and that it will convince you that I shall make a painter. . . . Mr. West was also extremely delighted with it. He said it was not merely an academical figure, but displayed thought. . . . If it is my destiny to become GREAT, and worthy of a biographical memoir, my biographer will never be able to charge upon my parents that bigoted attachment to any individual profession, the exercise of which spirit by parents toward their children has been the ruin of some of the greatest geniuses. . . . I hope that one day my success in my profession will reward you in some measure for the trouble and inconvenience I have so long put you to."

Morse showed West a cast of this *Dying Hercules.* West called his son Raphael, and, pointing to the figure, said, "Look there, sir; I have always told you that any painter can make a sculptor." The picture painted from this figure Morse sent to the Academy Exhibition. His pains in its production were richly rewarded. To the day of his death he treasured a copy of *The British Press* of May 4, 1813, in which his picture is declared to be among the nine best paintings in a gallery of a thousand, which included canvases by Turner, Northcote, Lawrence, and Wilkie. This picture is now in the Art Museum of Yale University. His plaster model, furthermore, won a gold medal at the Exhibition of the Society of Arts. Both the model and a cast from it disappeared and left no trace behind. Twenty-five years afterward Morse came upon the cast in the Capitol at Washington. One day, in 1838, he was installing his telegraph in an upper room there. To locate his wires he descended to a vault which had long been closed. His quick eye was attracted by something white glimmering in the darkness. It was the cast of his *Dying Hercules;* it had been given to the architect of the Capitol, who had laid it aside and forgotten all about it.

While Morse was in London, the United States and England were at war. It testified to the courtesy and *savoir faire* of Morse, his unfailing characteristics through life, that he was everywhere received with hospitality and kindness. His illustrious compatriot, Benjamin West, suffered no cooling in the friendship which had long bound him to King George Third. In proof he related to Morse:

" While the King was on a visit to me, news was brought of an important victory over the rebels. Not finding him at the palace, the messenger immediately traced him to my studio, and communicated the intelligence.

" The messenger then said to me:

" ' Are you not gratified at the success of his Majesty's troops? '

" ' No,' I replied: ' I can never rejoice in the misfortunes of my countrymen.'

" ' Right,' said the King, rising and placing his hand approvingly on my shoulder. ' If you did, you would not long be a fit subject for any government.' "

One day Morse paid West a visit whilst he was painting his canvas of " Christ Rejected." West carefully examined Morse's hands, and remarking their delicacy, he said: " Let me tie you with this cord and take that place while I paint in the hands of the Saviour." When he released the young artist, West said: " You may now say, if you please, that you had a hand in this picture."

West was not the only man of eminence whom Morse met during this long stay in London. He heard more than

one monologue from Coleridge, and was a delighted junior
in the circle which gathered around Rogers, the banker-
poet. Wordsworth and Crabbe, also, he met. Of the great
artists of that era he saw something of Fuseli and Northcote, Turner, Flaxman, and Sir Thomas Lawrence. At
Yale he had learned quite as much from his fellow-students
as from his professors. In London he was as gainfully instructed by young artists, like himself, as by the formal
precepts of Allston, West, and their venerable compeers.
From youngsters of the brush he heard criticism and
comment without retouching or reserve. And as he
went from one studio to another as a welcome visitor,
he saw what patience and fidelity go to the making of
every good picture, from the first outline to the final var-
nishing.

Of his younger associates the most notable was his chum
and room-mate, Charles Robert Leslie, three years his
junior, born in England of American parents. Leslie was
a warm-hearted youth, of decided talent and unquenchable
enthusiasm. His portrait, in Spanish costume, was the first
that Morse painted in London; Leslie returning the compliment by limning his friend as a Highlander.

For a few months, in 1833, Leslie taught drawing at
West Point, but he found the Military Academy a poor
exchange for London, and thither he returned for good
and all, rising to popularity as a painter of *genre* and historical pieces. He wrote an admirable life of his friend
Constable, a handbook for young artists packed with solid
sense and wise counsel, and an autobiography published
after his death, which took place in 1859.

Men of the world are apt to prefer the company of
artists, such as Morse now became, to any other. Painters
see much of nature and human nature: they observe with
the adhesive gaze of men storing impressions for use.
Every portrait painter of mark cultivates the sympathy

which puts a nervous or impatient sitter at ease, that he may bring out a revealing glance of curiosity, of introspection, of self-approval: and this sympathy remains with the artist when he lays down his palette. Lessons not so important, but still valuable enough, were learned by our young student of art: he was quietly advancing in nicety and sureness of touch, both with plastic clay and with the brush. Thus it came about that, by-and-by, he could fashion his telegraphic recorder with his own hands, in happy independence of model-makers. It is much when an inventor has this measure of the builder in him: in the very act of making his model, its creator feels that here and there he can better its design or construction. And thus the query suggests itself, What have artists and inventors in common? Mainly breadth and vividness of imagination. Da Vinci devised canal-locks and painted *Mona Lisa*, for many years one of the glories of the Louvre. Michael Angelo, at twenty-one, carved his *Pieta;* in mature life he planned, as a roof for that *Pieta,* the dome of Saint Peter's. In less exalted ranks of this hierarchy of artist-inventors we may remark Fulton and Daguerre, Nasmyth and Alvan Clark. These men were craftsmen as well as artists; in both fields they passed from old to new, from inheritance to discovery. They divined what to other men was inscrutable: then they gave it form with pencil or brush, with chisel or file. They could descry the approach of dawn while to their neighbors darkness still prevailed.

To imagination Morse joined other gifts. He had a fair measure of mechanical ingenuity. His first telegraphic register, though clumsy, revealed the combining talent of a real inventor. And then he was fortunate in having a fresh eye, in viewing electrical experiments from outside the rut of professional treadmills. In New Haven and New York, in Albany and Princeton, hundreds of students had worked with electrical apparatus, some of it better than any that had fallen in Morse's way. Yet he was the only one of them all to bid electricity write its messages, throb by throb, with pencil or pen. Remote, indeed, was his easel from machine shops and chemical laboratories. That very remoteness, while it kept him ignorant of many important advances in knowledge, in all likelihood gave him a truer perspective of the distant possibilities of science than if he had been an engineer or a chemist.

In the course of his fifth year abroad, Morse deemed his studies to be fairly closed. On August 21, 1815, he sailed from Liverpool for Boston on the *Ceres*. In Boston, four miles from his native Charlestown, he promptly opened a studio. By way of introduction he exhibited *The Judgment of Jupiter*, for which the public encouraged him with its voice and with nothing else. He received no offer for his picture, and no sitter favored him with a call. With no work for his brush, his mind reverted to the mechanical contrivances which had often suggested themselves to his ingenuity. He devised, with the aid of his brother Sidney, an improved pump, and adapted it to fire engines. This pump was commended by that acute critic, Eli Whitney, inventor of the cotton gin. But, alas! like the portraits Morse stood ready to paint, it was not in demand. What resource could he fall back upon? Nothing but touring from town to town with his easel in quest of patrons. In the autumn of 1816, and the following winter, he traveled through New Hampshire and Vermont. Let us see how he fared. From Concord, on August 16, he wrote to his parents:

" I am still here—I have painted two portraits at fifteen dollars each, and have two more engaged, and many more talked of. I think I shall get along well. I believe I could make an independent fortune in a few years if I devoted myself exclusively to portraits, so great is the desire for portraits in the different country towns."

During the next month he met at a party Miss Lucretia Pickering Walker, the beautiful and accomplished daughter of Charles Walker, a leading citizen of Concord. It was a case of love at first sight, with an early betrothal. Morse continued his tours, making friends wherever he went, and earning fair prices for his work. At length he felt warranted in assuming the responsibilities of matrimony, which, for two years, he had cherished in contemplation. On October 1, 1818, he was married to Miss Walker at Concord. Their union was of happiness unalloyed: to the end of her days Morse and his wife were lovers. The one supreme sorrow of his life was the early death of his devoted helpmate.

He had now entered upon the checkered career of an artist whose work was, at times, in pressing demand, with long intervals of idleness and the imminence of sheer want. In this regard, as in every other, his lot was one of sunshine just after his wedding at Concord. When he had reaped the Northern field pretty thoroughly, he went, at a friend's invitation, to Charleston, where he met with cheering success. For the Common Council of Charleston, he painted a portrait of President James Monroe. With his wonted public spirit, he took part in founding the South Carolina Academy of Fine Arts, of which a friend, Joel R. Poinsett, was chosen to be president. Every day that Morse remained in Charleston increased his vogue. In a few weeks he had listed one hundred and fifty patrons at sixty dollars each. He drew a good many portraits with the understanding that they were to be completed in the North, whither he must soon return to rejoin his wife. He now conceived a picture of the House of Representatives at Washington, in which the portraits of seventy leading members should appear. He hoped that this work might lead him from simple portraiture to historical painting, for which he felt that he had talent. He executed his large canvas in the autumn of 1822, and disappointment was again his portion. Nobody wanted it, although it was exhibited far and wide, and much admired. After many vicissitudes, the picture came into the hands of the late Daniel Huntington, of New York, whose gallery it long adorned. It is now in the Corcoran Art Gallery at Washington.

Morse's skill as an artist and as a mechanic came into play during the summer of 1823, when he devised a sculpturing machine in New Haven. In constructing and operating this machine he was aided by Mr. Auger, who carved busts of Apollo and other statuary, with no particular profit to Morse or himself. On August 27, 1823, Morse wrote to his wife:

" The more I think of making a push at New York as a permanent place of residence in my profession, the more proper it seems that it should be at once. New York does not yet feel the influx of wealth from the Western Canals, but in a year or two she will feel it, and it will be advantageous to me to be previously identified among her citizens as a painter. It requires some little time to become renowned in such a city."

During the ensuing month Morse took up his residence in New York, and wrote to his wife:

" I have obtained a place to board at friend Coolidge's at $2.25 per week, and have taken for my studio a fine room in Broadway [No. 96], on the corner of Pine Street, opposite Trinity Churchyard, for $6.50 a week, fifty cents less than I expected to pay. . . ."

In this studio the first portrait he painted was that of Chancellor Kent, who proved to be a nervous and fidgety subject. Morse would have been glad of other sitters, just as troublesome. But the Chancellor was not followed upstairs by any other patron, and on December 21, 1823, with Christmas at hand, Morse wrote to his wife in anything but a festal key:

" My cash is almost gone, and I begin to feel some anxiety and perplexity to know what to do. . . . I have thought of various plans, but which to decide upon I am completely at a loss, nor can I decide until I hear definitely from Washington in regard to my Mexico expedition. I wrote to General Van Rensselaer, Mr. Poinsett, and Colonel Hayne, of the Senate, applying for some situation in the legation soon to be sent to Mexico."

He was duly appointed attaché. But Mr. Edwards, who was to have been Minister to Mexico, and Morse's chief, through a quarrel with the powers that were, did not enter on his mission, and once more the poor artist knew the bitterness of balked hopes. But, after much cloudy weather, Morse was to enjoy a little sunshine. He was commissioned by the City of New York to paint a portrait of Lafayette. He proceeded to Washington forthwith, to find Lafayette as agreeable in a studio as in a drawing-room. While he was painting this picture, he received word that on February 8, 1825, his wife had suddenly died. This blow was almost more than Morse could bear. He and his wife had been devotedly attached to one another, and that she should pass away in his absence added pang to pang. An aggravation of his grief was the six days and nights' constant travel which then divided Washington from New Haven. To-day the journey may be accomplished in less than seven hours. On his return to Washington, utterly heartbroken, Morse finished his portrait of Lafayette, which hangs in the City Hall of New York.

He now resumed work in his Broadway studio, and although his canvases commended themselves to the fraternity of artists, he painted too few of them to yield him a living. Of his high standing with his brethren of the brush there was soon unmistakable proof. Colonel Trumbull, the historical painter, was then president of the American Academy of Arts, the one society of artists in New York. He was accused of inhospitality to young students, and on other grounds he was generally disliked. In their discontent, a group of painters and sculptors proposed to found a National Academy of the Fine Arts of Design. Accordingly, on January 15, 1826, fifteen artists were chosen by ballot as foundation members, with Morse as president, a post he held until 1845, with honor to himself, with usefulness both to his associates and the public. The Academy, its name shortened, still flourishes in New York, with art-classes much expanded and strengthened in the recent years of its history.

While Morse was at work with his wonted industry, there came to him bad news from New Haven. His father, to whom in every extremity he could turn for sympathy and aid, was dying. On June 9, 1826, the Rev. Dr. Morse expired in his sixty-fourth year. With the children of his son Samuel, he had resided in New Haven for six years. In 1823, three years before their father died, Samuel's brothers, Sidney and Richard, removed to New York, and established *The Observer*, a family journal of a religious character. After a severe struggle their newspaper became profitable, thanks to their energy and ability.

Samuel Morse, in his devotion to art, had not lost sight of the amazing developments in science of each passing year. In 1820, during a brief stay in New Haven, he often visited the laboratory of Professor Silliman, which had recently acquired from Dr. Hare, of Philadelphia, a galvanic calorimotor and his deflagrator for the combustion of metals. But it was not in producing high temperatures that Morse was to use electricity. The path of his interests and of his ultimate triumph was cleared and broadened when, seven years later, in 1827, he attended in New York a course of lectures by Professor James Freeman Dana, of Columbia College. Now came warmth and light to the seeds long ago planted in his mind at Yale. He observed with wonder how a straight wire conveying electricity deflected a nearby compass needle, an effect noticed first by Romagnesi at Trent in 1802, and independently remarked by Oersted in 1819, at Copenhagen. He saw how, following an experiment devised by Professor Schweigger, of Halle, this wire, when bent as a ring, deflected the needle much more than before. But what particularly impressed him was an electro-magnet invented, in 1825, by William Sturgeon, of Woolwich, near London. Here was a strip of soft iron, curved as a horseshoe, around which were coiled a few feet of copper wire. By way of insulation the iron had received a coat of varnish. When an electric current passed through this wire, at once the iron became magnetic, only to lose its magnetism the instant that the current was cut off. This action, so much more positive and energetic than the swaying of a compass needle, rooted itself deeply in Morse's brooding mind. It was this clutching effect that he chose, and most wisely, for the register he eventually designed. Other inventors, less sound in judgment, preferred a vibrating needle as their agent, and force of habit saddles that choice upon their army of successors.

But Morse's interest in electrical progress at this time was but an incident in a life devoted to art: he turned to the laboratory for the refreshing which comes with a change of outlook. His practice as a painter had steadily grown, until now he was offered more commissions than he could execute. Amid this pressure of toil, he prepared and delivered a series of discourses on the fine arts. These were among the first lectures on art ever heard in America. Their quality widened his circle of friends, and bore fruit in a professorship five years afterward. Yet for all his goodly income as an artist, Morse, now in his thirty-ninth year, was dissatisfied with his pictures. He resolved to visit Italy, there, at leisure, to become familiar with the masterpieces of all time, to refine his taste, and improve his tech-

nique. A score of his friends at once subscribed $2,800
for canvases which he was to paint while abroad, either as
copies or original works. He sailed from New York on
November 8, 1829, landing in Liverpool twenty-six days

CHAPPÉ TELEGRAPH

thereafter. In England he met Leslie and other intimates
of his youth, and, proceeding through France, took his
way to the Italian frontier. Near Lyons, on his southward
course, he saw the waving arms of a Chappé semaphore,

such as he was to banish from the world.   On February 20 he found himself in Rome: without losing a day he began to copy Raphael's *School of Athens* for Robert Donaldson, of New York.   In the Vatican and other great galleries of Italy, he copied with industry, learning many a golden lesson as he plied the brush.   William Dunlap, in his " History of the Arts in America," says:

" Mr. Morse has told me that he formed a theory for the distribution of colors in a picture many years since, when standing before a picture by Paul Veronese, which has been confirmed by all his subsequent studies of the works of the great masters.   This picture is now in the National Gallery, London.   He saw in it that the highest light was cold; the mass of light, warm; the middle tint, cool; the shadow, negative; the reflections, hot.   He says that he has tried this theory by placing a white ball in a box, lined with white, and convinced himself that the system of Paul Veronese is the order of nature.   Balls of orange, or of blue, so placed, give the same relative result.   The high light of the ball is uniformly cold in comparison with the local color of the ball.

" ' I have observed in a picture by Rubens,' said Morse, ' that it had a foxy tone, and, on examination, I found that the shadow (which, according to my theory, ought to be negative) was hot.   Whenever I found this to be the case, I found the picture foxy.'   On one occasion his friend Allston said to him, while standing before an unfinished painting, ' I have painted that piece of drapery of every color, and it will not harmonize with the rest of the picture.'   Morse found the drapery belonged to the mass of light, and said, ' According to my theory, it must be warm; paint it flesh-color.'   ' What do you mean by your theory? '   Morse explained it.   Allston immediately said: ' It is so; it is in nature;' and has since said, ' Your theory has saved me many an hour's labor.' "

Morse, during his sojourn in Italy, formed many delightful friendships.   His desire to please and help others always made others desire to please and help him.   He became intimate with the great Danish sculptor, Thorwaldsen, of whom he painted a speaking likeness. James Fenimore Cooper was then in Italy: no sooner did the novelist and the artist meet than an attachment began, only to end with Cooper's life. Morse owed to his father a close intimacy with Baron Von Humboldt, who had corresponded with the author of the "American Geography." Sometimes the great explorer would seat himself beside Morse as he painted at the Louvre, and discourse with the utmost charm from his vast store of observation and thought. During a later visit to Paris, and afterward at Potsdam, the two friends, so far apart in their labors, and, perhaps, for that very reason, fraternized with enthusiasm.

His portfolios filled, his commissions for pictures duly despatched, Morse deemed his post-graduate course at an end. On October 1, 1832, he embarked at Havre for New York on the *Sully*, for the most memorable voyage of his life. Soon after the shores of France had receded from view, the talk at dinner turned on electro-magnetism. Dr. Charles T. Jackson, of Boston, a discoverer of anesthesia, who sat near Morse, spoke of the length of wire in the coil of an electro-magnet, and a neighbor asked, "Is the velocity of electricity reduced by the length of its conducting wire?" Jackson replied that electricity passes instantaneously over any known length of wire. He cited Franklin's experiments with several miles of wire, in which no appreciable time elapsed between a touch at one end and a spark at the other. Then Morse uttered the conviction which determined his life ever after: "If the presence of electricity can be made visible in any part of the circuit, I see no reason why intelligence may not be transmitted instantaneously by electricity."

The talk proceeded, but Morse was now silent. So far as he knew, nobody else had ever entertained a project for electrical telegraphy. Of what Schilling, Gauss, and

Weber had accomplished in needle telegraphy in Germany, he was wholly ignorant. Nor had news reached him of the still more striking experiments of Joseph Henry, at Albany, a few months prior. Here was a remarkable instance of how an inventor may independently devise a scheme long before embodied in apparatus he knows nothing about. In truth, the times were ripe for practical telegraphy. The electro-magnet of Sturgeon, the galvanometer of Schweigger, had enabled several ingenious men, each advancing in a path of his own, to cross, at last, the threshold of electrical communication. If this could take place in Germany, France, England, and America, why not also on the bosom of the Atlantic? The feat was feasible wherever there were brains to take newly created tools and build with them, wherever there was imagination to pass from the known to the beyond. Morse had one of the unfailing marks of greatness. His confidence in himself and in his purposes could not be shaken. Many a stubborn obstacle might confront him. He would overcome it. As his ship neared Sandy Hook he said to her commander, Captain Pell: " Well, Captain, should you hear of the telegraph one of these days, as the wonder of the world, remember the discovery was made on the good ship *Sully.*"

Morse had unconsciously prepared himself, in more ways than one, for the task he now took up with a stout heart. His native ingenuity had been exercised in constructing his pump and his sculpturing machine. From boyhood he had been drawing and sketching, so that, as the *Sully* bowled along toward New York, he drew rapidly and precisely his plans for a telegraph. These plans, as then outlined, are preserved in the National Museum at Washington. All his life his imagination had swept broad horizons, and he foresaw what mankind would reap by the instantaneous conveying of intelligence: the prospect spurred him day and night, and became a sheer obsession. On the practical side of his project, he was happy, as no rival inventor was happy, in choosing as his servant the electro-magnet, with its forceful grasp.

On his return to New York Morse found, to his deep chagrin, that he had lost his place in its procession of artists. In his absence of three years he had dropped from the memory of many acquaintances from whom, had he remained at home, patrons would undoubtedly have been recruited. So far, therefore, from having means to carry out telegraphic experiments, he had hardly cash enough to pay his landlord and grocer. His commissions for portraits were so few that he was obliged to give lessons. Only rigid economy enabled him to keep together body and soul. His room, which served as a studio, workshop, and dormitory, was on the fifth floor of a building on the northeast corner of Beekman and Nassau Streets. In succession to that structure stands the present Morse Building. Near the window stood a lathe on which he turned out the brass apparatus which he devised and slowly improved. His diet was mainly tea of his own brewing and crackers. From Nassau Street he removed to University Place, but with no improvement of income. General Strother, of Virginia, a well-known contributor to magazines as " Porte Crayon," thus sketched Morse at this crisis in his fortunes:

" I engaged to become Morse's pupil, and subsequently went to New York, and found him in a room in University Place. He had three other pupils, and I soon found that our professor had very little patronage. I paid my fifty dollars for one quarter's instruction. Morse was a faithful teacher, and took as much interest in our progress as— more, indeed, than—we did ourselves. But he was very poor. I remember that, when my second quarter's pay was due, my remittance did not come as expected, and one day the professor came in, and said, courteously: ' Well, Strother, my boy, how are we off for money?'

" ' Why, professor,' I answered, ' I am sorry to say I

have been disappointed; but I expect a remittance next week.'

" ' Next week,' he repeated sadly; ' I shall be dead by that time.'

" ' Dead, sir? '

" ' Yes, dead by starvation.'

" I was distressed and astonished. I said hurriedly:

" ' Would ten dollars be of any service? '

" ' Ten dollars would save my life; that is all it would do.'

" I paid the money, all that I had, and we dined together. It was a modest meal, but good, and, after he had finished, he said:

" ' This is my first meal for twenty-four hours. Strother, don't be an artist. It means beggary. Your life depends upon people who know nothing of your art, and care nothing for you. A housedog lives better, and the very sensitiveness that stimulates an artist to work, keeps him alive to suffering.' "

Morse, a man with the utmost dread of debt, never made known his distress to friends who would gladly have come to his aid. And he felt comfort, dire though his straits might be, in the high esteem accorded him by his fellow-artists. As President of the Academy of Design, he exerted an influence as wide as the Union, and his methods were copied by a score of artists more successful than himself. Of the distinction he had won as a painter, signal proof was at hand, to be followed by grievous disappointment. As we have already seen, he was ambitious to paint historical canvases, such as were now required for the rotunda of the National Capitol. A Congressional committee was authorized to appoint artists to paint these pictures. The artists of America urged the selection of Morse, who stood second only to Allston, who was not in the running. John Quincy Adams, ex-President of the United States, a member of the committee, offered a resolution that foreign artists be allowed to compete, alleging the incompetency of

American painters. This gave offense to American artists and their friends. A severe reply to Mr. Adams appeared in a New York journal from the pen of James Fenimore Cooper, who did not sign his letter. Mr. Adams believed the writer to be Morse, but Morse had never heard of Mr. Adams' affront until he read Cooper's letter. Mr. Adams caused Morse's name to be rejected by the committee. To the last years of his long life the artist could not recall this blow without emotion. And yet the rebuff was a blessing in disguise: it transmuted Morse the painter into Morse the inventor. Had he set up his easel in the Capitol, it is altogether likely that his telegraphic project would have faded from his mind. In his present dismay a group of friends rallied to his relief and comfort, subscribing $3,000 for a large historical painting such as his rotunda picture would have been. Morse chose as its subject *The Signing of the First Compact on Board the Mayflower.* When his labors on the telegraph made it impossible to proceed with the work, he returned to his friends their subscriptions.*

Rescue from another quarter was at hand, none too soon. In 1835, Morse was appointed professor of the arts of design in the New York City University at a fair salary. Before his rooms were quite ready he hastily removed from his lodgings in Greenwich Lane to the University building. This structure, torn down in 1894, was for sixty years a picturesque landmark on Washington Square. Morse's apartments were on the third floor of the north wing, looking forth on a broad stretch of grass and trees. Let us now hear how his models took form, day by day, under his hands in his new home:

" There," he says, " I immediately commenced, with very

*In *Scribner's Magazine*, March, 1912, Edward Lind Morse, himself an artist, has an illustrated article on his father's pictures, "Samuel F. B. Morse, the Painter."

limited means, to experiment upon my invention. My first instrument was made up of an old picture or canvas frame fastened to a table; the wheels of an old wooden clock, moved by a weight to carry the paper forward; three wooden drums, upon one of which the paper was wound and passed over the other two; a wooden pendulum suspended to the top piece of the picture or stretching-frame, and vibrating across the paper as it passes over the center wooden drum; a pencil at the lower end of the pendulum, in contact with the paper; an electro-magnet fastened to a shelf across the picture or stretching-frame, opposite to an armature made fast to the pendulum; a type-rule and type for breaking the circuit, resting on an endless band, composed of carpet-binding, which passed over two wooden rollers, moved by a wooden crank, and carried forward by points projecting from the bottom of the rule downward into the carpet-binding; a lever, with a small weight on the upper side, and a tooth projecting downward at one end, operated on by the type, and a metallic fork also projecting downward over two mercury-cups, and a short circuit of wire, embracing the helices of the electro-magnet connected with the positive and negative poles of the battery, and terminating in the mercury-cups. When the instrument was at rest, the circuit was broken at the mercury-cups; as soon as the first type in the type-rule (put in motion by turning the wooden crank) came in contact with the tooth on the lever, it raised that end of the lever and depressed the other, bringing the prongs of the fork down into the mercury, thus closing the circuit; the current passing through the helices of the electro-magnet caused the pendulum to move and the pencil to make an oblique mark upon the paper, which, in the meantime, had been put in motion over the wooden drum. The tooth in the lever falling into the first two cogs of the types, the circuit was broken when the pendulum returned to its former position, the pencil making another mark as it returned across the paper. Thus, as the lever was alternately raised and depressed by the points of the type, the pencil passed to and fro across the slip of paper passing under it, making a mark resembling a succession of V's. The spaces between the types caused the pencil to mark horizontal lines, long or short, in proportion to the length of the spaces.

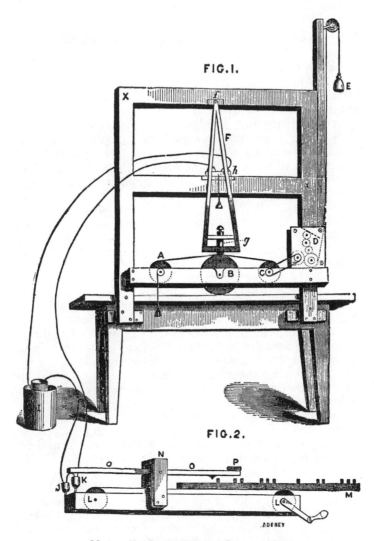

FIG.I.

FIG.2.

.ADENEY

MORSE FIRST TELEGRAPH INSTRUMENT

Fig. 1. A, cylinder from which paper was unrolled. B, cylinder on which paper received its records. C, cylinder on which paper was afterward wound. D, clockwork. E, weight for clockwork. F, wooden pendulum pivoted at f. g, pencil carrying a weight. h, electro-magnetic armature. I, voltaic cell.

Fig. 2. MORSE PORT-RULE. L, L, cylinders united by a linen belt. M, rule or composing stick. N, standard. O, O, lever suspended from N, which, when depressed, plunged into J and K, two cups of mercury, completing an electrical circuit.

" With this apparatus, rude as it was, and completed before the first of the year 1836, I was enabled to and did mark down telegraphic intelligible signs, and to make and did make distinguishable sounds for telegraphing. Having arrived at that point, I exhibited it to some of my friends early in that year, and, among others, to Professor Leonard D. Gale, who was a colleague in the university. I also experimented with the chemical power of the electric current in 1836, and succeeded in marking my telegraphic signs upon paper dipped in turmeric and a solution of the sulphate of soda (as well as other salts), by passing the current through it. I was soon satisfied, however, that the electromagnetic power was more available for telegraphic purposes, and possessed many advantages over any other, and I turned my thoughts in that direction. Early in 1836 I procured forty feet of wire, and, putting it in the circuit, I found that my battery of one cup was not sufficient to work my instrument. This result suggested to me the probability that the magnetism to be obtained from the electric current would diminish in proportion as the circuit was lengthened, so as to be insufficient for any practical purposes at great distances; and to remove that probable obstacle to my success I conceived the idea of combining two or more circuits together in the manner described in my first patent, each with an independent battery, making use of the magnetism of the current on the first to close and break the second; the second, the third, and so on; this contrivance was fully set forth in my patents. My chief concern, therefore, on my subsequent patents, was to ascertain at what distance from the battery sufficient magnetism could be obtained to vibrate a piece of metal, knowing that, if I could obtain the least motion at the distance of eight or ten miles, the ultimate object was within grasp. A practical mode of communicating the impulse of one circuit to another, such as that described in my patent of 1840, was matured as early as the spring of 1837, and exhibited then to Professor Gale, my confidential friend.

" Up to the autumn of 1837 my telegraphic apparatus existed in so rude a form that I felt a reluctance to have it seen. My means were very limited—so limited as to preclude the possibility of constructing an apparatus of such mechanical finish as to warrant my success in venturing upon its public exhibition. I had no wish to expose to ridicule the representative of so many hours of laborious thought. Prior to the summer of 1837, at which time Mr. Alfred Vail's attention became attracted to my telegraph, I depended upon my pencil for my subsistence. Indeed, so straitened were my circumstances that, in order to save time to carry out my invention and to economize my scanty means, I had for some months lodged and eaten in my studio, procuring my food in small quantities from some grocery, and preparing it myself. To conceal from my friends the stinted manner in which I lived, I was in the habit of bringing my food to my room in the evenings, and this was my mode of life many years." *

Morse's relay, an indispensable link in his telegraph, was an original device of his own. In days of old, when letters were borne by a chain of messengers, each of them bore a pouch for a stage of his journey. A carrier, at the end of his trip, might arrive utterly fagged out, but if he had just strength enough to pass his budget to the next man, it was enough. In the simple relay due to Morse, electricity, by a slight and feeble movement, trigger-fashion, opens a new flood-gate of power. An attenuated pulse from a distance arrives barely able to lift the armature of an electro-magnet. That lifting brings two wires into contact, and a second current, of much strength, carries the message for a second long journey; and so on, indefinitely. To-day so powerful are the currents in general use that single circuits of a thousand miles are common. Relaying, therefore, is not so important now as at first.

Professor Joseph Henry, then the acknowledged chief of American physicists, whose discoveries had been adopted by Morse as essential features of his telegraph, was ready to

* Taken by the kind permission of D. Appleton and Company, New York, from "The Life of S. F. B. Morse" by Samuel I. Prime, copyright 1874. Other extracts from the same work follow in this chapter.

answer any questions that the inventor might submit. These questions Morse reduced to writing. Duly followed by their answers they ran thus:

(1) " Have you any reason to think that magnetism cannot be induced in soft iron, at the distance of a hundred miles or more, by a single impulse or from a single battery apparatus?"   " No."

(2) " Suppose that a horseshoe magnet of soft iron, of a given size, receives its maximum of magnetism by a given number of coils around it, of wire, or of ribbon, and by a given sized battery, or number of batteries, at a given distance from the battery, does a succession of magnets introduced into the circuit diminish the magnetism of each?" " No."

(3) " Have you ascertained the law which regulates the proportion of quantity and intensity from the voltaic battery, necessary to overcome the resistance of the wire in long distances, in inducing magnetism in soft iron?" " Ohm has determined it."

(4) " Is it quantity or intensity which has most effect in inducing magnetism in soft iron?" " Quantity with short, intensity with long, wires."

Professor Henry wrote to Morse this inspiring word:

" PRINCETON, February 24, 1842.
" MY DEAR SIR: I am pleased to learn that you have again petitioned Congress, in reference to your telegraph, and I most sincerely hope you will succeed in convincing our representatives of the importance of the invention. In this you may, perhaps, find some difficulty, since, in the minds of many, the electro-magnetic telegraph is associated with the various chimerical projects constantly presented to the public, and particularly with the schemes so popular a year or so ago, for the application of electricity as a motive power in the arts. I have asserted, from the first, that all attempts of this kind are premature, and made without a proper knowledge of scientific principles. The case is, however, entirely different in regard to the electro-magnetic telegraph. Science is now fully ripe for this application, and I have

not the least doubt, if proper means be afforded, of the perfect success of the invention.

"The idea of transmitting intelligence to a distance, by means of electrical action, has been suggested by various persons, from the time of Franklin to the present; but until within the last few years, or since the principal discoveries in electro-magnetism, all attempts to reduce it to practice were necessarily unsuccessful. The mere suggestion, however, of a scheme of this kind is a matter for which little credit can be claimed, since it is one which would naturally arise in the mind of almost any person familiar with the phenomena of electricity; but the bringing it forward at the proper moment, when the developments of science are able to furnish the means of certain success, and the devising a plan for carrying it into practical operation, are the grounds of a just claim to scientific reputation as well as to public patronage.

"About the same time with yourself, Professor Wheatstone, of London, and Dr. Steinheil, of Germany, proposed plans of the electro-magnetic telegraph: but these differ as much from yours as the nature of the common principle would well permit; and, unless some essential improvements have lately been made in these European plans, I should prefer the one invented by yourself.

"With my best wishes for your success, I remain, with much esteem,
                    "Yours truly,
                              "JOSEPH HENRY."

Morse's invention of the relay enlisted him a lieutenant without whom his projects might have come to naught. This was a student at his University, Alfred Vail, a son of Judge Stephen Vail, owner of the Speedwell Iron Works, at Morristown, New Jersey. In February, 1837, the Secretary of the United States Treasury, at the request of Congress, issued a circular of inquiry regarding telegraphs. A copy of this circular came into Morse's hands. It spurred him to complete his model of the telegraph, and if possible, have it accepted by the Government. On September 2, 1837, Morse exhibited his apparatus, somewhat developed, at the University, with Alfred Vail in the audience. Vail was convinced that this telegraph, duly improved in form and arrangement of parts, would open a new world to human power. What was more to the point, he strongly desired to be the man who should remake the crude apparatus which clicked and swayed before him. His wish rested on solid ground: he was a mechanic and an inventor to the tips of his fingers. But a vital question was unsettled: Could electricity impel a message far enough for practical success? When Morse showed him his relay, and demonstrated how it lengthened indefinitely a line of communication, Vail decided to embark in the enterprise, and, as he afterward said, "sink or swim with it." He persuaded his father to advance $2,000, which was deemed enough to build an instrument acceptable by Congress, and defray the cost of patents. Morse now granted Vail a partnership, with one-fourth interest in the United States patents: it being agreed that Vail should improve the apparatus to the best of his ability, and exhibit it on request.

Vail rolled up his sleeves and began work. On the upper floor of a small mill near his father's house in Morristown, in months of untiring labor, he produced instruments improved in every detail. They are used to-day in essentially the forms he bestowed upon them. His family, with just pride in one of the great inventors of all time, have kept the mill in repair to this hour. With its crumbling waterwheel it recalls one of the supreme expansions of electrical empire. In a case on the main floor of the National Museum, in Washington, is the original Morse telegraph as it came into the hands of Vail. Beside it are the instruments developed from that telegraph a few months thereafter by Vail.

Morse's mechanism, in its first form, before Vail saw it, would send a message for only about forty feet. This meant failure, unless much longer distances were feasible.

Here Professor Leonard D. Gale, who occupied the chair
of chemistry at New York University, gave Morse help so
vital that he was admitted to a partnership. Morse was
using only one voltaic cell. Gale, drawing upon the telegraph of Joseph Henry, set up in Albany in 1831, bade
Morse use several cells; and told him to wrap his electro-
magnet with many coils of wire instead of one coil. This
was promptly done: at once the distance to which a message
could be sent was multiplied a hundred-fold, and all hazard
of failure was at an end.

Morse's signals were at first numerals only, such as for
many years had been used in the navies of the world. In
sending a despatch every word had to be translated into its
number, as set forth in a dictionary. Thus 3842, let us
suppose, meant "wheat." When 3842 was received at a
distant station, it was retranslated into "wheat." Each
numeral was signaled by type which bore protruding teeth
of corresponding number, suitably spaced. Each type was
mechanically moved along a tape, automatically making and
breaking an electric circuit. From this expedient Morse
passed to his chief invention, that of an alphabet represented by dots and dashes, produced by saw teeth and flat
spaces on the metallic bars which completed a circuit.

This code was the final term in a series of symbols,
worthy to follow that supreme stride in language, the reduction of spoken sounds to written signs. An alphabetical
code of signals is recorded by Polybius, one hundred and
fifty years before the birth of Christ. In that scheme the
twenty-four Greek letters were distributed in five tablets,
each comprising five letters, except the fifth tablet, which
had one space vacant. Torches, one to five, exposed on the
left side, indicated a particular tablet: similar torches on
the right side indicated a particular letter on that special
tablet. This plan was copied, varied, and simplified in many
ways, issuing at last in the codes of modern armies and

navies. Written codes once occupied the leisure of Francis
Bacon, who in " The Advancement of Learning," published
in 1605, showed how " a's " and " b's " could be arranged
in fives to signify an alphabet. For example, he represented

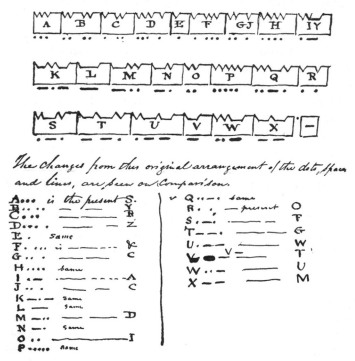

A ROUGH DRAWING MADE BY MORSE IN 1870 TO SHOW THE FIRST
FORM OF THE ALPHABET AND THE CHANGES TO THE PRESENT FORM
[By permission from *The Century Magazine*, New York, March, 1912.]

" e " by " aabaa." He said: " This contrivance shows a
method of expressing and signifying one's mind to any distance by objects either visible or audible, provided that they
are capable of two differences, as bells, speaking-trumpets,
fire-works, or cannon." Abraham Rees, in his Cyclopedia,
published in 1809, revived the code of Bacon, using " 1 "

and " 2 " instead of " a " and " b " as elements. Thus " e " was denoted by " 11211." In 1829, James Swaim, of Philadelphia, published " The Mural Diagraph; or the Art of Conversing Through a Wall," in which knocks and scratches were the two diverse signals. He saw that fewer than five signals would suffice for part of his code; " e," the letter oftenest used, he represented by a single scratch; one knock stood for " a." In the middle of several letters he introduced a space, and this defect, copied by Morse, to this day afflicts five letters of his alphabet. For example, " c " is represented by " .. . ", and is thus liable to confusion with " ie," " i " being " .. ", and "e" being ".".

In Germany the first electric telegraphs employed a magnetic needle, whose swayings to the right or left signified the alphabet and the ten numerals. In this field Schilling was the pioneer, probably as early as 1830; in his code a single movement to the right was " e," a single motion to the left was " t," ranking in its frequency second to " e." Gauss and Weber, in 1833, devised a like code; they signified " e " by one motion to the left. Three years later Steinheil devised a code which differed but little from its forerunners.*

It is clear that the German code-makers sought to give the briefest signals to the letters most in use. Long before their day printers had ascertained in what proportions the various letters are used in composition. In English " e " comes first, then " t," " a," " n," " o," and " s "; " z " is employed once while " e " is required sixty times. Alfred Vail, as Morse revised his signals, took counsel from *The Jerseyman*, then as now the local newspaper of Morristown, carefully noting in what quantities its types were divided in its " cases." Morse's original recorder, as we have seen, held a pen or pencil which, as it swayed from side to side,

* William B. Taylor in the Smithsonian Report, 1878, has a memoir on "Henry and the Telegraph." At page 357 he describes alphabetic binary notation in its successive phases.

marked a zigzag on the paper traveling beneath. Vail
improved this instrument by giving its armature an up
and down motion, as in the familiar sounders of to-day.
In this he returned to Morse's sketch on board the *Sully*,
given in Prime's "Life of Morse," page 255. He thus

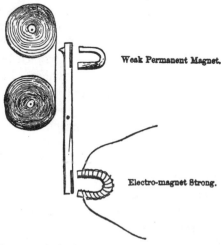

registered dots and dashes in a continuous line, scoring an
inestimable advance on the unrecordable swings of German
needles, or the zigzag lines of Morse's first register. Alfred
Vail died in Morristown on January 18, 1859. It has been
repeatedly declared that he and not Morse devised the dot-
and-dash alphabet, a claim set forth in detail by the late
Franklin Leonard Pope, in the *Century Magazine* for April,
1888. In the same magazine for March, 1912, Edward
Lind Morse, a son of Professor Morse, controverts Mr.
Pope, adducing evidence newly discovered. A decisive fact
is that Alfred Vail, in his book, "The American Electro-
magnetic Telegraph," issued in Philadelphia in 1845, gives
an illustrated description of the dot-and-dash alphabet,
which he credits to Professor Morse, adding two pages of
messages in its symbols.

The amended Morse alphabet was introduced to the public on January 24, 1838, at New York University: its signals were transmitted easily and clearly through ten miles of wire. In a few days Vail conducted an equally successful exhibition at the Franklin Institute, Philadelphia, amid applause. Judge Vail, encouraged by these successes, now authorized Morse to apply for patents in Europe. With high hopes Morse and Vail next proceeded to Washington to exhibit the telegraph to Congress. The Chairman of its House Committee on Commerce was the Hon. Francis O. J. Smith, of Maine, through whom an exhibition was arranged in the Capitol. President Van Buren, his Cabinet, and other public men of distinction, on February 21, 1838, viewed the telegraph at work with astonishment and commendation. The Hon. Mr. Smith was instructed to report a bill appropriating $30,000 to build an experimental line from Washington to Baltimore. His faith in the telegraph was as fervent as that of Morse. He agreed to resign from Congress and become a partner with one-fourth interest in Morse's patent. This fourth was contributed in equal parts by Morse and Vail, reducing Vail's interest, be it noted, from one-fourth to one-eighth. Smith was to be the legal adviser of the partnership, and accompany Morse to Europe to obtain patents, Smith paying all expenses and fees.

In the course of a long letter to Mr. Smith, Morse uttered a prophecy since more than fulfilled:

" From the enterprising character of our countrymen, shown in the manner in which they carry forward any new project which promises private or public advantage, it is not visionary to suppose that it would not be long before the whole surface of this country would be channeled for those nerves which are to diffuse, with the speed of thought, a knowledge of all that is occurring throughout the land; making, in fact, one neighborhood of the whole country."

But the fulfilment of Morse's prophecy came with leaden feet. On May 16, 1838, he sailed from New York for England. In London he found that Professor Wheatstone and Mr. Cooke had patented a telegraph based on the deflections of five magnetic needles, and requiring six conductors between its terminals. Morse demonstrated that his system was much more simple and economical, while it included an indelible record. He was denied a patent for England on the ground that his telegraph had been " published." A full description had appeared in the *London Mechanics' Magazine* for February 10, 1838, copied from *Silliman's Journal* for October, 1837. Morse then proceeded to France, where he had no difficulty in securing a patent. He next sought to introduce his telegraph in Russia, and accordingly entered into a contract to that end with the Russian Counsellor of State, Count Meyendorff. But the Czar refused to ratify the contract, as he thought that malevolence could easily interrupt communication.

Morse's visit to Europe, while a failure so far as his main purpose was concerned, enabled him to form one of the warmest friendships of his life. In Paris he heard of the achievements of Daguerre, whose photographs were then exciting the civilized world. He invited Daguerre to examine his telegraph, and requested permission to see the results of Daguerre's experiments in the art of painting with sunbeams. Daguerre received Morse with open arms, and explained every detail of his process, with a view to Morse introducing it in America. Thirty minutes were required for an exposure at that time, so that portraiture was out of the question until quick plates were devised. When Morse returned to America his brothers, Sidney and Richard, erected on the roof of their new building on the site of the present Morse Building, on the northeast corner of Nassau and Beekman Streets, New York, " a palace for the sun," as Mr. S. E. Morse was pleased to name it, a room with a glass roof, in which Professor Morse experimented with the new and beautiful art. While this structure was in progress, he pursued his experiments with great success in his rooms at the New York University on Washington Square. In a letter of February 10, 1855, he said:

"As soon as the necessary apparatus was made, I commenced experimenting with it. The greatest obstacle I had to encounter was in the quality of the plates. I obtained the common plated copper in coils at the hardware shops which, of course, was very thinly coated with silver, and that impure. The first experiment crowned with any success was a view of the Unitarian Church, from the third-story window on the staircase of the University. The time, if I recollect, in which the pate was exposed to the action of the light in the camera, was about fifteen minutes.

"In my intercourse with Daguerre, I specially conversed with him in regard to taking portraits of living persons. He expressed himself somewhat skeptical as to its practicability, only in consequence of the time necessary for the person to remain immovable. The time for taking an outdoor view was from fifteen to twenty minutes, and this he considered too long a time for any one to remain sufficiently still for a successful result. No sooner, however, had I mastered the process of Daguerre, than I commenced to experiment, with a view to accomplish this desirable result. I have now the results of these experiments taken in September, or the beginning of October, 1839. They are full length portraits of my daughter, single, and also in group with some of her young friends. They were taken out-of-doors, on the roof of a building, in the full sunlight, and with the eyes closed. The time was from ten to twenty minutes. . . . For five or six months I pursued the taking of daguerreotypes as a means of income. I abandoned the practice to give my exclusive attention to the telegraph, which required all my time."

Regarding the possibilities of this new art, Morse wrote to Washington Allston:

"Art is to be wonderfully enriched by this discovery. How narrow and foolish the idea which some express that it will be the ruin of art, or, rather, artists, for every one will be his own painter. One effect, I think, will undoubtedly be to banish the sketchy, slovenly daubs that pass for spirited and learned; those works which possess more general effect without detail, because, forsooth, detail destroys general effect. Nature, in the results of Daguerre's process, has taken the pencil into her own hands, and she shows that the minutest detail disturbs not the general repose. Artists will learn how to paint, and amateurs, or, rather, connoisseurs, how to criticise, how to look at Nature, and, therefore, how to estimate the value of true art. Our studies will now be enriched with sketches from Nature which we can store up during the summer, as the bee gathers her sweets for winter, and we shall thus have rich materials for composition, and an exhaustless store for the imagination to feed upon."

Morse became so skilful with his camera that, in November, 1840, he records taking a portrait in ten seconds. As Daguerre's process was not patented in the United States, a good many enterprising young fellows came to Morse for instruction in photography, that they might travel through the country and reap a goodly harvest. In this way he launched at least twenty camerists who acquired local fame.

Apart from his friendship with Daguerre, Morse's visit of ten months to Europe bore no fruit whatever. He came home in April, 1839, having failed to induce any government to adopt his telegraph. The only patent he secured, that from France, was tied up with conditions which rendered it worthless. Meanwhile not only had Congress omitted to vote the $30,000, which Morse and his partners had confidently expected, but the House had fallen into utter apathy regarding the whole scheme of electric telegraphy. At this ebb in their fortunes, Judge Vail became thoroughly disheartened, and no wonder. His advances in

cash were much more than at the outset Morse had estimated. His son had radically improved and simplified
the instruments of Morse. He had conducted the exhibitions in New York, Philadelphia, and Washington, which
had been reported with eulogy to Congress. To secure the
coöperation of Mr. Chairman Smith, Alfred Vail had
parted with one-half his original interest in the net returns
from the Morse patent. And what added to Judge Vail's
depression of mind was the financial panic which had just
swept the country, laying a heavy hand upon the Speedwell Iron Works. But Morse, although near the end of
his tether, was no Mr. Ready-to-halt. His hopes, dashed
and chilled, were irrepressible. He was willing to take a
slice of bread if refused a loaf. He modified his request
for aid from Congress, asking a grant of $3,500 to build a
line between the White House or one of the Departments,
and the Capitol, or the Navy Yard. This appeal met with
no response. Faint, yet pursuing, Morse wrote to Smith:

" While, so far as the invention itself is concerned,
everything is favorable, I find myself without sympathy
or help from any who are associated with me, whose interest one would think would impel them at least to inquire if they could render some assistance. For nearly
two years past, I have devoted all my time and scanty
means, living on a mere pittance, denying myself all pleas-
ures, and even necessary food, that I might have a sum to
put my telegraph into such a position before Congress as
to insure success to the common enterprise. I am crushed
for want of means, and means of so trifling a character, too,
that they who know how to ask (which I do not) could obtain in a few hours. . . . I will not run in debt if I lose the
whole matter. So, unless I have the means from some
source, I shall be compelled, however reluctantly, to leave
it; and, if I once get engaged in my profession again, the
telegraph and its proprietors will urge me from it in
vain. . . .
" 'Hope deferred maketh the heart sick.' It is true,

and I have known the full meaning of it. Nothing but the consciousness that I have an invention which is to mark an era in human civilization, and which is to contribute to the happiness of millions, would have sustained me through so many and such lengthened trials of patience in perfecting it."

In December, 1842, Morse took his final stand; once again he applied for aid to Congress, resolved that in case he received no for an answer he would return to his easel and abandon telegraphy for good and all. He was greatly heartened when the Committee on Commerce, for the second time, recommended an appropriation of $30,000 in furtherance of his plans. The bill passed by a vote of 89 Yeas to 83 Nays; all the New Jersey votes, six in number, thanks to the activity of Judge Vail, were Yeas. Had these votes been withheld, or adverse, the appropriation would have been lost. In the Senate, during the last hour of its session, March 3, 1843, the bill was passed, and then duly signed by the President. Morse long afterward wrote to a friend:

" This was the turning point in the history of the telegraph. My personal funds were reduced to the fraction of a dollar; and had the passage of the bill failed from any cause, there would have been little prospect of another attempt on my part to introduce to the world my new invention."

On March 4, 1843, Morse wrote to Vail:

" You will be glad to learn, doubtless, that my bill has passed the Senate without a division, and without opposition, so that now the telegraphic enterprise begins to look bright. . . . The whole delegation of your State, without exception, deserve the highest gratitude of us all."

Morse forthwith became superintendent of the telegraph line which was to unite Washington with Baltimore. His

Born September 25, 1807.   Died January 19, 1859

[From a daguerreotype taken about 1853, in the possession of his son, James Cumming Vail, Morristown, N. J.]

salary was $2,500 a year. On March 31, Vail became assistant superintendent: three dollars a day was his modest remuneration, plus expenses. He began work with his customary skill and verve. He soon found out how to unite several circuits with a single battery, a feat of importance as telegraphy lengthened and interlaced its lines He further improved his register, and in masterly fashion. Instead of either pencil or pen, liable to become blunt or broken with use, he attached a steel point to his armature, which embossed the paper strip as it rolled around its cylinder. To aid this indenting effect, the cylinder was belted with a narrow groove, just where it received the steel point. In one detail, Vail's judgment, usually sound, was at fault. With British experience in mind, he believed that his wires should be laid in underground conduits. Defective insulation brought this plan to failure. Then he resorted, and with success, to aerial suspension, as advised by Professor Henry. This method, had Vail but known it, had long before approved itself in the lines of Dyar in America, and of Weber in Germany. Ezra Cornell, who had been a traveling agent for a patent plow, took the contract for rearing the poles and suspending their wires. This was his first venture in telegraphic construction, an industry which yielded him a handsome fortune, part of which went to found Cornell University at Ithaca, New York.

Cornell began stringing his wires from pole to pole in Washington, on April 1, 1844; on May 23, he belted the last insulator at Mount Clare, in Baltimore. A Grove battery of one hundred cups was provided, and the instruments, through their forty miles of wire, throbbed with a gratifying resonance. Next day, May 24, Morse sent from Washington to Vail, in Baltimore, the famous message suggested by Miss Ellsworth, "What hath God wrought!" (Numbers xxiii:23). The signals received at Baltimore were repeated to Washington. Then followed a familiar conversation between the two cities, the first in a series which shall end only with the last page of American history. At first, both in Washington and Baltimore, skepticism prevailed as to this mysterious telegraph. But this was to be banished, and within two days after Miss Ellsworth's despatch, when on May 26, the National Democratic Convention met in Baltimore, to nominate candidates for its ticket, the Vice-Presidency was offered to Silas Wright. His declination, received by telegraph, was hailed by the delegates with incredulity. When their messenger from Washington confirmed the telegram, doubts were at an end.

But such faith in the telegraph as might exist bore little fruit in works. For its first four days its income was, in all, one cent—at the Washington office. On the fifth day the receipts were twelve and a half cents. The sixth day was Sunday. On the seventh day sixty cents came in; next day, one dollar and thirty-two cents; next day, one dollar and four cents. Almost two years later, for the quarter ending March 31, 1846, the receipts of the line were only $203.43. Let us recall the rates: at first one cent for four characters: afterward, from Washington to Baltimore, ten cents for ten words, and one cent for each additional word; from Washington to New York, fifty cents for ten words, and five cents for each extra word.

Disappointing as his financial returns undoubtedly were, Morse now carried out a highly important scientific application of his telegraph. In 1839 he had suggested to Arago, in Paris, that the telegraph could determine longitudes with a new accuracy. On June 12, 1844, Captain Charles Wilkes, who had commanded the famous expedition around the world, ascertained by telegraph that Battle Monument Square, in Baltimore, is 1 minute, 34.868 seconds east of the Capitol in Washington. About this time Morse recast and improved his alphabet, failing, however, to drop the spacings, which, to this day, mar his code. In European

codes these spacings do not occur. In a minor detail of
communication, Morse now inaugurated a practice which
has greatly economized the time and cost of telegraphy, by
devising brief and simple abbreviations of the words and
phrases most in use. His lists, much extended since his
day, have spread from telegraphers to stenographers and
ordinary note-takers, with gain all round. Usually the letters chosen for an abbreviation suggest the word, as " atc "

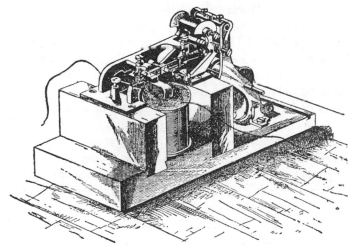

THE BALTIMORE RECORDING INSTRUMENT OF 1844
Now in the National Museum, Washington, D. C.

for " Atlantic." Parallel with the shortening of words has
proceeded the development of secret codes. In these codes,
the words must be as unlike as possible, and each, of course,
bears no suggestion of the phrase or the sentence which it
signifies. " Medehulp " in a cable code means " your order
for additional goods received too late to ship with previous
order: will forward at once." By an international agreement, no code-word may exceed ten letters. Astonishing
accuracy is attained in handling these codes, especially when

one remembers that the words follow one another in arbitrary succession, in what seems to be sheer nonsense. An operator in New York, receiving code messages from an Atlantic cable, has fallen into but one error in a year and a half. But from the fruitage of to-day let us return to the hard work of planting the seeds of modern telegraphy.

Congress, in addition to its original grant of $30,000, voted $8,000 toward the maintenance of the line joining Washington with Baltimore. Further aid, urgently needed, was refused. Morse offered his patents to the Government for $100,000. The Hon. Cave Johnson, Postmaster-General, reported: " The operation of the telegraph between Washington and Baltimore has not satisfied me that, under any rate of postage that could be adopted, its revenues could be made equal to its expenditures." Thus ended the hopes of Morse that his telegraph should be a governmental mode of communication, supplementing the Post Office, as now in Great Britain and the leading countries of Continental Europe. Morse and his fellow-owners of the telegraph patent, thus finding impossible the national adoption of their enterprise, on May 15, 1845, organized " The Magnetic Telegraph Company," for the purpose of constructing and operating a telegraph line from New York to Washington. All concerned were confident that the longer a line, within reasonable limits, the more business per mile it would enjoy. Their company, the first of many such companies in America, received subscriptions to the amount of $15,000. A leading house of bankers in Washington, Corcoran & Riggs, headed the list with $1,000. Among the subscribers of $500 each was Ezra Cornell. This time Morse's hopes were not merely fulfilled, but exceeded. With the extension of wires from Baltimore to New York began the triumphs of American telegraphy. As soon as April 20, 1846, he was able to say: " A few weeks more and Boston, New York, Philadelphia, Baltimore, and Washington will be connected, 428 miles; and also New York, Albany, and Buffalo, 433 miles. Besides these are many branch lines of 30 to 40 miles each. I have a telegram in which 94 characters were distinctly written in one minute. In one instance a battery of two cups operated a line of 130 miles with perfect success."

As to the speed of transmission, he had this to say on December 15, 1846:

" The President's message, on the subject of the war with Mexico, was accurately transmitted to the Baltimore *Sun* at the rate of 99 letters per minute. My skilful operators have printed these characters at the rate of as many as 177 letters per minute. . . . He must be an expert penman who can write legibly more than 100 letters per minute; consequently, my mode of communication equals, or nearly equals, the most expeditious mode known of recording thought."

Morse at first found Vail not quite careful in sending his signals. He wrote him: " You confound your ' m's,' ' t's,' and ' l's,' and do not separate your words. Sometimes your dots were not made. It is not the fault of our local battery here, for at other times it worked perfectly well, but for want, I think, of perfect contact in touching at your end. . . . Be particular to-day. . . ." And again: " Strike your dots firmer, and do not separate the two dots of the ' O ' so far apart. Condense your language more, leaving out ' the ' whenever you can, and when ' *h* ' follows ' *t*,' separate them so that they shall not be ' *8*.' The beginning of a long common word will generally be sufficient—if not, I can easily ask you to repeat the whole, for example,—' Butler made communication in favor of majority rule.'—' Butler made com- in fav-- of maj. rule '. . . ."

Although Vail's expertness as an operator came to him slowly, his commanding ability as an inventor was in full swing from the morning that telegraphy was installed as a business enterprise. At first a receiving relay weighed 185 pounds: this he rapidly reduced. To-day an effective relay is but four ounces in weight. Vail, who had the ear and touch of an accomplished musician, soon found that he could send well-timed free-hand signals, discarding the port-rule, or type-carrier, of Morse, with its incidental botheration. In a few weeks he constructed a circuit-closer in the shape of a finger key, by which signals could be readily sent, improving upon a design of Morse. Vail's key, in its essential features, is to-day under the touch of every telegraph operator in America.

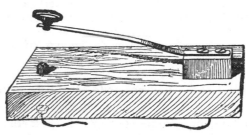

VAIL'S ORIGINAL FINGER KEY OF 1844
[In the cabinet of the Western Union Telegraph Co., New York.]

A further simplification of equal worth entered next, and quite unbidden. Operators of quick ear soon interpreted signals solely by the sound of the armature-lever. Morse always regarded the permanent marking of signals on paper as the core of his system, and, dreading liability for error, he stoutly opposed this reading by ear. But it extended itself irresistibly; it was simple, and, to everybody's astonishment, it was accurate as well. Hearing was discovered to be able to do new work, and to do it perfectly. The Morse recorder has passed out of use except in schools where, to learners in pairs, it declares how they stand in speed and accuracy from day to day. Sounds, at first merely incidental, are now the one means of receiving a telegram. To augment their efficiency, modern receiving instruments are manufactured to emit a loud, clear note.

In the instrument of Morse and Vail, as modified by later inventors, much survives of the simple apparatus devised by Joseph Henry in Albany, in 1831, a year before Morse embarked on the *Sully*. Henry's battery of several cells, affording him an intense current, his wire circuit, his electro-magnet of many coils, his armature-lever, and the bell struck by that lever, all serve to-day on the operator's table, greatly bettered in form and material, but changed in no essential particular. Henry's rough-and-ready transmitter, a wire dipped in mercury, is replaced by Vail's finger-key. The adjustable stops, between which the armature plays, borrowed by Henry from Page, maintain themselves as in-dispensable. Vail joined two or more circuits from one battery; he next gave six wires a common return circuit. These were pioneer steps in an art which at last invited Canada to speak to California, and Puget Sound with Texas.

Often the question arises, Why did not Vail lay claim to perfecting the Morse apparatus? The late Franklin Leonard Pope discussed this question in the *Century Magazine,* of April, 1888, in an article already mentioned. After a review of the facts, he concluded that Vail deemed that he had merely improved the inventions of Morse; although in reality, he transformed them almost beyond recognition. Vail, too, seems to have believed that, as a partner with Morse, he was debarred from taking out patents in his own name. Moreover, the Morse patents were constantly and bitterly assailed in the courts, and Vail, as a co-proprietor of them, could neither with honor, nor safety, set up any per-sonal claims. To use his own words, inscribed on a model of his indenting register, he " wished to preserve the peaceful unity of the invention." In the joint venture of Morse and himself, Morse was undoubtedly the captain of the ship. And his first mate in his talents and loyalty was worthy of his chieftain.

While Morse was experimenting with his telegraph, in the summer' of 1842, he proved that its signals could take their way through water as well as overland. He took copper wire, one-twelfth of an inch thick, and insulated it with pitch, tar, and India rubber. The cable thus produced was laid from the Battery at the foot of Manhattan Island to Governor's Island, about a mile off. Three or four characters had been transmitted, when the line was severed by the anchor of a passing ship. During the following December Morse repeated this experiment, with gratifying success, in the canal at Washington. He naturally regarded with confidence the project for an Atlantic cable. On September 30, 1854, he wrote to Faraday:

" Taking for granted a successful result of the experiment on the propulsion of a current to the required distance, that is to say, from Newfoundland to Ireland, I have proposed that the cable conductor be constructed in the following manner : The conducting wires of the circuit to be the purest copper, each not less than one-eighth of an inch in sectional diameter. Each wire to be insulated to the thickness also of one-eighth of an inch with gutta percha. If it should be decided by the company that, in the first instance, a single conductor shall be laid down, then a thin tube of lead, about one-sixteenth of an inch in thickness, is to be drawn over the wire conductor and its gutta percha covering, and then a series of strands of common iron wire and of hempen cord, or rope yarn of the same size, say four or five of the former and the rest of the latter, are to be laid parallel with the interior conducting wire, on the exterior of the tube, and these are to be confined in place by two spiral cords wound in contrary directions and crossing each other around the cable at intervals, of, say, nine or twelve inches "

When the steam frigate *Niagara* was commissioned to lay the first Atlantic cable, Morse was an invited guest. He took a keen interest in the unremitting labor of paying out the line and testing its conductivity. On the fateful morning of August 11, 1857, the line parted abruptly, and Morse was obliged to return to England. Next year a second cable was laid, only to prove a failure. For a decisive experiment, the *Great Eastern,* much the largest steamship of her day, was laden with a strong and carefully manufactured cable, sailing on July 13, 1866. Two weeks thereafter the wire was landed on the American shore, to enter upon long and faithful service.

But let us turn back a page or two of telegraphic history, and note how Morse, as soon as his telegraph was an assured triumph in America, sought to introduce it in Europe. On this errand he sailed from New York on August 6, 1845, arriving in Liverpool nine days afterward. The General Commercial Telegraph Company of London was then operating the British telegraphs with Wheatstone and Cooke's needle instruments, which required two wires to complete a circuit, with only one-half the speed of the Morse apparatus. He offered the Company his instruments for a thousand pounds, plus one-fourth of the cash they would save their purchasers. This offer was declined. On October 9, Morse wrote to his daughter:

" I know not what to say of my telegraphic matters here yet. There is nothing decided upon, and I have many obstacles to contend against, particularly the opposition of the proprietors of existing telegraphs. But that mine is the best system, I have now no doubt; all that I have seen, while they are ingenious, are more complicated, more expensive, less efficient, and easier deranged. It may take some time to establish the superiority of mine over the others, for there is the usual array of prejudice and interest against a system which throws others out of use."

In Vienna Morse exhibited his telegraph to the Emperor and Empress of Austria. Proceeding to Paris, he renewed his acquaintance with Arago, who presented him and his telegraph to the French Chamber of Deputies. Here, as elsewhere throughout his tour, Morse received hearty commendation, only vocal, however, and with this and nothing else to cheer him he returned home. In 1846 his American patent was reissued: it defined with new precision the claims of his original patent of 1840. From day to day he could watch, with fatherly pride, the building of telegraph lines as they radiated from New York, Boston, and Washington. It was apprehended that the Hudson River might not be crossed with success. A cable, duly laid, worked perfectly from the moment of its immersion. Regarding a printing telegraph, he wrote on April 20, 1846, to M. Brequet, a French electrician:

". . . My friend and co-proprietor in the Telegraph, Mr. Vail, some time in 1837, was intent on producing a printing telegraph, and gave the project much thought. I uniformly discouraged him, however, on the ground, not that such a plan was impracticable, but, in comparison with the method I had devised, worthless, since, were such a mode perfectly accomplished and in actual use, my more simple mode would inevitably supersede the more complicated mode. Mr. Vail, in his work entitled ' The American Electro-magnetic Telegraph,' discusses the whole matter. Experience has proved that when my system is put to the test in competition with the common letter-printing telegraphs of Europe, mine has proved superior. In Vienna, for example, Mr. Bain's letter-printer, the most ingenious of all, was examined with mine publicly before one of the largest and most learned assemblies ever convened in that capital, and the American Telegraph carried the day by acclamation, and is now adopted by that Government."

Until 1847, when Morse was fifty-six years of age, he was all but homeless from the day he left his father's house in his youth. Soon after his marriage in 1818, he had established himself in New Haven, but he had to earn his bread elsewhere, and seldom could he sit by his hearthstone. This was a severe hardship to a man of his warm domestic feelings. To be virtually homeless sharpened the sting of poverty, and he may well have often doubted whether he had been wise in choosing art as his career. Now, at last, not his easel, but his telegraph, began to yield him a moderate income, with a prospect of steady increase. He felt warranted in rearing a roof-tree for his remaining years, and in sharing it with a wife. As a homestead he chose Locust Grove, near Poughkeepsie, New York; and he married Miss Sarah E. Griswold, the daughter of a cousin. He next placed his business affairs in the hands of a trusty friend, the Hon. Amos Kendall, formerly United States Postmaster-General, and then retired to what he hoped would be rest and peace. But this hope was unfulfilled; he was constantly obliged to withstand infringers of his patents. Again and again in the courts he had to adduce evidence that always won him victory. But these victories were costly, and robbed him of a goodly part of earnings which, even in the gross, were but moderate. A well-informed estimate of his net returns from his American patents places them at $80,000, and no more. His first patent, granted in 1840, expired June 19, 1854. It was extended for seven years, chiefly through the recommendation of Professor Joseph Henry.

When legal contentions were intermitted, Morse's life at Locust Grove was placid and simple. He rose at half-past six o'clock, and remained in his study until eight o'clock, when he had breakfast. Most of his day was occupied with reading and writing. On a table at his side stood a telegraph key: by its aid he could converse with friends hundreds of miles away. He had conferred a nervous system upon America; it vibrated at his will, greatly to his aid and

cheer.   Some years after taking up his residence at Locust
Grove, he bought a commodious house at No. 5 West
Twenty-second Street, New York, the third house west of
Fifth Avenue.   This became his home in winter, and a
charming home it was, with its broad library and study,
adorned with pictures from his own brush.   Here the present writer was presented to him in his eightieth year.   Even
then he stood erect, with a dignity and courtesy unaffected
by his burden of years.   He said that he had just received
pleasant news from Germany: " Many German inventors
have devised new and ingenious telegraph instruments, but
from every quarter of the empire they ask for the Morse."

Morse, as we have seen, obtained but one patent in
Europe, namely, from France, and this was burdened with
conditions which made it valueless.   Far and wide throughout Europe, however, his apparatus went into service, and
details of practice, worked out in America at his instance,
were adopted in all the leading countries of the Continent.
In view of these facts, and in view of the comparatively
scant remuneration which he had enjoyed from his American patents, Morse, in 1857, by the advice of friends holding high official stations, issued a memorial claiming some
indemnity from the Governments of Europe within whose
borders his telegraph was at work.   General Lewis Cass,
Secretary of State, sent copies of this memorial to Min-
isters of the United States in Europe, soliciting their good
offices on behalf of the inventor.   His appeal was favorably
received.   Count Walewski, Minister of Foreign Affairs for
France, acted as secretary of the international committee
which took a testimonial in hand.   He addressed to Morse
this cordial note:

" Paris, September 1, 1858.
" Sir: It is with lively satisfaction that I have the honor
to announce to you that the sum of four hundred thousand
francs will be remitted to you, in four annuities, in the name

of France, of Austria, of Belgium, of the Netherlands, of
Piedmont, of Russia, of the Holy See, of Sweden, of Tus-
cany, and of Turkey, as an honorary gratuity, and as a reward, altogether personal, of your useful labors. Nothing
can better mark, than this collective act of reward, the sentiment of public gratitude which your invention has so justly
excited. . . ."

In this gratifying mode, as an act of justice, Morse
received from Europe compensation equal to that accorded
him in his native America. The note from Count Walewski
was followed by a word from Professor Steinheil, the director of German telegraphs. It was this distinguished man
who discovered that the earth may serve instead of the second wire which, originally, was deemed indispensable as a
return line. This discovery, which at a stroke cut down
the cost of construction by one-half, never brought him a
penny. Professor Steinheil was a gentleman: never for a
moment was his mind warped or clouded by professional
jealousy. He had invented an elaborate telegraph instrument: but Morse's was better, and he always said so. This
is Steinheil's note to Morse:

" MUNICH, October 30, 1858.
". . . What we have done for telegraphy stands side by
side. The contributions of the one do not encroach on the
contributions of the other—do not make the other superfluous. You have contributed the quickest, simplest, and
most beautiful mode of communication. I have reduced to
one-half the conducting wire, and also made it surer and
cheaper. Now it will be a satisfaction to me if this my
contribution toward solving the great problem should be
rewarded by my friends in Europe. But I cannot suppress
the wish that, as I contributed to procure the acknowledgment of your invention in Europe, so you may be inclined to
procure my portion of reward in America. It would certainly be a noble example, seldom seen in the world's history, the example of two men who had spent a great part
of their lifetime in solving the same problem, appearing not

as rivals, but as friends, each striving that the services of the one should be rewarded in the land of the other."

The example of Europe in behalf of Morse was not followed by America with regard to the eminent German electrician. His great contribution to the wealth of the United States never brought him anything beyond vocal thanks.

When Morse was well advanced in the eighth decade of his life, his friends, a numerous and influential band, resolved to accord him a public banquet at Delmonico's. This entertainment took place on December 29, 1868. Chief Justice Chase, who had been Secretary of the Treasury in the Cabinet of President Lincoln, was chairman. Daniel Huntington, the eminent artist of New York, who had been a pupil of Morse's, paid him an eloquent tribute as an artist whose successes at the easel had prefigured his triumphs in telegraphy.*

Morse was a man of clinging affections. Gratitude, once aroused in his heart, was undying. Of Allston, his master

---

*On October 5, 1911, the Western Union Telegraph Company, at its headquarters in New York, reported the following interesting facts and figures. They present a wonderful advance within a period of less than seventy years from May 24, 1844, when Professor Morse sent his famous despatch from Washington to Baltimore—

The longest land line of the Company, without a repeater, stretches from Ogden, Utah, to Portland, Oregon, 908 miles. Its longest ocean cable unites Canso, Nova Scotia, with Land's End, England, 2,563 nautical miles apart. During the past thirty years manual transmission has not increased its pace. Ordinary operators send 25 words a minute; the quickest men reach 40 words a minute, with an occasional spurt of 52 words. Many operators receive their messages directly on a typewriter.

Mechanical transmission is gaining ground steadily. First of all the signals are reduced to perforations in a paper strip. This strip is rapidly swept between two metallic springs; at each perforation these springs meet, allowing an electric pulse to enter the line. On the line connecting Chicago and San Francisco by the southern at the easel, and in youth his generous friend, he ever spoke with loving veneration. In token of this feeling to the artist and the man, he presented Leslie's portrait of Allston to the National Academy of Design, New York, of which he himself had long been president. He did honor to Allston's memory a second time, and notably, in presenting to Yale College Allston's celebrated painting of *Jeremiah*. This picture, which cost Morse seven thousand dollars, was followed by a donation of ten thousand dollars to the Theological Department of Yale. An equal donation went to the Union Theological Seminary, New York, to endow a lectureship to bear his father's name, on " The Relation of the Bible to the Sciences." Long before this, indeed as far back as 1846, Yale College, with commendable promptitude, had conferred upon Morse the degree of Doctor of Laws. This honor came from the hands of President Day, who, as professor of physics, had undoubtedly given Morse his first impulse toward the telegraph. This degree from

route, 2,785 miles in length, a speed of 70 to 80 words a minute is attained by automatic transmission. Similar apparatus is employed on ocean cables, with the result that on the best lines 250 letters a minute are forwarded   On submarine wires two messages may be simultaneously despatched without confusion; on land wires four such messages seem to be the limit of feasible practice. Between New York and Chicago, New York and Boston, and several other pairs of cities, the automatic receivers print their messages on typewriters.

The original wire from Washington to Baltimore was placed underground; because of defective insulation it failed utterly. To-day a subterranean line is being completed which will link together Washington, Baltimore, Philadelphia, New York, and Boston, for a service at once telegraphic and telephonic. This will eliminate all risk of a break in communication by storms or snowfalls. In aerial lines four wires are often so disposed that four telegrams are sent from each terminal at once, while, at the same time, three telephonic conversations are in progress.

At the end of 1910, the Western Union Telegraph Company had 30,163 operators in its employ.

his *alma mater* was the most cherished of the scores of distinctions showered upon him by colleges and universities, by learned societies at home and abroad, and by nations all the way from Turkey to Sweden. Devotion to Yale was always part and parcel of Morse's religion.

As he advanced in years he suffered the inevitable infirmities of old age. One morning in the summer of 1869, as he was going upstairs, he fell and broke a leg. This kept him in bed three weeks: he endured the severe pain and imprisonment with serenity. Thanks to his unimpaired constitution, shortly after he was able to come downstairs, he threw away his crutch and walked about almost as erect as ever.

Other afflictions befell him, harder to bear. In the autumn of 1868, his brother, Richard, the youngest of the trio, died abroad. In 1871, Sidney, his only surviving brother, passed away. The ties of affection binding these three together were strong. It may be fitting here to mention an act in which they joined to do honor to their father's memory. Rev. Dr. Morse died, leaving no estate whatever, and his debts, amounting to a considerable sum, were assumed by his sons. At first Samuel could contribute nothing. When prosperity came to him, he insisted upon paying one-third, so that all the brothers might share and share alike.

Much comes to a man by remaining on earth, even when he remains long after the labors which have won him renown. In his eighty-first year, Morse received the unusual honor of having his statue reared in the city which had long been his home, and where he had accomplished his great work. This statue, of heroic size, was unveiled in Central Park, New York, on June 10, 1871. It was modeled by Byron M. Pickett, and cast in bronze by Maurice I. Power. It stands close to the portal at Seventy-second Street. Another statue, this time of Benjamin Franklin, was erected soon afterward, and, most appropriately, in Printing

House Square, New York. Its inauguration was fixed for January 17, 1872. The committee in charge requested Morse to unveil their statue of a great American who, like himself, had subjugated electricity with the hand of a master. Morse was now in feeble health, sinking in strength a little every day. But he insisted on accepting the invitation. The day had been unwisely chosen; it was bitterly cold, as might have been expected in midwinter. After Morse had withdrawn the cord that removed the covering from the bronze, he said: " Mr. De Groot and Fellow-citizens : I esteem it one of my highest honors that I should have been designated to perform the office of unveiling this day the fine statue of our illustrious and immortal Franklin. When requested to accept this duty, I was confined to my bed, but I could not refuse, and I said, ' Yes, if I have to be lifted to the spot.' Franklin needs no eulogy from me. No one has more reason to venerate his name than myself. May his illustrious example of devotion to the interest of universal humanity be the seed of further fruit for the good of the world."

He went home to die. Neuralgia seized him, and all his fortitude was demanded to bear its pain. He died on April 2, 1872. His funeral took place from the Madison Square Presbyterian Church, on April 5.

So ended the life of the remarkable man who established American telegraphy. Those of us who remember him as he would occasionally stroll through Madison Square, recall a figure quite six feet in stature, erect and firm, almost to the last. His large brown eyes had the steady look which sees men and things as they are. Here was a gentleman of the old school, with dignity as his chief characteristic. In a circle of friends he was fond of fun, with strangers his manner was that of highbred reserve. In his family he was regarded with veneration. Those who knew him best loved him most.

CHARLES GOODYEAR

AIR and water, food and shelter, were the first gifts of Nature to man. Amid his lowly kindred he soon declared his primacy by wielding sticks and stones as weapons and tools, by plaiting leaves and grass into roofs, by rending hides into raiment. Next he shaped flints into rude chisels and knives, and, using as an awl a thorn plucked from a cactus, he bade a sinew fasten one hide to another. In a golden hour he caught a spark struck from flints, and thus harnessed flame to hollow a tree into a canoe, to harden clay into pottery, to smelt lead and iron from their ores. In new intensities, fire fused sand into glass, and alloyed carbon with iron to form steel. Meantime arts of equal dignity arose without aid from fire: hides were tanned into leather, paper was unrolled from birchbark, from the papyrus, from the fibers of many other plants. Thus were gifts of Nature exalted in value by art: the tanner added new strength and durability to a sheepskin; the steelmaker bestowed upon iron a heightened elasticity. Tanning, steelmaking, and their sister arts date back so far that their birth has faded even from myth and legend. From those remote times to the present day there has been but one worthy addition to glass and pottery, leather and paper, namely, the vulcanized rubber due to Charles Goodyear. Were it as cheap as glass or steel, it would be just as commonly and usefully employed.

Charles Goodyear was born in New Haven, Connecticut, on December 29, 1800, of that sound New England stock which has given many leaders to America. His father, Amasa Goodyear, was descended from Stephen Goodyear, successor to Governor Eaton as head of the company of

Chas Goodyear

[From the painting by G. P. A. Healy, Museum of the Brooklyn Institute of Arts and Sciences.]

London merchants who, in 1683, founded the colony of New Haven. Charles Goodyear, as a boy, was studious and resolute, giving clear promise of the man. In youth he had some thought of entering the Christian ministry: throughout life his religious faith was an unfailing staff in every onset and repulse. At seventeen he went to Philadelphia, where he mastered the hardware trade in an apprenticeship of four years. The experience thus gained he turned to good account at a later period, as we shall note. At twenty-one he returned to New Haven, and became a partner with his father in the firm of Amasa Goodyear & Son. They manufactured metal buttons and spoons, scythes and clocks. Several of their other products were farm tools of steel, devised by the elder Goodyear. Of these the best were the forks, which slowly supplanted clumsy tools forged from wrought-iron at local smithies. As customers grudgingly bought these steel forks, young Goodyear learned a lesson he never forgot. The forks were light, springy, and durable; yet their very lightness and fine finish often excited suspicion. Not seldom a well-to-do farmer deemed that he paid the inventor a compliment in accepting one of his forks as a present. In producing other tools of like novelty, and some simple farm machinery, the elder Goodyear was constantly at work. His example acted as a spur to his son, who, like himself, was brimming with Yankee ingenuity. And yet, with characteristic candor, Charles Goodyear disclaimed any special talent as a mechanic. He says:

" I do not claim to have a mechanical talent, but, on the contrary, have an aversion to bestowing thought upon machinery when there is anything complicated about it. . . . Independently of all pecuniary considerations, I have taken great satisfaction in trying to improve articles of necessity or convenience, for the use of men. Those which first engaged my attention were in the hardware line, and such as were immediately connected with my·occupation. Whenever I observed an article in common use in which there was obviously a great defect, I commonly applied my mind to the subject to find, if possible, the best way of improving it, or removing the defect, always contesting the common maxim that, for the interest of trade, 'things should be made so that they will not last too long.' "

In 1824, Goodyear married Clarissa Beecher; their happy union was blessed with seven children.* No matter how dire the straits into which Goodyear repeatedly fell, his wife bore her part with unrepining cheerfulness. During her husband's long battle, she looked for victory with his own invincible faith. In the second year of their marriage, Goodyear returned to Philadelphia, where he established a hardware store, mainly stocked from his father's workshop in New Haven. At first this business thrived, but Goodyear gave credit too freely, and in 1830 he was obliged to suspend payment, his creditors granting him a long period for the discharge of their claims. He refused to avail himself of the bankrupt law, partly because bankruptcy would divest him of titles to unfinished inventions. His decision was unfortunate: his prestige in banking circles was gone, and his difficulties went steadily from bad to

---

*Of these children two survive; Miss Clarissa Goodyear of Winsted, Connecticut, and Professor William Henry Goodyear, Curator of the Department of Fine Arts in the Brooklyn Institute of Arts and Sciences. He has acquired international honors as a student and author in the field of fine art. Especially acute and fruitful are his studies of refinements in architectural design.

Nelson Goodyear, of New York, a grandson of Charles Goodyear, is the inventor of a variety of acetylene and other gas apparatus, both for illumination and for generating and burning combustible gas, in connection with oxygen, as a source of intense heat. He represents the fourth generation in a remarkable line of inventors. His father, Charles Goodyear II., greatly improved the welt-sewing machine that bears his name.

worse. Under the cruel laws then in force, he was, during
the next ten years, again and again imprisoned for debt.
Happily he found merciful men among his jailers, who allowed him to use a bench and tools. More than once he
thus earned enough in prison to send bread to his wife
and children. He faced all this hardship without flinching
or complaint. As to his feelings in bondage, he wrote:
" My anticipations of ultimate success in life were never
changed, my hopes were never for one moment depressed."
    In those dark days, the profits from his ingenuity, though
small, determined Goodyear to set up as an inventor. From
boyhood he had worked with tools; as a manufacturer and
a merchant he had learned just what people wanted, and
what good things they were likely to leave unbought. He
believed with his father, that it was high time that many
an old appliance gave place to something new and better.
His father had made his mark by improving the tools and
machinery for farms. Why did not Charles Goodyear stick
to this goodly field? What led him to gum elastic as the object of his thought and toil? This is his answer:

    " While yet a schoolboy, the wonderful and mysterious
properties of this substance attracted my attention, and made
a strong impression on my mind. A thin scale, peeled
from a bottle or a shoe, afterward came under my notice,
and suggested that this would be very useful as a fabric,
if it could be made uniformly thin and could be prepared
so as to prevent its adhering and becoming a solid mass, as
it soon did from the warmth and pressure of my hand."

    Gum elastic first came to the United States about 1800,
mostly from Brazil, where the natives derived it from the
juice of the Hevea and other trees. Even in its crude
lumps and flakes, as imported from Para to New York, it
was a substance to excite the curiosity of a brain so in-
quisitive and exploring as Goodyear's. He noticed that,

while this gum was soft and yielding, it was tough in an extraordinary degree; it would stretch further than any other material he had ever handled; it was waterproof, so as to be made into overshoes and raincoats. But with all these excellent qualities, gum elastic had glaring faults. The natives who gathered the gum molded it into galoshes that lasted for years, although in winter they froze to the hardness of iron, and in summer became as soft as suet. All the wares made in North America had the same limited serviceability. Yet why should not Yankee ingenuity and skill surpass the crude and faulty manufactures of Indians in Brazil? Over and over again the manufacturers of Connecticut and Massachusetts believed that they had come upon the secret of preserving and curing gum elastic, only to land in one disastrous failure after another. That the last and worst of these failures was impending came to Goodyear's knowledge in an unexpected way.

In New York, one morning, at the wareroom of the Roxbury Rubber Company, he examined a life-preserver, to find that its mode of inflation was defective. Some weeks afterward he revisited this wareroom, offering for sale a new and improved tube which he had devised for this life-preserver. At once the Roxbury agent saw that there stood before him an inventor of talent. He disclosed to Goodyear that rubber, as then manufactured, was liable to decompose at a temperature of 100° Fahrenheit, or so. He declared that if Goodyear could prevent this ruinous change, he would not only enrich himself, he would ward off bankruptcy from factories whose owners had risked their all. Goodyear had supposed that, before huge fortunes had been embarked in this business, its obstacles had been wholly surmounted. He went home to ponder deeply what he had heard. For weeks he revolved in his brain the problem of curing or tanning rubber into an indifference such as leather displays to ordinary cold and heat. Surely, he

thought, there must be some way to do this. He came
to the conviction, from which he never budged, that every
obstacle to successful curing would yield to persistent assault, and that he and nobody else was the man to conduct
that assault. He tells us:

" I was blessed with ignorance of the obstacles I had
subsequently to encounter, but soon learned that the difficulties attending the experimenter in gum elastic obliged
him to await the return of both warm and cold weather, at
least twelve months, and often much longer, before he could
know with certainty that his manufactures would not decompose. . . . I was encouraged in my efforts by the reflection that what is hidden and unknown, and cannot be
discovered by scientific research, will most likely be discovered by accident, if at all, and by the man who applies
himself most perseveringly to the subject, and is most observing of everything related thereto."

This bold prophecy was more than fulfilled, as we shall
presently see. And its fulfilment lay in that very great
agent, heat, which melted gum elastic much as if tallow
from the shambles. This was why manufacturers of rubber goods avoided working at temperatures above 100°.
Indeed, Macintosh, who produced rubber raincoats, warned
his customers against bringing them near a fire.

With the hope before him of a goodly reward, Goodyear
began experiments with some Brazilian gum elastic. At
first he worked in his small dwelling, where he mixed his
gum by hand, spreading it with a rolling-pin lent by his
wife. Soon his admixtures were applied to emboss cam-
brics, for which there was at that time a fair demand. A
friend, Ralph B. Steele, of New Haven, now advanced him
a little capital, and Goodyear soon covered his shelves with
hundreds of pairs of rubber shoes, attractive in style, easy
to put on and take off. But were they as good as they
seemed? We shall see. Goodyear all along had been both-

ered by the persistent stickiness of his gum. He thought this due to the turpentine he used as a solvent. If he could secure a supply of gum elastic, not dissolved in turpentine, a fair test would condemn or acquit the accused solvent.

He rejoiced when he was able to buy a few casks of gum, kept liquid by a little alcohol and nothing else. Shortly after the casks were rolled into his premises, he was called out by an errand for an hour or two. In that interval, Jerry from Ireland, his man-of-all-work, resolved to acquaint himself with that liquid gum, so he applied it to his trousers with no sparing hand. To his alarm in a few minutes his legs were cemented together, and he was firmly glued to his bench. Only when a pair of shears had been diligently plied around him, was Jerry once more a free man. This adventure was decisive. It taught Goodyear that the stickiness of gum elastic inhered in itself, and was not chargeable to any solvent whatever.

And what of the rubber shoes he had molded in hundreds of handsome and convenient pairs? By way of test he left them alone until warm weather. Then, a single hot day melted them into formless and reeking dough. Goodyear had been so sanguine of success that this failure was mortifying in the extreme. His friends, to whom he was in debt, withdrew all further aid. Why should they throw good money after bad? Goodyear placed his family in a nearby village, where, soon afterward, his wife, to pay their way, had to sell linen she had spun at her wheel. Goodyear betook himself to New York, where a friend, John W. Sexton, provided him with a lodging in Gold Street. A good-natured druggist, Silas Carle, advanced him the chemicals he required. One of his first compounds was a union of gum elastic and magnesia; this, when boiled in lime water, underwent a tanning, with banishment of stickiness so far as surfaces went. This method enabled him to make a few sheets of rubber of fair quality, and some small ornamental articles. For these, in the autumn of 1835, he received prizes at the fairs of the Mechanics' and American Institutes. But Goodyear soon saw that this lime-water process had but slight value. Its products might, at any moment, touch vinegar or other acid, when at once the surface coat of lime was neutralized, uncovering sticky gum beneath. " I have not used lime enough," was his comment. So he employed lime in larger proportions, only to find the resulting mixture too biting for his hands. He, therefore, resorted to machinery, with its tougher fibers of wood and iron. In Greenwich Village, now part of New York City, he hired a bench in Mr. Pike's mill, where machinery and motive-power were available. To this mill Goodyear often carried a gallon jug of slaked lime from his room in Gold Street, three miles away. But lime intermixed with gum elastic produced a compound of so little elasticity and strength as to be worthless. Shortly after this balking discovery, a sunbeam lighted up Goodyear's work-table, and none too soon.

One morning he ornamented a piece of gum elastic with bronze, and boiled it in a weak solution of lime. On removing the fabric from its bath, he saw that part of the bronze had been washed off. To detach the remainder he touched it with nitric acid. This instantly darkened the gum, which he impatiently threw aside as spoiled and useless. But there was something in the look and feel of that shriveled sheet that clung to his memory. A day or two later he picked it out of his rubbish-heap, and examined it,—with a rich reward. Wherever the nitric acid had touched the gum, all stickiness had departed, and its surface was virtually tanned. Goodyear sagaciously followed up this golden hint; before a week had passed he was producing thin rubber sheets, cured through and through. From these he patterned table-covers and aprons, which he printed in handsome designs.   This acid-gas process, as he afterward called it, he gradually improved in every detail.   By dipping his wares in a weak solution of nitric acid, and then in water mingled with a little chloride of lime, he avoided the scorching which had pestered him in early experiments.   All the cold processes for curing rubber, whether devised by Goodyear or his successors, date from his happy observation of the effect produced by a touch of nitric acid.*

At this period of Goodyear's experiments, his wife was his constant helper.   She it was who first built schoolroom globes from sheet rubber.   Had she been absent, the scraps of her husband's pasteboard patterns would have gone to waste.   Her deft fingers dovetailed them into bonnets, worn at church by herself and her daughters.

Goodyear's thin fabrics were so novel and durable that they readily found a market.   This attracted the interest of William Ballard, of New York, who proffered financial aid to the inventor.   With little delay the firm of Goodyear & Ballard was formed, and began manufacturing, first in Bank Street, New York, and later in Staten Island.   Preparing for a large business, they rented a wareroom on Broadway.   But the panic of 1836 forced Mr. Ballard into bankruptcy, and the factory had to be closed.   Again Goodyear's fortunes dropped to a low ebb.   One afternoon, in Staten Island, he could not pay his fare to New York; so he pawned his umbrella with the ferrymaster, afterward famous as Commodore Vanderbilt.

*In 1846, Alexander Parkes, a chemist of Birmingham, in England, invented a vulcanization requiring no heat.   He immersed gum elastic in a mixture of 100 parts bisulphide of carbon and 2½ parts of chloride of sulphur.   After an immersion of from 1½ to 3 minutes, depending upon the thickness of the goods, he employed a drying stream of air at about 78° Fahrenheit.

A vapor cure, requiring but moderate temperatures, is sometimes employed for thin fabrics.   The vapor of heated chloride of sulphur is sent into a container in which the goods fully expose their surfaces.

To keep the wolf from his door, he resumed the making of aprons and tablecloths, but the demand for these goods slowly fell to zero. His scanty tableware, under stress of want, dwindled to little more than a few cups which, by turns, held weak tea, or mixtures of gum, not so weak. His straits at last grew desperate. One morning his family arose without a crumb in the cupboard, without a penny to buy food. He put a valued keepsake in his pocket, and sped toward a pawnshop. On his way thither he met a creditor from whom he had reason to dread reproaches. Great was his astonishment to be asked: " What can I do for you? " When Goodyear was sure that no affront was intended, he said that a loan of fifteen dollars would be most useful. In a moment the cash was in his palm. The keepsake remained in Goodyear's pocket, but only to reach the pawnshop a fortnight later. When, at last, everything that could be pledged had passed out of his hands, Goodyear borrowed a hundred dollars from James DeForest, a brother-in-law. This loan tided him over two or three months of experiments which proceeded all day and far into the night. Never was a discoverer more obsessed by his aims than was Goodyear. His thoughts centered in rubber; they were circumferenced by rubber. When he saw garments of wool, boats of ash, sails of canvas, it was only to imagine how much better all would be if molded in rubber.

At that time, the largest rubber factory in America was in Roxbury, now part of Boston. Thither Goodyear directed his steps, hoping that at least a few branches of its work might be alive and stirring. With an eye to business he took in his wallet a few samples of his best wares. In Roxbury he met Harry Willis, who had been his fellow apprentice in Philadelphia, and who treated him most hospitably. And never did Goodyear need a friend more than now. Roxbury and its neighborhood were suffering from an utter collapse in the rubber trade. In this trade, as recently as 1834, there had been a boom of the wildest. Thousands of speculators, small and great, had plunged into rubber as recklessly as, in later days, other victims launched their all, and more, in worthless gold-mines and oil-wells. To-day it seems incredible that New Englanders, deemed to be shrewdness incarnate, should have embarked fortunes in producing goods liable to offensive putrefaction. But so it was; and to the craze had now succeeded a panic, and Goodyear found nobody to look at his samples, or to listen to his projects.

There was nothing for it but to return to New Haven, where, in the winter of 1837-38, Goodyear resumed the manufacture of overshoes, in improved qualities. His new methods of production he patented, selling licenses in connection with his acid-gas process. This gave him a decent income, and for a brief season his skies were cloudless. Good fortune now paid him a second visit, leading him to the very threshold of vulcanization by the friendly hand of Nathaniel Hayward, who had been a foreman in the Eagle Rubber Company at Woburn, Massachusetts. When this Company failed, Hayward was permitted to use its factory, where he produced a few rubber goods on his own account. In a dream, he said, he had been bidden to combine sulphur with gum, and expose the compound to sunshine. This ghostly counsel he had obeyed. His reward was rubber freed from all stickiness, with a surface well cured or tanned. At Goodyear's suggestion, Hayward patented this process; when Goodyear bought the patent. He did not then know that he was never to do a better stroke of business in his life, for this purchase was the first and indispensable step toward vulcanization. That gum elastic loses its viscosity in a solution of sulphur in turpentine had been discovered in 1832, by Dr. L. Leudersdorff, a German chemist, who had published the fact in his " History of India Rubber." His knowledge came to him, not in a vision of darkness, but in ordinary experiments by daylight. He remained, however, wholly ignorant of the new values conferred on sulphurized rubber by high temperatures.

Goodyear now felt that his feet were firmly set in the right track at last. When he placed thin sheets of united rubber and sulphur in a sunbath for hours together, he obtained almost as good a tanning as afterward from the heat of ovens. Then and always he marveled that solar rays, of quite moderate temperature, were as effective as much greater heats from fuels. This remarkable fact is still a mystery, and might richly repay investigation. Without pausing to resolve this puzzle, Goodyear took advantage of solarization, as he called it, to produce new varieties of thin rubber wares. On some of these he printed newspapers; a few others he shaped into attractive ornaments. All went well so long as his fabrics were thin enough to be tanned from surface to surface. When his wares were bulky he found, to his chagrin, that, beneath their hardened skin, the gum was nearly as sticky as ever.

This discovery came suddenly, and as a crushing blow. The Postmaster-General gave Goodyear an order for a large supply of mail bags. This order the inventor noised abroad, as it indorsed his rubber in a most influential quarter. He manufactured the bags with all despatch; and, although the season was summer, they kept their shape and promised to keep it permanently. He thought it well to hang them up for a prolonged test before delivery at Washington. Then, to refresh his jaded body and mind, he took a holiday. When he came back, unutterable was his dismay to see his mailbags on the floor in malodorous decomposition. To give them a leathery hue he had used chromes, white lead, and vermilion. These admixtures he blamed for the wreckage which met his eye. But if his pigments were at fault, more blameworthy was a curing which sank but little into the body of his wares. That season he had not only manufactured mail bags, but life-preservers, cushions, and other goods. All these, as disgusting refuse, were thrown on his hands by their purchasers. Again the ill-starred inventor sank to the sorriest plight. His aged father and mother were sharing his home; they had to be deprived of the scanty comforts necessary to their advanced age. Indeed, at this pinch, it was not a question of comforts, but simply of bread and a roof. He tells us:

"For four years I had attempted in vain to improve a manufacture that had entailed ruin on all concerned. It was generally agreed that a man who could proceed further in such a course fairly deserved all the distress brought upon himself, and was justly debarred from sympathy. I was not unfrequently reminded that I could at any time improve my circumstances by returning to the hardware trade."

In his heart's core Goodyear's faith was unshaken that he would yet make rubber in masses as he had long made it in films. He was a dreamer, but he always took care to dream with his feet on a rock. Now, for a few months, he earned an occasional dollar by making fabrics in thin rubber, eking out his modest expenses by recourse to pawnshops. Then came the day when, through utter absence of demand for his wares, he was obliged to cease manufacturing. Hayward, who for some time had been his assistant, had to be dismissed. Here, indeed, stood a hero, unsustained by the excitement and pomp of a battlefield, continuing a fight as faithfully as ever did an enlisted champion. Day after day, cold and hungry in a dingy room, he kept up his tests of new compounds, sustained as firmly as if he distinctly beheld what the next few months would unfold to his view. He says:

"I applied myself with unabated ardor and diligence to detect the cause of my misfortune and, if possible, retrieve the lost reputation of my invention. As on former occasions, I had hardly time enough to realize the extent of my embarrassment, before I became intently engaged with another experiment, my mind buoyant with new hopes and expectations; which, as it afterward proved, were to be, for the time at least, more than realized."

How Goodyear, at the end of years of baffled quest, at last alighted upon vulcanization, he narrates:

"While on a visit to Woburn, I carried on at my dwelling-place some experiments to ascertain the effect of heat on the compound that had decomposed in the mail bags and other articles. I was surprised to find that a specimen, being carelessly brought into contact with a hot stove, charred like leather. I endeavored to call the attention of my brother and others, who were present, and who were acquainted with the manufacture of gum elastic, to this remarkable effect, unlike any before known, since gum elastic always melted when exposed to a high degree of heat. Nobody but myself thought the charring worthy of notice. My words reminded my hearers of other claims I had been in the habit of making in behalf of other experiments. However, I directly inferred that if the charring process could be stopped at the right point, it might divest the compound of its stickiness throughout, which would make it better than the native gum. Upon further trials with high temperatures I was convinced that my inference was sound. When I plunged India rubber into melted sulphur at great heats, it was always charred, never melted. I then exposed a similar fabric before an open fire with the same result. What was of supreme importance was that upon the border of the charred fabric there was a line, or border, which had escaped charring, and was perfectly cured."

Goodyear's daughter has left this word regarding her father's first unwitting vulcanization:

"As I was passing in and out of the room, I casually observed the little piece of gum Father was holding near the fire, and I noticed that he was unusually animated by some discovery which he had made. He nailed the gum outside the door in the intense cold. Next morning he brought it in, and held it up exultingly. It was perfectly flexible, as when he nailed it up. This was proof enough of the value of his discovery."

His first successful treatment of sulphurized rubber took place in front of a fire in his bedroom. There, with the assistance of his family, he cured a square yard of rubber-cloth, thicker than any fabric he had hitherto treated, through and through. Part of it went into a cap for himself, to prove lasting and pliant, while resistant to heat and cold. But no such moderate and changeful temperatures as those of a fireplace would meet the demands now clearly in Goodyear's vision. He required a high and steady heat, under strict control. At first he had put up with the oven where his wife baked her loaves. This oven, laden with a batch of rubber, he would watch far into the night, observing how the rubber slowly hardened until six hours had passed. Beyond that period, he found that only harm was wrought. At other times he held rubber against the steaming nose of a tea-kettle. Yet again, he coated a lump of rubber with ashes or sand, to toast it for an hour or during a whole day, altering, on occasion, the proportion of sulphur to rubber. Expedients of manufacture which have long been built into a routine had, in those gloomy days, to be fumbled for and found by this lonely and ill-equipped explorer. All honor to his sagacity and to his unswerving resolution!

For months after Goodyear had mastered the art and mystery of vulcanization, he was vexed by rubber peeling off the cloth on which he spread it. He tried one textile fabric after another, until he had experimented with everything in the market. All in vain; no cloth had a lasting grip. Then he simply mixed cotton fiber with rubber, and he had just the cloth he wanted. Goodyear deemed this fabric second only in importance to vulcanized rubber itself. Clad in a complete panoply from his oven, he now walked abroad, a marked man. He tells us that an acquaintance of his was once asked: " How shall I recognize Goodyear, in case I happen to see him?" The response was: " If you meet a man who has on an India rubber cap, stock, coat, vest, and shoes, with an India rubber purse without a cent in it, that is he!"

Goodyear's health, never robust, underwent a strain all but fatal in these years of tribulation. Now that triumph dawned upon him, he was a martyr to dyspepsia and gout. But neither qualm, nor pain, could chill his ardor in attacking the obstacles which remained in his path. Often in the night he would arouse his wife to jot down directions for fresh experiments, as these suggested themselves to him after hours of incessant thought. When a long dictation came to an end, he would fall asleep through sheer exhaustion. One field of rich promise at this time was the use of steam as a vulcanizer; within what limits, and with what precautions, it behooved him to ascertain. He must have access to a comprehensive steam plant; and just such a plant his friends at Lynn, Baldwin & Haskins, placed at his disposal. Here for several weeks he conducted fruitful experiments. Then, well satisfied with his progress, he returned to Woburn, once more to attack the chief difficulties of vulcanization until, at last, they were surmounted. It is altogether improbable that one unaided man fused the first glass, or tanned the first leather, or spread the first sheet of paper. In all likelihood it was a long sucession of toilers who bestowed each of these great boons upon mankind. It is the unique distinction of Goodyear that he arrived at his discovery by himself. He, and no one else, saw the splendid prize of perfected rubber. He, all alone, through the struggles and defeats of years, was true to that vision. When Fortune, that exacting mistress, crowned him with laurel at last, there stood beside him neither partner nor lieutenant.

Are we to call it accident that brought Goodyear first to his acid-gas process, and then to the supreme discovery of vulcanization? On this point his convictions were clear:

". . . I was for many years seeking to accomplish this object, and allowed nothing to escape my notice that related to it. Like the falling apple before Newton's gaze, it was suggestive of an important fact to one whose mind was previously prepared to draw an inference from any occurrence which might favor the object of his research. While I admit that these discoveries of mine were not the result of scientific chemical investigation, I am not willing to admit that they were the result of what is commonly called accident. I claim them to be the result of the closest application and observation."

In truth, golden accidents, such as befell Goodyear, happen only to explorers who deserve them, who try both likely and unlikely experiments with equal care; who test new compounds, often with no definite expectation as to what properties they may reveal. They dare to employ new, and possibly dangerous, intensities of heat and light, of mechanical pressure, of electrical strain. They are well aware that at times the paths of Nature return upon themselves, in what seems, and only seems, to be anomaly and contradiction. They have seen a boomerang fly forward during one-half its sweep, and then fly backward to the feet of its thrower. They have observed water slowly contract during one degree after another of its cooling, and then quietly expand just before it freezes. Sulphur thickens at a moderate temperature, only to flow freely at a higher temperature. Rubber united with sulphur has a discontinuity even more remarkable: at first it softens with heat, but heighten that heat, and the compound hardens, and takes on new and priceless qualities.

When Goodyear had at last perfected vulcanization in its essentials, he found to his sorrow that if invention is difficult, persuasion is still more difficult. Far and wide he offered vulcanized rubber, much more elastic than its parent gum, nearly as durable as leather, unaffected by heat or cold. But who would take up its manufacture and create its market? It was nearly two years before he could convince anybody that his rubber had value. And those two years renewed his familiarity with downright want. During this final siege of the wolf he was offered liberal terms by a leading firm in Paris, Rattier & Guibal, for the exclusive use in France of his acid-gas process. This process, he told them, would be almost wholly supplanted by his new and better method, vulcanization. This offer from Paris, with news from other European cities where the manufacture of rubber was thriving, greatly cheered the anxious inventor. He went on producing articles of new design, and of a quality steadily improved. For the most part his profits were trifling; at times they were nothing at all; so that, as often before, he came to the verge of starvation. He recites:

" During the winter of 1839-40, during a long and severe snowstorm, when even those who were blessed with health were confined within doors, I found that my family was left without food or fuel. My feeling was that the face of nature was a fit emblem of my own condition—cold and cheerless. But the recollection of a kind greeting received some time previous from Mr. O. B. Coolidge, of Woburn, suggested a visit to him, although he was almost a stranger. He resided at a distance of some miles, yet, enfeebled by illness as I was, I resolved to reach his house through the storm. In making my way against the driving snow I was all but exhausted. At last I reached the dwelling of Mr. Coolidge, and stated to him my condition and my hopes of success from my discovery. He received me cordially, and not only supplied me with a sum adequate to my immediate wants, but also with facilities for continuing experiments on a small scale."

While awaiting, in misery, the day when the public should awake to what vulcanization meant for its convenience and gain, Goodyear did not fold his hands and bemoan his fate. He diligently sought to overcome the difficulties which clogged the detailed working of his process. From the outset of his labors, he had been plagued by the fermentation of his compounds. He traced this to delay between mixing and baking his rubber. He was taught what the bread-baker had learned long before, that there must be despatch betwixt the kneading trough and the oven. In another quarter he was sorely perplexed. Often his goods showed blisters where, of course, breaks soon followed. He found that some blisters sprang from small quantities of acid which had carelessly been allowed to enter his turpentine. So, also, if his white lead, magnesia, or other admixture, carried any impurity, however slight, this, when heated, would generate gas and raise blisters. Another constant offender was moisture, giving rise to steam. As a final precaution, Goodyear found it necessary to lift his temperatures slowly and evenly, taking pains never to carry them unduly high. While he was thus patiently banishing faults from his process, he explained its great merits to listless ears and averted eyes. Whatever faith he had once inspired in his public seemed to have died beyond hope of resurrection. But neither hunger at home, nor indifference abroad, could swerve him from his purpose or chill his enthusiasm. He tells us:

" I felt in duty bound to beg in earnest, if need be, sooner than that the discovery should be lost to the world and to myself. . . . My inability to convince others of the truth of my assertions, or to bring them to comprehend the importance of the subject, gave me intense anxiety as to the results, and produced a state of mind such as could have been ill endured but for the excitement caused by efforts to surmount the obstacles I met with. How I subsisted at this period, charity alone can tell, for it is as well to call things by their right names, and it is little else than charity when the lender looks upon what he parts with as a gift. The pawning or selling some relic of better days, or some article of necessity, was a frequent expedient. My library had long since disappeared, but shortly after the discovery of vulcanization I collected and sold at auction the school-books of my children, which brought me the trifling sum of five dollars; small as the amount was, it enabled me to proceed. At this step I did not hesitate. The occasion, and the certainty of success, warranted the measure which, in other circumstances, would have been sacrilege. I had now grounds of assurance which had never existed with regard to previous improvements. My discovery (of vulcanization) was made in winter, and its specimens did not stiffen by cold. Summer returned and they were not softened by heat: there could be no danger on this score, as they were made at a temperature of 270°. The next thing to be done was to manufacture specimens of sufficient size to satisfy others of the merit of the invention by a trial of the goods. At first I was unaware of the difficulties in the way of operating on a large scale. All my previous specimens were made from thin fabrics, which could be heated before an open fire. When a specimen of considerable dimensions was heated, it seemed impossible to avoid blistering, and this inflicted great loss before it was at last overcome.

"In the spring of 1839 I had manufactured some tolerably perfect specimens, heating them before an open fire with brushwood which the kindness of my neighbors allowed me to gather in the fields, as I was unable that summer to supply myself with more substantial fuel. When these specimens were exhibited, some of my fellow townsmen were induced to assist me in building a brick oven, about six feet square, in which some comparatively large goods were to be baked. But before vulcanization could be attempted, the gum fermented, as the weather was warm, and there was nothing for it but to be content with a few specimens which had been manufactured before an open fire in my own dwelling. These I wrapped up with intent to show them in New York. A former employee of mine, at that time in Boston, promised that if I would call on him in that city he would lend me fifty dollars. When I arrived in Boston, he disappointed me. . . . I strayed into East Cambridge, and stayed at the house of a friend who made me comfortable for the night. Early next morning I walked home, a distance of ten miles, to learn on the threshold that my youngest boy, two years of age, who was in perfect health when I left home, was then dying. I thanked God for being turned back to the rescue of my family, for a dealer had refused to keep his promise to provide them with subsistence.

" I then wrote a note to a sincere friend of mine in Boston, representing the situation of my family. I was confident that he would help me, and he did. Out of regard for my wife and children he sent me seven dollars, with a severe reprimand for not turning my attention to some occupation that would support my household. A stranger to me, who happened to be in my friend's office when he received my letter, sent me a barrel of flour, which was a source of heartfelt gratitude. I next addressed myself to a brother-in-law, Mr. William DeForest, from whom I obtained fifty dollars. This enabled me to go to New York, and lay my project before Mr. William Rider, who agreed to furnish capital for manufacture on joint account. To the firmness and perseverance of this friend, and to the skill and assiduity of his brother, Mr. Emory Rider, even more than to their pecuniary aid, am I indebted for practical success. This success had barely time to receive fair public demonstration when Mr. William Rider failed, leaving me once more without resources.

" In the fall of 1841," continues Goodyear, " before Mr. Rider's failure, I commenced operations at Springfield, Massachusetts, having a short time before manufactured some rubber compound in sheets, uniformly heated. They were passed through a heated cast-iron trough. At this time I invented the shirred or corrugated goods which afterward became famous, both on account of their intrinsic merit, and through the many lawsuits to which they gave rise. Some elegant ribbons which I shirred, attracted the attention of Mr. William DeForest, who brought them to public notice and favor. . . . He furnished the capital for their manufacture, so that I was able to proceed with my improvements in the vulcanizing process." *

One morning, while Goodyear was baking a batch of rubber, a bailiff called to demand the immediate payment of a considerable debt. In default of compliance, Goodyear was escorted to jail. Often before he had been led to prison, but now, with commercial success almost within his grasp, his resentment was keen. His long maintained opposition to bankruptcy at last gave way: he accepted its relief, determined that his merciless creditors should badger him no more. In a few months the tide of his fortunes turned, and he was receiving a goodly revenue from his licenses. At once he paid his debts to the last penny, disbursing in all $35,000. For a brief season he now entered a quiet sea and enjoyed fair weather. As he recalled the storms and stresses now receding into the past, he was philosopher enough to say:

" Although sometimes disheartened by the apparent loss of time from hindrances, I have, on the whole, good reason to be reconciled to these temporary delays, being well aware that the law of necessity, under one form or other, is the only one under which invention will thrive or accomplish much. Millions might have been spent without effecting anything in comparison with what has been done. Money is indispensable for the perfecting of improvements, but it is trial and necessity chiefly that are effectual in bringing hidden things to light. In other words, however indispensable money may be to carry out an enterprise or perfect the

---

*Shirring deserves a word of description. A parallel series of thin rubber cords, while stretched, are interwoven in a warp of cotton or silk. As the fabric leaves its loom, the rubber is allowed to contract. In so doing it produces the puckering effect called shirring.

improvements of an inventor, it will avail but little in bringing to light that which is unknown, especially where the subject cannot be approached by any known laws of science."

As the qualities of vulcanized rubber unfolded themselves
under the eager tests of Goodyear, his rosiest dreams were
far outsped. He says:

" I did not expect materially to improve upon the good
qualities of the original gum. My object in experiment was
limited to restoring gum to its original state, and even that
I almost despaired of. My success in imparting to gum
elastic new and valuable properties, and at the same time
retaining all the useful qualities it had at first, has not
ceased to surprise mankind wherever it has become known.
This substance, aside from the difficulty of treating it
chemically, was in its native state as wonderful and mysterious as any in nature, and is rendered yet more wonderful by the change wrought in vulcanization. This
change may be compared to that wrought in a perishable
skin or hide by tanning, which converts it into a beautiful
kid or substantial leather; or, to that wrought when iron
is baked with carbon, and issues as steel. This comparison
with steel holds good, not only as to result, but also as to
method, except that, instead of carbon, sulphur is employed.
In both cases a high temperature is required. . . . From the
vulcanizing oven is removed an article fundamentally
changed in its properties as contrasted with its ingredients.
The most powerful solvents of gum elastic affect it but
slightly, or not at all. Gum elastic melts at a comparatively
moderate heat, and cracks with the ordinary cold of a winter day. Vulcanized rubber is indifferent to extremes of
both heat and cold. My process works no mere improvement of a substance, but, in fact, produces a material
wholly new. The durability imparted to gum elastic by
vulcanization not only improves it for its own peculiar and
legitimate uses, but also renders it available for a variety
of new purposes never before imagined. It may appear ab-
surd to compare the lasting quality of rubber with that of
wood and metal, yet because rubber resists corrosion and
decay, it is far preferable to oak or iron, as experience

proves. Nitric acid quickly dissolves iron, copper, and brass, and is without effect on rubber. Without injury a rubber vessel holds potash; and potash promptly destroys leather and wood. Many other substances are hurt or ruined by water; rubber is waterproof. So is its parent, gum elastic, a fact turned to account long before vulcanization." *

In 1848, Goodyear, with his unfailing skill, began making hollow balls and similar goods. Against a containing mold, he forced a layer of rubber by air slightly compressed. Of

*Gum elastic is not the only substance which is greatly exalted in value by simple treatment. A parallel discovery to vulcanization was that of John Mercer in 1850. This English chemist and dyer found that cotton fabrics bathed in a solution of sulphuric acid, or caustic soda, were almost doubled in strength. He proved, also, that paper and linen are improved in the same way by like immersion. His method, familiar as mercerization, to-day produces many cotton textiles which resemble silk, and also the papers, like parchment, used to cover jars of preserved fruit, and to wrap the costlier kinds of crackers and sweets.

Mercer's original discovery, like Goodyear's, was quite unintentional. He thought that an alkaline solution passed through a thick cotton filter would be weakened. To test this supposition he made a filter from six folds of fine, strong bleached cotton fabric pressed thrice through a calender to make it compact. On this filter he poured a caustic soda solution of 60° on the Twaddell scale. The filtration was very slow, and it fulfilled Mercer's expectation: the solution as it left the cotton showed a strength of but 53° on the Twaddell scale. And now John Mercer, as an observer, came forward as of kindred to Charles Goodyear. He noticed that the cotton filter had undergone remarkable changes: it had become semi-transparent, and had gained thickness at the expense of length and breadth. Most important of all, a weight of 22 pounds was now needed to break off a piece of mercerized cloth, as compared with the 13 pounds which had sufficed before treatment. In dyeing his new fabrics, Mercer found that their receptivity of color had been greatly increased. Strange to say, he found that heat checked the mercerizing process; at 212° Fahrenheit, it wholly ceased. This in contrast to the strength added to rubber at temperatures gradually heightened to 270°.

equal value were the thin veneers he now vulcanized between hot plates. But it was in compounding, not in details of manipulation, that he took his next great stride. His brother Nelson discovered that to increase the percentage of sulphur added hardness to a compound. Charles Goodyear, following up this discovery, soon created a diversity of products quite as useful as soft rubber, and unlike soft rubber in not being liable to slow oxidation, with its eventual brittleness and decay. One brand of his hard rubber replaced bone and whalebone; another kind superseded ivory and horn. Goodyear shrewdly pointed out that, in most cases, these new rubbers could be used instead of tusks and whale fibers, steadily growing scarcer and dearer. The specially tough varieties of hard rubber known as ebonite and vulcanite, have created an important field for themselves. They may be turned in a lathe, or carved by steel tools, as if ebony or boxwood, for cabinet-work. As they are impervious to water, uncorroded by acids, and non-conductors of electricity, they afford electrical insulators of unapproached quality, and form indispensable parts of the best telegraphic and telephonic instruments. These hard rubbers, almost metallic in appearance, remind us that at first Goodyear called his wares "metallic gum elastic," supposing their sulphur to be as metallic as their lead. Copper has often been used by portrait painters instead of canvas or wood, and Goodyear determined that hard rubber should be tested for a like purpose. Accordingly he had a series of family portraits executed on hard rubber, and with gratifying results, as this material is unaffected by dampness or wide fluctuations of temperature, and is liable neither to crack, warp, nor decay. One of these pictures, a portrait of himself, is reproduced for this chapter. It was executed in Paris, in 1855, by George P. A. Healy. Rubber, hard or soft, is prepared by vulcanization—a word not coined by Goodyear. James Brockedon, a partner of Macintosh, in the manufacture of raincoats, with the Vulcan of mythology in mind, called the Goodyear process " vulcanization." This term has taken firm root in the English language.

To understand how much art and science owe to Goodyear, let us place side by side a piece of vulcanized rubber, and a bit of gum elastic, such as his process begins with. Except for its dinginess, the gum reminds us of wheaten dough. Both gum and dough are elastic at common temperatures; and both become brittle in wintry air. Two joined lumps of dough adhere so firmly that they cannot be separated; just so with gum. As new and golden qualities appear in a baked loaf, unpromised in the parent paste, so gum, properly compounded and heated, blossoms into a new wealth of properties not foretold in the crude juice of a rubber plant. Vulcanized rubber is much more elastic than gum. When free from adulteration it is much tougher, so that it forms durable gloves and shoes, belts or tires. Because born at a temperature of 270° or so, it can bear all heats not exceeding these extremes. Happily, it is just as indifferent to cold; gum, in touching ice, loses its elasticity; when vulcanized, it is as flexible as ever. To bring rubber to brittleness demands the cold of liquid air, 312° below the zero of Fahrenheit. Because the stickiness of gum has vanished in the oven, it may be kept as clean as glass. Before it is heated, a rubber compound is perfectly plastic, so that it may be molded and modeled as if wax. This makes the manufacture of its shoes and garments as simple as the pasting together of their paper patterns. To round out its circle of adaptability, rubber lends itself to every art of the printer. It takes perfect impressions from steel and copper plates, from type and stone; and, unlike paper, it asks for no preliminary dampening. It is easily bronzed, gilded, or japanned. It readily combines with pigments, especially with lead oxides, which shorten the time needed for

baking. Last of all, as Goodyear remarked, it is a capital
electrical insulator. Since his time, electricity has expanded
its empire a thousandfold, so that rubber to-day covers
millions of wires bringing currents into offices, factories,
and homes, and helps to build, in even greater number,
dynamos and motors, telephones and sounders, in designs
all but faultless, of efficiencies nearly perfect.

Of late years, the manufacture of rubber has become, for
the most part, highly specialized. A few large concerns
produce a large variety of wares which may demand as many
as four hundred formulas in their preparation. The period
required for heating each article is determined, and the right
temperature is maintained with precision. Steam, because
easily regulated, is employed to heat the ovens: its pressure may reach 600 pounds to the square inch. Rubber,
when prepared and vulcanized with the utmost care, may
retain its original excellence for ten years.

To produce artificial rubber has long been the aim of leading chemists. In 1892 Professor William Tilden derived
isoprene, a colorless liquid resembling benzine, from turpentine. A few weeks afterward he noticed that a bottle
of isoprene had spontaneously formed several lumps of
rubber. Isoprene and rubber are alike in the number and
variety of their atoms; they differ solely in the architecture
which unites these atoms as molecules. Professor Tilden
found that his artificial rubber, like the natural product,
consisted of two substances, one of which was more soluble
in benzine or carbon bisulphide than the other. Yet more:
this artificial product entered into combination with sulphur,
forming a tough, elastic compound. As striking was a discovery by Dr. F. E. Matthews who, in July, 1910, sealed up
isoprene and sodium in a tube. In the course of the next
month he observed that the liquid had become viscid, and
contained a little rubber of prime quality. Sodium thus
enters upon a new career as an important means of trans-

formation. Other modes of converting isoprene into rubber have been discovered by Dr. Fritz Hofmann and Professor Karl Harries; and researchers of distinction are now endeavoring to cheapen isoprene as a basis of manufacture. Tires for motor-cars molded from artificial rubber have worn as well as if Para rubber: a test so severe is putting planters on their mettle. Their hope is that, by improved and enlarged cultivation, they may face their chemical rivals as successfully as have the planters of camphor trees.

The elasticity which so strongly characterizes rubber is shared, in minor degrees, by many other substances, a few of them easily produced by the chemist. A white substitute for rubber is obtained by stirring sulphur chloride into linseed, or other fatty oil, mixed with petroleum spirit. After a few minutes' thorough stirring, the oil thickens, and becomes a somewhat elastic mass. A similar substance, dark in color, is derived from a vegetable oil heated to about 380° Fahrenheit, when flowers of sulphur are added. As the mixture thickens, it develops elasticity. But every substitute for rubber is extensible in only a comparatively slight degree. In this chief quality, rubber and its next of kin stand far apart, reminding us of the immense disparity in magnetism between iron and its nearest relation in the magnetic family, nickel.

Of late years, the art of blending rubber with cheaper substances has been highly developed. Here, as in every other field of this manufacture, the pioneer was Goodyear himself. He mixed rubber with many oils, with carbon from coal tar, with earths, metallic oxides, metals, and ores finely pulverized. He found that a little lampblack in a compound conferred resistance to wind and weather. To produce articles specially light, he strewed sawdust and powdered cork into his kettles. Let him tell how he mixed and treated his compounds:

" Sulphur is sometimes mixed with the gum in the process of crushing or grinding, in the proportion of half an ounce of sulphur to a pound of gum. At other times it is dusted as flour upon the goods before they are placed in the heater; this is commonly done when the mixture contains white lead, or when the coat of gum is thin and the goods light. . . . Another mode is to generate sulphurous gas in the heater containing the goods. . . . When fabrics thinly coated with rubber are taken from the spreading machine, they are as adhesive as the native gum, and great care and skill are required to prevent their surfaces adhering together. As a precaution, the sheets are rolled up in cloth, or dusted with flour. The articles to be manufactured are first cut out from a sheet, their seams are washed clean from flour, and the cleansed parts are brought into contact and pressed either by the fingers or a small band roller, so as to unite them firmly. Then the article is ready to be vulcanized. Some articles, such as shirred goods, air pillows, and the like, are cemented. Other articles, shaped without cloths, require to be put on forms or lasts, or into molds or must be otherwise supported. This prevents change of shape, for the first effect of heat is to soften the rubber compound; only afterward does hardening take place. . . . The ovens are heated either by steam or hot air. Steam is not used in the cases where it causes discoloration. For car and other springs, drapery, stayed compounds, and much else, steam is preferred. Vulcanization usually requires four to six hours, during which the temperature is gradually raised from about 250° to 270° Fahrenheit. Variations in temperature and in time of exposure follow upon diversity in the thickness of goods, and also turn upon the kind of compound employed."

While Goodyear was applying his rubber to art and industry, in fields for the most part profitable, he was not to be lured into manufacturing as a vocation. He maintained his family in comfort, and then devoted the remainder of his income to experiment. His notebook, a priceless heirloom to his children, shows how fruitful and sweeping were his designs. His sketches, drawn with skill and spirit, are certainly divergent enough. Here are anchor-buoys and sails, hammocks and umbrellas, overshoes for horses to wear on icy pavements, tarpaulins and tents, printers' rolls and engine packing, self-inflating beds and baptismal pants, floor-mats and baby-jumpers. He offers us a hat with a receptacle for papers in its crown, secured by a rubber cord. To a traveler on shipboard he presents a waistcoat, easily distended with air in case of shipwreck.

Goodyear strangely overlooked an important application of rubber, to the tires of vehicles, as invented and patented in 1845, by Robert William Thomson, an Englishman, who took pains to exhibit his wheels in America as well as at home. To-day a leading branch of the rubber industry furnishes tires, solid or pneumatic, to wagons and carriages, to bicycles and motor-cars. Thomson's tires came out just forty years too soon for acceptance. As devised in 1845, they are essentially the tires rolling at this hour through the Main Streets and Broadways of America. Thomson, to give him the credit long unduly withheld from him, was the worthiest of all the successors of that wonderful man who first made a wheel, for Thomson gave the wheel a new efficiency by bidding it tread upon air. His tire was a hollow belt of India rubber, inflated with air by a condenser from which the pump of to-day is lineally descended. His belt was formed of several thicknesses of rubber, soaked and cemented in dissolved rubber, with careful vulcanization of the tube as a whole. What attracted most attention in his tires was their width of five inches. Thomson had skill as well as ingenuity; from the first his tires proved sound and durable. One set of them ran twelve hundred miles without distress. But these "aerial wheels" excited only the Oh's and Ah's of empty wonder; they were regarded as mere freaks of invention, and then quite forgotten.

About 1868, tires of solid rubber began to encircle the

wheels of heavy traction engines in England. Soon afterward they appeared on the wheels of chairs for invalids, and
trucks for baggage and freight. When velocipedes came in,
their vogue was stimulated by the use of rubber tires; thence
they passed to the supplanters of velocipedes, bicycles and
tricycles. A destiny of renown attended a tricycle owned
by a lad of Belfast, who, wishing to outrun his comrades,
appealed for aid to his father, John Boyd Dunlop, a vet-
erinary surgeon. Mr. Dunlop came to his son's assistance
most memorably. He took three pieces of stout rubber
tubing, welded each into a circle, inflated this circle with
air from a pump to form a tire duly fastened with tape to a
wheel of the tricycle. Forthwith that machine outstripped
every rival on the ground. Dunlop patented his invention,
only to find that he had been anticipated forty-five years
before by Thomson. But Dunlop saw that, while he was
in the nick of time, Thomson had been nearly half a century too early. Dunlop and his friends at once formed a
joint-stock company, and possessed themselves of patents
for clinchers and other indispensable auxiliaries. Then they
proceeded to make and market their tires with so much skill
and address that soon they were masters of a huge business, with branches throughout the world.

Since 1898, motor-cars have been perfected, and are now
adapted to touring, to the transportation of passengers and
freight, in scores of excellent models. Despite recurrent
competition from leather, wood, or steel, rubber for tires
holds the field. In many cases it is armored with leather,
and usually this leather bears studs of steel. The preference accorded to rubber is justly earned. In resilience it far
outlives leather, its most formidable rival; it drinks, as the
French say, a stone which would perceptibly lift a leather
tire, and severely jar a tire of wood or steel. Motor-car
tires become hot at high speeds, so, to avoid further vulcanization, they contain but little free sulphur. A dusty

bloom on a tire betokens its presence. Much ingenuity has been exercised upon sectional tires, and upon chains intended to bite the dust. Many heavy freight wagons bear tires of solid rubber in twins, each wheel having two distinct series of rubber pads or paws which surround it. Each circle has, let us suppose, thirty intervals without rubber; opposite each interval on the adjoining circle appears a rubber paw. A wheel thus armed runs better than if its rubber were disposed in one uniform circle. A further advantage is that, if a paw becomes worn or damaged, it is easily and cheaply replaced, whereas a pneumatic tire would need costly repairs.

Good tires are never made of pure rubber, but of rubber combined with such metallic oxides as produce a compound more tough and durable. But in many wares the admixtures of cheap ingredients with rubber are adulterants and nothing else. Not only mechanical mixture with rubber, but the chemistry of vulcanization has been closely studied of late years. For boots, shoes, and raincoats, three per cent. of sulphur is added to rubber; of this quantity two per cent. combines, leaving one per cent. free. Vulcanization takes place only when there is a little sulphur in excess. For mechanical goods and mold work, as much as six to ten per cent. of sulphur is admixed; in vulcanites and other hard goods, the proportion becomes one-half. For all that many diverse processes, with and without heat, have sought to supplant Goodyear's method, his practice to-day is but little departed from. That remarkable man struck the bull's-eye of his target; nothing but its outer circles remain for his successors.

Goodyear was not a mere draftsman, to sketch a design and go no further. When he had outlined a lifeboat and its sail, for instance, he knew no rest until that boat was launched and its sail unfurled. His workshop afforded him facilities but scant as compared with those of the well-appointed factories now vulcanizing his wares, so he sought to lay one of these concerns under contribution. From among them he chose the Naugatuck Company of Connecticut, directed by personal friends, manufacturing on a vast scale elastics for shoes, suspenders, and the like. It was agreed that in their mixing-rooms and ovens Goodyear should have new compounds tested and new articles produced. But the inventor found it so difficult to have his instructions carried out, that he soon abandoned the attempt. In experiences of this kind, he discovered how wide a gulf divides manufacturers from researchers. Often when he broached a fresh project or design to a man of business, he met with the remonstrance: " Why bother to test novelties when so many wares devised long ago enjoy a profitable demand? "

Goodyear's first invention in rubber was an improved valve for a life-preserver. This, it will be remembered, he offered to the New York agent of the Roxbury Company, whose approval of his ingenuity heartened him greatly. From the hour when first he examined a life-preserver, until the close of his life, nothing molded of rubber was oftener in Goodyear's mind than his devices for safety at sea. He gave months to designing and testing life-preservers shaped like accordions, and in other ingenious forms. He wished that every table and chair, cushion and footstool, bolster and pillow, aboard ship, should be hollow and instantly inflatable, to insure escape from peril. He believed the constant loss of life at sea to be mainly due to sheer neglect. Regarding his devices he wrote:

" A proper investigation and public trial of the proposed articles will demonstrate that there is no real necessity for such constant loss of life by mariners as now occurs. Must men continue to be drowned because their fathers were? Must treasures continue to go to the bottom of the deep because there are offices where they can be insured?

HORSEMAN IN WATERPROOFS

[Drawn by Charles Goodyear.]

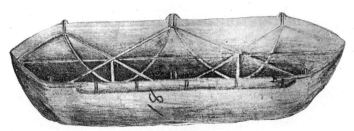

LIFE-BOAT

[Drawn by Charles Goodyear.]

The loss to the world is none the less on that account, and such a state of things need not, and ought not, to exist."

In his endeavor to safeguard the mariner, Goodyear was thwarted less by declared opposition than by stolid indifference. Nobody but himself took to heart the drownings which year by year he summed up with grief and indignation. He marveled that millions of pairs of galoshes and suspenders should be sold every twelvemonth, and seldom a swimmer's belt, and never a rubber lifeboat. He began to see how much the art of the merchant is needed to create a market for the inventor, whose wares, without an adroit and persistent canvass, may utterly miss public favor. Reviewing these and other obstacles to success, Goodyear said, toward the close of his volume on " Gum Elastic":

". . . It is a mistaken notion that an invention consists in the first vague idea of it. It takes far more than that to entitle one to the merit of an invention, for, between the bare conception of an idea, and the demonstration of the practicability and utility of the thing conceived, there is almost always a vast amount of labor to be performed, time and money to be spent, and innumerable difficulties and prejudices to be encountered, before the work is accomplished. An individual who performs all that is necessary in these ways to bring an improvement to the notice of the public, and causes them to appreciate and understand it by dint of perseverance, is in some countries considered the author of an invention, even though the first idea did not originate with him.

" It is often repeated that ' necessity is the mother of invention.' It may with equal truth be said that inventors are the children of misfortune and want. Probably no class of the community, in any country, receive a smaller compensation for their labors than do inventors. A volume might be written on the peculiar difficulties and embarrassments to which they are subject, but the whole may be summed up in a few words,—as a general rule their labors begin, continue, and end in ' necessity.' Their hard fortune often calls forth the expression of pity and compassion from the public; at the same time, there are too many ever ready to encroach upon their inventions. However valuable and important an improvement may be, it is seldom that the rightful owners are benefited by it. There is, however, in such cases one alleviating and consoling reflection to well-disciplined minds,—success has crowned their attempt, and they can leave the world better off for having lived in it. In most cases an inventor at first knows little of the difficulties he has to encounter. His attempts may be foreign to his occupation, obliging him to resort to a mechanic or a machinist for the various parts of the thing he designs. He usually finds it the most difficult of all tasks to persuade mechanics to perform a novel task whose utility they do not perceive. Often a well-conceived plan comes to failure, because wrong materials are chosen, or from a defect or oversight in construction. Defeat only confirms the projector in his conviction that he is right; he sees in his mind's eye his invention working as much to the admiration of others as to that of himself. So he renews his attempts until the machine does all he expected it to do. But he has little idea how much remains to be done to make his invention profitable. He has probably exhausted his own resources and the resources and patience of his friends in completing his devices; he has not the means needed to manufacture the article, and this deprives him of all reward for his ingenuity and toil.

"He takes out letters-patent for his invention, which he counts as property, but which amount chiefly to a permission by government to fight his own battles. Patents are commonly evaded, and the patent law is so ineffectual for their protection, that the public does not value them much, nor can they be expected to do so, for in too many cases the purchase of a patent is equivalent to the purchase of a lawsuit. If the discovery is of unlimited importance and universal application, the danger of its loss by the inventor is proportioned to its utility and importance. There will be found persons in every community unprincipled enough to pirate the invention, especially if they can make some slight alteration and evasion of it. The community cannot always be expected to understand the merits of the cause; or, if they do, since competition has given the thing they want at less cost, they are apt to encourage encroachments for an interested reason. The thing, they say, is so simple that any one would have thought of it, and no one is entitled to the monopoly of thought. It would be certainly more just to say that the inventor should be rewarded on that very account, because his improvement is simple and, therefore, practical, avoiding the great error in most attempts at improvements, that of complication and mystery."

These remarks plainly tell us that Goodyear's experience as a patentee had been unfortunate. In truth, he was dilatory in seeking such protection as patents might grant him. He always wished to incorporate in his claims the advances in method which constantly arose under his hands. And he found that every new step but broadened the horizon for fresh experiment and research. Thus it came about that his American patent was dated June 15, 1844, just five years after his discovery of vulcanization. This delay opened the door to a shrewd rival in England. For twenty years prior to Goodyear's discovery, Macintosh & Company, of London, had manufactured rainproof coats of gum elastic, using naphtha as a solvent. A partner in this firm, Thomas Hancock, received from America a piece of vulcanized rubber, unaccompanied by any information as to how it had been produced. Its odor, however, betrayed the presence of sulphur. Mr. Hancock had long been combining sulphur and rubber in his own experiments: his next steps are recalled in his " History of India Rubber Manufactures ":

" I found that when submitting the compounds containing sulphur to heat it was necessary, after ascertaining the temperatures that suited any compound, to find also the period of exposure to heat that produced the best result. Until I noticed this necessity I was often sadly perplexed, as the same compounds exposed to the same temperature were sometimes good and sometimes bad in practice; the variation in time being often from one hour to between six and seven hours, or even more. All the way through these experiments for producing the 'change' (vulcanization) I had no other guide, of course, than to watch for any promising appearance in any of the scraps and to improve upon them. But I now know I was frequently thwarted by my want of information as to what caused the differences in appearance, and particularly in regard to the temperature I employed, which was somewhat at random, knowing how freely I could use it, within certain limits, without injury.

"A thought now occurred to me that in the end proved extremely valuable. Revolving in my mind some of the effects produced by the high degree of heat I had employed in making solutions of rubber and sulphur, in oil of turpentine, it occurred to me that, as the melting-point of sulphur is only about 240°, which I knew would not be injurious to rubber, it would be well to see what would ensue on immersing a slip of sheet rubber in sulphur at its lowest melting-point. I accordingly melted some sulphur in an iron vessel, and immersed in it some slips of cut sheet rubber about half an inch wide and one-sixteenth of an inch thick. After they had been immersed for some time I examined them, and found that the surface had assumed a yellowish-tan color. I immersed them again. On withdrawing them the second time I cut one of them across with a wet knife, and found that the rubber was tinged of this tan color to a considerable depth. I immersed them again. On the third examination I found that the tan color had quite penetrated through the slip. This was strong evidence that the rubber had freely absorbed the sulphur, and I fully expected to find these slips 'changed.' In this I was greatly disappointed, for, on applying the tests, I found that not the least 'changing' effect had been produced. I now replaced them and raised the temperature of the sulphur and allowed them to remain immersed for a considerable time. On the fourth withdrawal I found to my great satisfaction that one slip of the rubber was perfectly 'changed,' retaining the same tan color throughout. The other slips remained in the sulphur while the examination was going on, and on withdrawing them I found the lowermost, the slip nearest the fire, turning black and becoming hard and horny, thus at once indubitably opening to me the true source and process of producing the 'change' in all its pure and pristine simplicity."

Hancock, having thus arrived at the vulcanization of surfaces by immersing gum elastic in molten sulphur, took out a patent in England on November 21, 1843. It was not until January 30, 1844, that Goodyear, through his agent, William Newton, patented his method in England. On the 8th of the same month, this agent secured a patent in France.

By this lack of promptitude as a patentee, Goodyear lost severely. And yet he was a man of much shrewdness, as we may observe in the publicity which he managed to give his wares. In 1849, he heard that two years later London would hold an International Exhibition; he resolved that his display should be one of the most striking in the Crystal Palace, and it was. He received one of the five council medals which came to the United States. Especially commended by the official judges was his array of hard-rubber ware, much of it exquisite in design.

In August of the next year, 1852, Goodyear's case against Horace H. Day, an infringer of his patents, came before the United States Circuit Court, at Trenton, New Jersey. Daniel Webster, as attorney for the prosecution, argued this as his last case, with all his wonted eloquence and power. He won the verdict, receiving as his fee $10,000. In the course of his plea, the great lawyer said:

" It is well known that the articles manufactured of gum elastic up to the year 1834 were entirely useless. If they were exposed to the sun, they became sticky; you could not separate them after their surfaces came in contact; and if exposed to the cold, they became hard and rigid. I well remember that I had some experience in this matter myself. A friend in New York sent me a very fine cloak in India rubber, and a hat of the same material. I did not succeed very well with them. I took the cloak one day and

set it out in the cold.   It stood very well by itself.   I surmounted it with the hat, and many persons passing by supposed they saw standing by the porch, the Farmer of Marsh-
field."

Mr. Webster continued:

" In January, 1844, Mr. Goodyear went to Naugatuck, in
Connecticut, and started a factory.   It would be painful
to speak of his extreme want—the destitution of his family, half clad, he picking up with his own hands little billets
of wood from the wayside, to warm the household—suffering reproach—not harsh, for no one would bestow that
upon him—receiving indignation and ridicule from his
friends.   Here is a letter of his written in a good spirit and
cheerful vein, but particularly affecting from that circumstance:

" ' DEBTORS' PRISON, BOSTON, April 21, 1840.
" ' MR. JOHN HASKINS OR LUKE BALDWIN:
" ' GENTLEMEN—I have the pleasure to invite you to call
and see me at my lodgings, and to communicate with my
family, and possibly to establish an India Rubber Factory
for myself, on the spot.   Do not fail to call on the receipt
of this, as I feel some anxiety on account of my family.
My father will probably arrange my affairs in relation to
this Hotel, which, after all, is perhaps as good a resting-
place as any on this side of the grave,
" ' Yours truly,
" ' CHARLES GOODYEAR.' "

Later in his plea, Mr. Webster said:

" I ask again if there is anybody else than Goodyear who
made this invention, who is he?   Is the discovery so plain
that it might have come about by accident?   It is likely to
work important changes in the arts everywhere.   It in-
troduces quite a new material into the arts, that material
being nothing less than *elastic metal*.   It is hard like metal,
and elastic as pure gum elastic.   Why, that is as great
and momentous a phenomenon occurring to men in the

progress of their knowledge, as it would be for a man to show that iron and gold could remain iron and gold, and yet become elastic like India rubber. Now, this fact cannot be denied; it cannot be discredited; it cannot be kept out of sight; somebody has made this invention. That is certain. Who is he? Mr. Hancock has been referred to. But he expressly acknowledges Goodyear to be the first inventor. I say that there is not in the world a human being that can stand up, and say that it is his invention, except the man who is sitting at that table, Charles Goodyear."

When Mr. Webster had won his case, Goodyear, accompanied by his family, took passage to Europe. His claims as a patentee in America were greatly strengthened by the decision at Trenton; he crossed the Atlantic in the interests of his European rights, and to promote the manufactures which bore his name throughout Europe. In London he was called upon by Mr. Hancock's partner, Macintosh, the famous manufacturer of raincoats, who offered him one-half the Hancock patent to relinquish a suit for infringement. This offer Goodyear declined, believing that equity was on his side; but the legal verdict went against him.

Mrs. Goodyear had left America in poor health; to her husband's sore affliction, her symptoms grew steadily worse. In March, 1853, she passed away. During the summer of 1854, Goodyear was united in marriage to Miss Fanny Wardell, of London, who survived him. To this union three children were born. Of these the only survivor is a daughter, Fanny, the wife of Dr. Emil Deckert, of the University of Frankfort-on-the-Main.

In 1855, Paris, to emulate the example of London, held an international exposition on a scale surpassing that of the British metropolis. Goodyear contributed a palatial booth, which, with its contents, cost him fifty thousand dollars, assembling every product of vulcanized rubber then known. His outlay was extravagant, and, joined to the depredations of an agent, his purse was emptied of its last dollar. He was unable to pay his debts, and was locked up in Clichy prison, near Paris. Toward the close of December he secured release, and at once posted to England to bring to bay certain audacious infringers. He had scarcely left his steamer when he was arrested on a claim originating in France. His friends proffered bail. He firmly declined bail, contending that the claim was fraudulent. This fact he clearly proved in court, when he was at once honorably discharged.

All this strife, legal and financial, came upon a man who had, for years, suffered disabling infirmity. With the shadow of death upon his brow, Goodyear took to his bed. He bade his family good-by, and sent farewells to his friends. His wife's skilful nursing led to a measurable return of strength. Early in April, 1856, he was able to travel to Bath, where he remained until May, 1858, when he sailed for New York. His stay in Bath was clouded by embarrassment. Bad health prevented his giving proper attention to his business, so that necessity again brought him into the clutches of usurers. To pay his way he had to pawn his wife's jewelry, and his own. Meanwhile his interests in America had fallen into confusion through neglect. Some of his licensees utterly ignored their contracts. To cap the climax, his trusted attorney embezzled a large sum from him. Once more in America, Goodyear's affairs were brought into something like order, and his health improved a little. Most justly his patent, which expired in 1858, was renewed for seven years, in view of the wholly inadequate returns it had yielded him. With the prospect of a respectable income from his licenses, Goodyear decided to make his home in Washington, where he hoped for peace and comfort in what remained to him of life. True to his chief purpose as an inventor, he fitted up in his house a large tank for tests of models of life-saving craft. One morning, while occupied with these models, word came from Connecticut that his daughter was dying. That he might clasp her hand in farewell, Goodyear started northward at once. On his way he was obliged, through sheer exhaustion, to pause in New York, taking quarters at the Fifth Avenue Hotel. There he learned of his daughter's death. That he should have been absent in her last hours was a final blow to this loving father. His symptoms every hour grew more alarming, and soon all hope was at an end. Early on Sunday morning, July 1, 1860, as the belfries of Fifth Avenue pealed their invitation to worship, he breathed his last.

JOHN ERICSSON

A BOY of nine, lively and vigorous, is seated on a bench in a little Swedish village. He is showing his father and mother a tiny pump, a toy sawmill, and a small set of drawing-instruments; he has made them all with no other tools than the jack-knife and gimlet beside him. The time is 1812, a year memorable in American annals; the place is Forsvik in Northern Sweden; and this wonderful boy is John Ericsson, who became the greatest engineer that Europe ever bestowed upon America. His father, Olof Ericsson, was a man of education, who for some years worked a small mine which he owned in part. He was sadly lacking in business ability, so that, after more than one call from the bailiff, his decent little property slipped through his fingers. Notwithstanding the poverty which thus befell him, he was faithful and most generous in the education of his three children. Ericsson's mother was of Flemish descent, with a Scottish strain in her blood: she was a woman of brains and force of character. It was from her that John Ericsson came by his unbending will and tireless energy. From the very first his bent was toward construction and nothing else. As a child in his native Langbanshyttan for hours together he would watch the machinery of his father's mine, discovering how the wheels and pinions were built, how they moved, and what they did.

When Ericsson was eight years old his father removed to Forsvik, a hundred miles away, as foreman of a gang of rock blasters on the Göta Canal, designed to carry the waters of Lake Venern into the North Sea. As the work proceeded, it drew from England a good many men trained by Telford, the famous builder of canals. From among them Olof Erics-

[From the painting by K. S. MacCord, 1889.]

son engaged teachers for his two sons, Nils and John. John's course included chemistry, algebra, and geometry. He was already a good draftsman when these lessons began; he was now taught field-drawing, in which he soon excelled. From the English controller of works nearby John learned English, and, as he spoke it whenever he had a chance, he was soon proficient. Meantime, in the variety of work going on around him, the lad received instruction as telling as that of classrooms. The details of blasting and excavating, of grading and building, were day by day drawing out his great natural powers to observe, and to knit cause to consequence. It was a striking case of rich soil enjoying the best culture. Years afterward a friend said to Ericsson: " It is a pity you did not graduate from a technological institute." Ericsson replied: " No, it was very fortunate. Had I taken a course at such an institution I should have acquired such a belief in authorities that I should never have been able to develop originality and make my own way in physics and mechanics, as I now propose to do."

That John Ericsson was a born commander was proved in his fourteenth year, when he was given charge of six hundred Swedish troops employed as laborers on the Göta Canal: he was then so short that he had to stand on a stool to reach the eye-piece of his leveling instrument. At seventeen, three years later, he was irresistibly drawn to military life; who could tell but that he might become a general and win national renown? He joined the Twenty-third Rifle Corps, and soon Ensign Ericsson was one of the best marksmen on its roster. By grace of the Crown Prince of Sweden he was accorded, in 1827, when he was twenty-four, the rank of captain in the Swedish Army, a title which he retained with pride as long as he lived. This sally into the profession of arms threatened the loss of Ericsson to the engineering world. It but added a new field to the empire in which he became the unapproached master. He now took up with enthusiasm the study of guns, and was soon drawing their details as swiftly and accurately as in later years he drew plans for engines and hoists, bridges and culverts. From the contours of guns he passed to a study of the explosive forces which guns are built to resist. His experiments included all the explosives then used in Sweden, and he became familiar with 80-pounders on the Baltic, at a time when there was nothing larger than a 40-pounder in the United States Navy. It was in these days and nights of eager study that Ericsson acquired a firm grasp of military and naval practice, to stand him in good stead in after life, and on both sides of the Atlantic.

A word as to Ericsson, the man, as he now stood on the threshold of his career:

" At twenty-one," says his biographer, Mr. W. C. Church, " he is described as handsome and dashing, with a cluster of thick, brown, glossy curls encircling his white massive forehead. His mouth was delicate but firm, nose straight, eyes light blue, clear, and bright, with a slight expression of sadness, his complexion brilliant with the freshness and glow of healthy youth. The broad shoulders carried most splendidly the proud, erect head." *

At that early age Ericsson had already left Sweden, proceeding to Havre, where he joined the staff of M. Mazeline, the famous shipbuilder. Here he remained about a year, learning much about the design and construction of ships, and comparing the newly devised screw propellers of Delisle and Sauvage. That of Sauvage commended itself to him,

* From "The Life of John Ericsson," by William Conant Church, two volumes, fully illustrated, copyright by Charles Scribner's Sons, New York, 1890. By the kind permission of its publishers this work has served as the chief source of information in writing this chapter. Mr. Church was for years an intimate friend of Captain Ericsson, who appointed him to be his biographer.

and, in improving its contour at a later day, he scored one of the triumphs of his career. Tradition has it that Ericsson chafed under the iron discipline of his French employer, so that he turned his eyes to England, where he sought a market for a new motor. With an old experiment of his father's in mind, he had designed before he left home an engine whose working cylinder should be filled with flame instead of steam. When his plans were embodied in brass and iron, the engines worked perfectly, and Ericsson for the first time knew a creator's joy. With $270 in borrowed cash, he went to England, arriving there on May 18, 1826, and at once set up his engine for a new test. It had been a success in Sweden, where its fuel was wood. In England the fierce heat of coal rapidly destroyed its working parts. His invention a failure, Ericsson sought employment as an engineer. Even to a casual eye the superiority of the man was always manifest: to the discerning vision of a master engineer and manufacturer, John Braithwaite, of London, Ericsson was just the assistant he was looking for. He engaged him at once, and soon admitted him to a partnership, the firm becoming Braithwaite & Ericsson.

The originality of the young Swede had now wide scope. At tin mines near Truro, in Cornwall, he installed an air compressor which worked a pump at a considerable distance. This was the first time that compressed air was used to transmit motive-power. Another task for air in motion next engaged him. He had long known that a blacksmith intensifies a blaze by a bellows; why not reap like profit by attaching bellows to the furnace of a steam boiler? From bellows in this application he soon passed to a centrifugal blower, a device which he patented in 1828. In so doing he was a pioneer of a new and great economy, that of mechanical draft, which heightens the value of all fuels, and makes it feasible to burn low-grade peats, refuse from

sugar-cane, and the like, with thoroughness. In 1829 Ericsson installed a boiler with a blower on the *Victory*, which
Captain John Ross commanded on his Arctic expedition. It was for this boiler that Ericsson devised his first
surface condenser,—an invention of remarkable nativity,
well worth recalling. James Watt, David Napier, and other
inventors had sought to replace water jets by surface-condensers, only to be foiled by a slowness of action which
Ericsson overcame. His firm was employed by Felix Booth,
a London distiller, to build his refrigerators and coolers.
These consisted of thin copper tubes, inclosing the vapor or
liquor to be chilled, and securely sealed from a surrounding
stream of cold water. At that time the exhaust steam from
engines was condensed by a jet of water which mingled with
the condensed steam and wasted much heat. This crude
process Ericsson saw could be gainfully superseded by his
distillery cooler. He built a condenser with sealed tubes
to contain exhaust steam, around which tubes might course
salt or fresh water to reduce the steam to pure water, afterward returned to the boiler for another cycle of duty. Surface-condensers, derived from this invention, are to-day indispensable in steamships and vessels of war. In addition
to building a surface-condenser on the *Victory*, Ericsson
introduced on that memorable ship the plan, now universal
in vessels of war, of protecting machinery from shot by placing it below the water-line.

From the sea this tireless innovator returned to the land.
He built the first steam fire engine ever constructed, and,
using a forced draft, it sent a stream over the tall chimneys
of a London brewery. But the municipal authorities saw
no good in this engine, and stuck to pumping by hand.
What if the water, often taken from gutters, did choke
their hose with gravel and filth? A steam engine, afloat on
a steamboat of nine miles an hour, was adopted in 1835 for
the protection of London, in so far as it could be protected

from the riverside; but for a land engine London had to
wait until 1860, thirty-two years after Ericsson's demonstration. So much for the official stupidity and inertia which
were to harass and balk him all his life.

His next great task was building the " Novelty," a locomotive which competed with Stephenson's " Rocket " in
October, 1829, at Rainhill, for a prize of five hundred

THE NOVELTY LOCOMOTIVE
Built by Ericsson to compete with Stephenson's Rocket, 1829.

pounds offered by the Liverpool & Manchester Railway.
The successful engine was to draw, at ten miles an hour,
three times its own weight, which weight was not to exceed six tons; the height of its chimney was restricted to
fifteen feet, and its boiler pressure to fifty pounds per square
inch. It must consume its own smoke: its price was to be
£550 ($2,677). Five months were granted to the competing
builders, but when Ericsson heard of the contest only seven

weeks of this period remained. Stephenson, with ample time for experimental runs, was able to correct minor faults in his design and to give his engine thorough workmanship. This good fortune did not fall to Ericsson's lot, so that, greatly to his chagrin, the flue-sheets of his " Novelty " gave way before it had completed the prescribed seventy miles. Stephenson's " Rocket " duly finished the course, and won the prize. While its pace never exceeded 24 miles an hour, the " Novelty " reached 32 miles, which even to-day would be creditable speed. In design the " Novelty " was the better engine of the two: its connecting-rods were horizontal, so that they ran with steadiness; those of the " Rocket " were diagonal, causing a severe racking motion from side to side. Stephenson adopted a steam-blast for his chimney: Ericsson used a blowing-machine with better effect.

Although Ericsson was defeated at Rainhill, the performance there of his locomotive was so remarkable as greatly to heighten his reputation as an engineer. He showed rare versatility in the tasks he now took up; let us glance at two of them. In 1831, at Birkenhead, opposite Liverpool, he set up a hollow metal drum, fitted inclined planes upon its inner surface, and, admitting steam at the center, the drum became a motor whirling 900 feet a second. To drive a pump, also of Ericsson's design, this swift motor had its speed reduced by hand-wheels; but the velocity was so high as to ruin the belts. Ericsson then built another rotary engine, actuated by pistons, only to score another failure. The steam-turbine was as yet below the horizon, to await steels of new tenacity, machine-tools of utmost precision, amended plans of lubrication, and, more than aught else, a feasible method for the reduction of steam pressures, step by step, until zero is approached.

All his life long, Ericsson was an unsparing critic of the steam engine. He believed it wasteful, but he never learned just how wasteful it was. In his early days, measurement as a science and an art had not reached exactitude; in his later years, he neglected its lessons. While he improved the design of steam engines again and again, and invented important adjuncts for their boilers and cylinders, he was convinced that steam would soon give place to a better prime-mover. To-day we know that his dissatisfaction was well grounded, and that engines using oil, or gas, explosively, are much the most economical converters of heat into work. It was neither oil nor gas, but air, that Ericsson chose as the medium by which he hoped to supersede steam. Unfortunately he greatly overestimated the energy contained in a pound of coal or other fuel. He was wont to quote with approval the dictum of Professor Harvefeldt that a common spirit-lamp might well drive an engine of 100 horse-power. All this, be it remembered, was long before Joule, in 1843, had proved that a pound of the best coal in burning gives out no more heat than, fully utilized, would yield one horse-power for 5 hours and 42 minutes.

In ignorance of this fundamental fact, Ericsson expected far too much from his regenerator. This device, in its simplest form, resembles the aspirator of metallic gauze which, a few years ago, was worn by many British folk under their nostrils in winter. The air as exhaled warmed the gauze, and this gauze then warmed the air as drawn through it into the lungs from the atmosphere. The principle of this aspirator was applied to air engines by Glazebrook, as long ago as 1797, in an English patent. His device was improved by Lilley in 1819, and by the Rev. Robert Stirling in 1827. In 1833, Ericsson perfected a new and excellent regenerator for the caloric engine, which he patented and exhibited that year. Through a fagot of small thin copper tubes the heated air passed out of the working cylinders into the cooler. On the outside of these tubes, cold air from the cooler passed in an opposite direc-

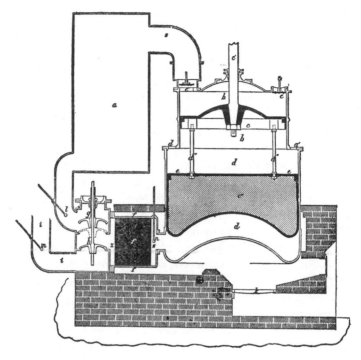

ERICSSON CALORIC ENGINE, 1851

a, air-receiver. *b b*, supply-cylinder. *e'*, self-acting valve for letting air into, and *e' e'*, self-acting valve for letting air out of the same. *c*, supply-piston; *c'*, piston-rod of the same, connected to the working-beam of the engine. *d d*, working-cylinder; *d' d'*, holes at the junctions of the two cylinders through atmospheric air passes in and out freely. *e e*, working piston. *d" d"*, rods connecting the two pistons together. *e'''*, air-tight vessel, below working piston filled with clay and charcoal to prevent transmission of heat from below. *f f*, regenerator. *f'*, discs of wire-net. *g*, valve, worked by engine, to admit air into regenerator and working-cylinder. *h*, valve for letting air out of same. *i i*, pipe, open to atmosphere, to carry off air after its passage through engine. *k*, fire-place.

tion on its way to the working cylinders. This engine, although only of five horse-power, had a working piston 14 inches in diameter. It was this necessity for large dimensions which proved fatal to Ericsson's hopes that air was to oust steam as a prime-mover. In the course of his long career he was so often a pathmaker that, perforce, he took a wrong turning more than once. In choosing air as the working medium of his engine, he fell into his chief and most costly error. Whether air be used directly from the atmosphere, or is compressed before use, it must be raised through 490° Fahrenheit to be doubled in pressure, that is, it must rise from, say, 60° to 550°. At 550° the metals in an engine are warped, lubricants are burned or decomposed, and the destruction of working parts begins. Hence a lower temperature, of about 390°, marks the limit to which heating is safely carried, and at that point only two-thirds is added to the initial pressure of working air. Contrast this with steam, which, at 390°, has a pressure of 200 pounds to the square inch, with no risk to working surfaces from overheating. Water, too, absorbs heat much more quickly than does air. Since 1833, the steam engine has been multiplied about tenfold in its economy, and to-day its rivals are not air engines, but motors driven, gun-fashion, by the explosions of oil-vapor or of gas. And be it noted that the modern air engine is much more efficient than when it left Ericsson's hands. It has been improved by Rider so as still to enjoy a field in pumping on farms, plantations, and country estates. It is largely used for irrigation, and for the water supply of villages and small towns. It is simple in design, asks no skill in its attendant, and, as it needs no water, it is suited to arid regions such as those of Arizona and New Mexico. Where winter is long and fuel dear, as in parts of Northern Canada, it may be worth while to burn all the fuel first for motive-power, converted into electricity, and then warm buildings solely with exhausts from engines. In such places caloric engines may find a new field.

In England, as in Sweden and America, Ericsson was a man who linked himself to a few friends and no more. In

Liverpool he formed the acquaintance of Francis B. Ogden, Consul for the United States, and this led to an intimacy fraught, as we shall see, with consequences of great moment to Ericsson. Mr. Ogden was an observant man, with a mechanical turn of mind. Inspecting, as he often did, the instruments on board vessels in port, he was struck, one day, with the notion that the ordinary sounding lead could be easily improved. He gave his suggestion for an improvement to Ericsson, who thereupon constructed a sounding gage which, slightly modified, is in general use to-day. Ericsson took a glass tube filled with air, closed it at the top, leaving its base open; as this tube sank in the sea, its air was compressed in proportion to its depth of immersion. This depth was registered on a dial in fathoms or feet. A lump of tallow, below the tube, told whether it had struck bottom or not. Thus, for the first time, mariners were enabled to take sounding without stopping their ships, affording them a new means of safety. Lord Kelvin improved this tube by lining it with silver chromate, discolored by the rising water.

This device, and others equally ingenious, were not the only objects of Ericsson's attention. His social circle in England, though limited, was large enough to include the woman who was to engage his heart. Among his earliest acquaintances in England was Mr. Charles Seidler, whose wife had a half-sister, Amelia Byam. When Ericsson first saw her, she was but ten years of age. She became a beautiful and lovely woman, the most fascinating he had ever beheld,—as he was wont to say,—intelligent, generous in disposition, and highly accomplished, especially in music. When Amelia Byam was nineteen, and Ericsson thirty-three, they were married in St. John's Church, Paddington. But Ericsson was already wedded to his engineering projects, and this pre-occupation meant neglect and unhappiness for his wife. In 1865 they parted, and although until her death, in 1887, they corresponded, they never met again. Only within narrow bounds was Ericsson ever master of the art of living with others. He was kind and generous to the point of magnanimity, but his temper was ungovernable, or, at least, it was quite ungoverned. His friends loved him; his enemies hated him with all their hearts. Where he felt himself to be right, it was hard for him to brook opposition. In plain terms, he had the defects of his virtues, and his masterful will often sank into sheer wilfulness. In the formative years of youth and early manhood he had been much the ablest mind in his little circle, and self-sufficiency became his habit, and, to some extent, his chief defect. This inured to his originality as a designer and an inventor, but, by standing aloof from his peers, he often missed the victories only to be won by brigade attack. To-day organized corps of engineers are testing steels, cements, and concretes for the behoof of their brethren the world over; bolts and screws, girders and rails, are standardized; fire-prevention proceeds apace, and the electrical corrosion of metal structures is investigated. Every leader draws freely upon the new knowledge and economy thus placed at his service: in requital he contributes what he can from his own experiments and experience; so that practice everywhere may rise to the level of the best anywhere. Nothing is more remarkable in Ericsson's career than his ignorance of advances in physical research, turned to profitable account by scores of contemporary engineers who, in native ability, hardly stood as high as his shoes.

His originality of conception had full play in his next great task. In 1833, he began experiments with propellers of various contours, on the London & Birmingham Canal. Three years later he built a steamboat model whose screw propeller gave it a speed of three miles an hour. Cheered by this pace in a mere model, Ericsson proceeded to build a real steamboat, 45 feet long, 8 feet beam, and 3 feet draught. She was launched in 1837, and named in honor of his friend in Liverpool, the *Francis B. Ogden.* Two propellers, 5 feet 3 inches in diameter, were so fitted to the vessel that either could be used. This little steamer moved at ten miles an hour, and Ericsson invited the Lords of the Admiralty to take passage in her for a trip on the Thames. They came, but only to shut their eyes to plain proof that a screw was a better propeller than paddles. Quoth the Surveyor of the Royal Navy, Sir William Symonds: " Even if the screw has the power to propel a vessel, it would be found altogether useless in practice, because, the power being applied at the stern, it would be absolutely impossible to make the vessel steer."

A few months later, in 1837, Ericsson designed a steam engine of a new and economical type. Its two cylinders worked at right angles to each other, and the connecting-rod coupled to their one crank-pin, directly turned the propeller shaft. This engine, applied to the iron steamer *Robert F. Stockton,* in 1838, was the first direct-acting engine ever built for propulsion.

The screw propeller was well known before Ericsson took it up; but he was the first to sketch a form so correct that at the outset it worked with high economy. Engines, as then employed for paddle-wheels, were much too slow for the direct actuation of screws. Ericsson's chief rival in England, Francis Pettit Smith, employed gearing in the actuation of his screw. Ericsson, with characteristic irreverence, threw tradition to the winds, and coupled his propeller directly to a fast engine. For a time his patent brought him a fair royalty, but he had to maintain a constant fight against aggressors. The final decision in the United States courts was that the screw propeller could not be protected by a patent. The British Government, for its use of the screw, divided $100,000 equally among five of its designers, Smith, Lowe, Ericsson, Blaxland, and Woodcroft. A striking case, this, of a device long neglected, and then independently revived by several projectors of mark.

All his life long, Ericsson was dominated by the ingenuity and boldness of his conceptions: seldom did he ask, " If carried out, will they pay?" Thus his career in England, though professionally brilliant, was a failure financially. In 1837, at a time of widespread panic, the firm of Braithwaite & Ericsson became bankrupt, and Ericsson for a time was immured in the Fleet, the famous prison for debtors. That year, through his friend, Mr. Ogden, he met Lieutenant Robert F. Stockton, of the United States Navy, who was building the Delaware & Raritan Canal, and was visiting England in quest of funds for the enterprise. He accompanied Ericsson on a trip of the *Francis B. Ogden* from London Bridge to Greenwich, and was so gratified that he immediately ordered for the United States Navy two iron steamboats, to be fitted with Ericsson's steam machinery and propellers. Returning home, Stockton was promoted to a captaincy, and ordered to the Mediterranean. On his way thither, he paused in London to consult his friends, Ogden and Ericsson, and to witness a trial trip of one of the vessels he had ordered, named by Ericsson the *Robert F. Stockton.* Its length was 70 feet, its beam 10 feet, its draught 3 feet. It was driven by a double-cylinder, direct-acting engine of 50 horse-power. An Ericsson spiral propeller completed its machinery. In January, 1839, Ericsson gave her a trial trip on the Thames, with Mr. Ogden, Lieutenant Stockton, and thirty other passengers. Her success was unqualified, inducing the *Times* to forecast " important changes in steam navigation." Ericsson applied his propeller to other English craft, with results equally good from an engineer's point of view. But commercially his demonstration bore no fruit: it required years of persuasion to bring British officials and the British public to adopt the screw propeller.

In 1839, Ericsson became superintending engineer for the Eastern Counties Railway; while in its service he devised a machine for constructing embankments. For some unrecorded reason, probably his constitutional impatience of control by others, he grew discontented with his post, and hailed with joy the prospect of a visit to America. Congress had authorized the construction of three warships, and, on Stockton's assurance that Ericsson would be allowed to build one of them, he sailed for New York on the *Great Western,* arriving, after a rough voyage, on November 23, 1839. He brought complete plans for a steam frigate, such as he expected to build. Every detail was worked out, including engines and motive power, her diverse guns, and the mechanism by which they were to be mounted, aimed, and fired. This Swedish artilleryman, fortified by his thirteen years of observation and study in England, offered America plans such as no other engineer in the world could then prepare. But opposition arose, and it was not until 1842, three years later, that the keel was laid of Ericsson's steam frigate. She was named the *Princeton,* in honor of Captain Stockton's place of residence in New Jersey.

Meanwhile Ericsson found much to do. First of all, he won with his fire engine a prize from the Mechanics' Institute of New York. And if the Navy hesitated about adopting his screw propeller, ordinary shipowners were alive to its merits. At a date not now ascertainable, probably in the summer of 1841, the canal barge *Ericsson,* built from his plans, plied on her first trip from Brockville to Montreal, one hundred and forty miles, in sixteen hours. This speed was moderate, but the *Ericsson* proved her ability to keep a safe course through the Longue Sault and Lachine Rapids, the most tumultuous of the St. Lawrence. Five other vessels, equipped with the Ericsson propeller, were placed upon the Rideau Canal and the St. Lawrence River, so that the name "propeller" came to signify a freight steamer driven by a screw. In the United States, the *Clarion,* plying between New York and Havana, was fitted with an Ericsson propeller, as also were seven vessels steaming out of Philadelphia to various southern ports. A like equipment was bestowed upon the Revenue Cutter *Jefferson* on Lake Erie. By the end of 1843, no fewer than forty-two vessels on American and Canadian waters were actuated by Ericsson screws.

Ericsson had been in New York two years when, in the fall of 1841, Stockton at last received orders from the United States Navy Department to build a steamer of 600 tons. He at once engaged Ericsson to draw its plans and supervise its construction, with the distinct understanding that he was to be paid for his services. This vessel, duly launched and equipped, was named the *Princeton.* She was exhibited with triumph. Unfortunately, during her construction, Ericsson and Stockton drifted apart. The irascible and imperious designer, conscious of his powers, grew weary of the condescension, not to say the arrogance, of the naval martinet. On February 5, 1844, Stockton reported to the Navy Department that the *Princeton* displayed " great and obvious advantages both over sailing-ships and steamers propelled in the usual way (by paddles). With engines lying snug in the bottom of the vessel, out of reach of an enemy's shot, making no noise, smoke, or agitation of the water, she can surprise an enemy and at pleasure take her own position and her own distance." All true. But Ericsson had no mention in a report from which might be inferred that it was Stockton who had designed the *Princeton.*

Her inaugural closed with a shocking fatality. On board were guns with self-acting locks, patterned after a wrought-iron gun which Ericsson had designed in England and brought to America. This model weapon, though forged of the best iron, had the faults of a forging: strong lengthwise, it was weak transversely, so that cracks appeared in its trial firing. As a remedy, Ericson adopted an expedient now universal. Hoops of wrought-iron, three and one-half inches thick, were shrunk over the breech of the gun up to its trunnion bands. These hoops were arranged in two tiers, one above another, so as to break joints, and these joints were so close that the outer band seemed a single piece of metal. Thus reinforced, the gun was fired about three hundred times with charges varying from 25 to 35 pounds of powder, and with shot of 212 pounds, so as to pierce a wrought-iron target 4½ inches thick. Prompted by this amazing result, Stockton designed a gun of his own, which he called the " Peacemaker." It was duly forged, and then sent to New York to be bored and finished under Ericsson's direction. It was of like caliber with his model gun, twelve inches, but a foot wider at the breech, and much heavier throughout. Its appearance of strength was deceptive. Harm had been suffered under the forging hammer, harm not discovered until too late. Ericsson, with a paternal partiality for his own gun, advised Stockton to use it instead of the " Peacemaker " on the inaugural day, but he does not seem to have doubted the strength of Stockton's gun. However, it burst, under a final charge, killing several members of the company, and severely wounding Captain Stockton. He was acquitted of blame by a court of inquiry which was promptly summoned. He had slighted Ericsson, who now stood aloof in Stockton's distress. Their differences naturally grew more and more embittered, as we shall observe. Ericsson's model gun on the *Princeton* had proved sound and safe, thanks to its reinforcing hoops. This source of strength was duly remarked. During the Civil War the Union looked to Major T. J. Rodman and Captain R. C. Parrott for its heavy guns, and these, as forged and hooped, were lineally descended from the Ericsson weapon on the *Princeton*.

Ericsson's services as her designer and builder now involved him in the most unpleasant contest of his life. In
March, 1844, he sent to the Secretary of the United States
Navy a bill for $15,080 for professional services in supervis-
ing the construction of the *Princeton,* including $5,000 as
inventor and designer of her apparatus, gun-carriage, and
spirit-level, by which the elevation of a piece of ordnance
might be readily and precisely ascertained, and her sliding
chimney, which could be reduced to a height of five feet
above the deck. If this slight projection had been carried
away, or damaged by a shot, the draft, because forced,
would nevertheless have been continued with efficiency.
Ericsson's bill was referred to Captain Stockton, who wrote
a long series of objections, concluding: " Captain Ericsson, at the time he volunteered his services, considered that
the opportunity accorded him to exhibit to the world the importance of his various patents would be satisfactory remuneration for all his services in getting them up on so
magnificent a scale."

So much for omitting to reduce to writing a weighty
matter of business, clearly understood at the outset, and
afterward warped by a bitter personal quarrel, and what
Ericsson termed " the deep rascality of Stockton." Ericsson, at the beginning, distinctly agreed that if his plans were
successful he was to be compensated. The success of his
plans was acknowledged, and not only in America, but in
France and England, where they received the flattery of
imitation. Besides, why should the Navy Department refuse to pay him for services strictly professional in super-
vising the building of the *Princeton?* Merely to execute
the drawings occupied him two hundred and seven days,
and his pace was twice that of an ordinary draftsman. One
hundred and thirteen days more had been consumed in superintendence and travel. The Naval Committee of the
House of Representatives unanimously reported a bill to

pay Ericsson his claim, but the House defeated it by a small majority. In 1848 a similar bill was defeated by an adverse report from the Senate Naval Committee. In March, 1856, the Senate ordered that Ericsson's papers be referred to the Court of Claims, then recently established. It decided in Ericsson's favor, and the Senate Committee reported a bill for its payment. Congress, however, neglected to appropriate the money, and Ericsson was never paid.

This injustice, and much ill usage on the part of national officers in later years, soured Ericsson to the core. This was one reason why he never really became an American, never took root in a country where he lived continuously for fifty years. At the first refusal of payment for his work on the *Princeton,* his anger was heightened by his dire poverty, solely due to his having disbursed as much as $6,000 in anticipation of full and prompt repayment. How with an empty purse could he meet his pressing debts? At one time his bank balance fell to $23. On September 16, 1846, he wrote to his friend, John O. Sargent: " I received your letter of the 14th yesterday afternoon, and opened it with a trembling hand. My worst fears were realized, and I turned nearly crazy for a few minutes. In my despair I resorted to the expedient of asking Delamater (the engine builder) to help me, and he has done so for to-day, appropriating the funds he has for meeting a bill at the end of next week. Now, if in addition to my anxiety already experienced, I should ruin the young man's credit by not being able to refund the money by next Wednesday, I shall have to cut my throat."

From this pecuniary distress he was for a time relieved by the sale to the Government of the steamer *Massachusetts,* in which he had an interest, and by the receipt of $4,300 for the application of his fresh-water apparatus to that vessel.

By 1848, Ericsson had climbed out of debt by sheer hard work. His rage against Stockton and the Government had calmed down: in October of that year he was naturalized as a citizen. But his drawing-board held him in a subjection never relaxed: he took no interest in politics until slavery threatened the life of the Union. Then his soul was aroused, for he could conceive nothing meaner than the desire of one man to live on the toil of another. How nobly and indispensably he served the nation we shall duly see.

Versatile in an extraordinary degree, Ericsson at this period entered many diverse fields, always as a conqueror. He improved his surface-condenser for steamships, giving it an engine of its own, so as to be independent of the engine driving the screw. Hence, in case that bad weather, or accident, checked or stopped the propelling engine, the task of condensation would not be interrupted. He was vitally interested in the intensity of flames beneath a steam boiler, or within a cupola furnace such as ironmakers employ. In measuring their extreme temperatures, he discarded, as worthless, the clay measures of Wedgewood, and devised a thermometer which registered the degree to which the heat expanded its confined gas. This method, in which he was once again pioneer, survives as one of the most trustworthy ever invented. But these and other creations were but the by-play of a mind intent on a supreme task, that of supplanting the steam engine as a prime-mover.

After he came to the United States, in 1839, Ericsson continued his experiments with hot air as a motor, building eight caloric engines between 1840 and 1850. He gradually enlarged their dimensions, until a cylinder of 30 inches diameter succeeded to the 14-inch cylinder of his first American design. All these engines had, as regenerators, metal chests with wire meshes in which the outgoing air left much heat for the incoming air to absorb. The difference in temperature between the incoming and outgoing streams was never less than 350° Fahrenheit. In 1851 he designed a ninth engine, to cost $17,000, having a two-foot stroke and two compressing cylinders of four feet diameter. Its two regenerators contained twenty-seven million cells, and Ericsson estimated that but eleven ounces of coal were burned in producing one horse-power for an hour. If this estimate was correct, Ericsson's engine surpassed any feat to-day possible to the best steam engines which, with multiple expansion, and the most elaborate auxiliaries for economy, never burn less than one pound of coal as against his eleven ounces. If his figures were wrong, Ericsson immovably held them to be right. How this led to the one great disaster of his professional career is told by him in his Contributions to the Centennial Exhibition at Philadelphia, in 1876:

" The regularity of action and perfect working of every part of the thirty-inch engine in 1851, and, above all, its apparent great economy of fuel, inclined some enterprising merchants of New York, in the latter part of 1851, to accept my proposition to construct a ship for navigating the ocean, propelled by paddle-wheels actuated by the caloric engine. This work was commenced forthwith, and pushed with such vigor that within nine months from commencing the construction of the machinery, and within seven months of the laying of the keel, the paddle-wheels of the caloric ship *Ericsson* turned around in the dock. In view of the fact that the engines consisted of four working cylinders of 168 inches diameter, 6 feet stroke, and 4 air-compressing cylinders of 137 inches diameter and 6 feet stroke, it may be claimed that in point of magnitude and rapidity of construction, the motive machinery of the caloric ship stands unrivaled in the annals of marine engineering."

To build this vessel required about half a million dollars, her engines costing $130,000. Her length was 260 feet, her breadth 40 feet, her draught 17 feet, with a tonnage of nearly 2,200. The keel was laid in April, 1852, five months later she was launched, and started on her trial trip January 5, 1853. Six weeks afterward, on February 16, 1853, she left New York for Washington, arriving there safely, notwithstanding a stormy passage. Her four working cylinders, each 14 feet wide, were bestowed in pairs midway of the vessel, two forward and two aft. Instead of resting on the keelsons, in the usual manner, they were suspended, like huge camp kettles, over the furnace fires. Above the working cylinders were four supply cylinders, or single-acting pumps, of 137 inches in diameter. Eight piston-rods, each 14 feet long, connected the mammoth pistons of each set of cylinders, and these pistons had a total capacity of 43 cubic feet. Ericsson expected to reach a pressure of 12 pounds to the square inch with his engine and calculated that this would give a speed of ten or even twelve miles an hour; but it was found impossible to exceed eight miles. This gait, slow as it was, fulfilled his promise, and a failure in speed would not have condemned his vessel if a quicker pace seemed feasible when his design received revision.

The *Ericsson* returned to New York, and was in many details much improved. Blowers were added to force the draft, and make good a deficient area of grate surface. But out of a fair sky fell a thunderbolt. During a trip on April 27, 1854, in New York Bay, the *Ericsson* was struck by a sudden squall and sank. This was her designer's account of the wreck, in a letter to his friend, Mr. Sargent:

" At the very moment of success—of brilliant success— Fate has dealt me the severest blow I ever received. We yesterday went out on a private preparatory trial of the caloric ship, during which all our anticipations were realized. We attained a speed of from twelve to thirteen turns of our paddle-wheels, equal to fully eleven miles an hour, without putting forth anything like our maximum power. All went magnificently until within a mile or two of the city (on our return from Sandy Hook), when our· beautiful ship was struck by a terrific tornado on our larboard quarter, careening the hull so far as to put completely under water the lower starboard, which, unfortunately, the men on the freight deck had opened to clear out some rubbish, the day being very fine. The men, so far as we could learn, became terrified and ran on deck without closing the ports, and the hold filled so rapidly as to sink the ship in a few minutes. I need not tell you what my feelings were as I watched the destructive element entering the fireplaces of the engines, and as the noble fabric, yielding under my feet, disappeared inch by inch. A more sudden transition from gladness and exultation to disappointment and regret is scarcely on record. Two years of anxious labor had been brought to a successful close, the finest and strongest ship, perhaps, ever built was gliding on the placid surface of the finest harbor in the world, and within a few cable-lengths of her anchorage; yet, with such solid grounds for exultation, and with such perfect security from danger, a freak of the elements effected utter annihilation in the space of a few minutes."

The unfortunate ship was lifted to the surface: it was decided to convert her into a steamer, as her air engines had developed but 300 horse-power. It had been proved, beyond dispute, that in very large dimensions, such as those of the *Ericsson,* air cannot compete with steam as a motive power. Bulk and weight, with all the inflexibility of arithmetic, oppose the project. The *Ericsson,* as a steamer, in 1858 bore the remains of ex-President James Monroe from New York to Richmond, Virginia, with the Seventh Regiment as an escort. During the Civil War she served as a transport. At last she was converted into a sailer, and carried coals on the Pacific Ocean under the Union Jack. All his life afterward, Ericsson maintained that his caloric ship was his masterpiece, both in design and construction. Its failure left him still believing that its motor, in principle, was the best ever built. In January, 1855, nine months after the *Ericsson* foundered, he wrote to his business associates, Mr. Stoughton, Mr. Tyler, and Mr. Bloodgood:

". . . On the principle of the improved caloric engine, more motive power may be obtained from a mass of metallic wires of two feet cube than from a whole mountain of coal, as applied in the present steam engine. Every experimental trial made has more than realized my anticipations as regards the rapidity and certainty of depositing and returning the caloric on this remarkable system. The practical application *alone* has presented difficulties. . . . In the meantime I find myself on the verge of ruin. I must do *something* to obtain bread, and vindicate to some extent my assumed position as the opponent of steam. Accordingly I have determined to return to my original caloric engine. The plan is less brilliant—less startling—but as it proved to yield power practically twenty years ago, so will it again. At any rate, it cannot fail to be sufficiently useful to save its author from starving. . . ."

A thousand of these caloric engines were sold in two years, the beginning of a demand which for a long period steadily widened. These Ericsson engines were yoked to printing presses, hoisting gear for warehouses, docks, and ships; they were busy in mines and mills; they were employed for pumping, for irrigation, and for the water supply of villages; many were applied on farms to threshing, on plantations to ginning and other tasks. Of late years air engines have suffered severely from the competition of lighter and more forceful engines burning gas or gasoline, as well as from the rivalry of electric motors.

While Ericsson overrated the regenerator, its worth was, nevertheless, substantial. In 1838 he sought to link it to the steam engine, but success eluded him. Now, thoroughly familiar with steam engines of new types, he had better fortune. His plan was to send exhaust steam through tubing, on the other side of which ran water on its way to the boiler. This feed-water heater, in modern forms, is always part of a steam engine of the best class. The exhausts from heat engines form much the largest item of loss; their utilization, especially to heighten the efficiency of engines themselves, still offers a promising field to ingenuity.

For the careful execution of his designs, and for securing a wide and growing market, Ericsson was indebted to Cornelius H. Delamater, the engine builder, and for many years owner of the Phœnix Foundry in New York. With him the inventor maintained the longest and most intimate of his friendships. Mr. Delamater was a clerk in the Phœnix Foundry when the engines for the *Princeton* were under construction in 1842. He had the utmost confidence in Ericsson's talents and integrity. To be sure, Ericsson's temper was at times most provoking; and yet, after every storm, the sunshine of his good will emerged all the warmer for a ray of repentance.

Another intimate friend of Ericsson's was Professor James J. Mapes, an engineer holding high rank as an expert in patent cases. Whenever Ericsson's ring was heard at their door, the Mapes children sprang to greet him, for his kindness and playfulness had wholly won their hearts. After a romp with the youngsters the inventor would discuss with the professor deep questions in physics and chemistry, soon reaching the horizons where inference leaps into conjecture. In his big and busy brain the great Swedish engineer had many compartments, and their contents were highly contrasted. Often at the fireside of his friend Mapes, he would glide from a page of Laplace's "Mechanism of the Heavens," or a theorem in Newton's "Principia," to recalling a Swedish ballad of his youth. His biographer, after Ericsson's death, found among his dusty diagrams and calculations a list of songs which included "Who are you, my girl?", "It is so sweet in

Spring," and "Oh, Robert, cruel is our parting." This man, who, when more than sixty years of age, would stand on his head for the amusement of the Mapes children, was a dreaded and gusty autocrat in foundries and engine sheds. At the drafting-table no man excelled him in celerity and accuracy. Yet, John Ericsson was, after all, a human being, and, therefore, liable to err, and to suffer lapses of memory, although at extremely long intervals. His own expertness made him an exacting master; and he required in execution a rigid adherence to every detail in his drawings. One day his assistants were filled with glee: they found that "the old man" had omitted a vent-hole in a drawing otherwise complete. In his life by Colonel Church appears this characteristic story:

"Charles Nelson, at one time draftsman in the Novelty Works in this city, had charge of the engines of the *Columbia,* designed by Captain Ericsson, and when the engines were finished it was customary in those days to get the length of the piston-rod from the engine itself, so that there would be no mistake in cutting the key-way on the piston-rod. Nelson was down in the *Columbia's* cylinder with a baton about fourteen feet long, when Ericsson came on board and stood right over him. He roared out: 'What are you doing there, sir?'

"'Getting the length of the piston-rod, Captain Ericsson.'

"'Is it not on the drawing, sir?'

"'Yes, sir.'

"'Then why do you come here with sticks, sir? Go and get the length from the drawing, sir. I do not want you to bring sticks when the drawing gives the size.'"

Charles Bernard, an old New York engineer, used to tell a similar story of Ericsson's accuracy. John Mars was putting in the engines of the *Quinnebaug,* and one of the details was a small connection as crooked as a dog's hind leg. Mars tried to get it into its place for a long time, but failed, and finally went to Ericsson and told him the rod could not be got in. Ericsson said:

" Is it right by the drawing? "
" Yes, sir," said Mars.
" Then it will go in," said Ericsson; and when Mars tried it again it did go in.

At the outbreak of the Civil War, in April, 1861, Ericsson was fifty-eight years of age, yet enjoying all the vigor usual at forty.   Twelve to fourteen hours a day, standing at his table, he drew plans for machinery and engines.   An occasional visit to a foundry or a machine shop, at rare intervals a call upon Professor Mapes or Mr. E. W. Stoughton, were the only breaks in his toil.   The attack on Fort Sumter, and the events which quickly followed, stirred him profoundly: as in many another case, the division of camps had converted a friend into a foe.   In former days at Washington, a Representative from Florida, the Hon. Stephen R. Mallory, had been a champion of his claims as designer of the *Princeton,* and had become thoroughly aware of his extraordinary powers.   Mr. Mallory was now the virtual head of the Confederate Navy: at his instance the frigate *Merrimac,* which had been burned and sunk in Norfolk Harbor, was lifted and repaired, to be clad with iron armor and work ruin to Union warships.   With but one establishment in the South capable of furnishing armor, the Tredegar Foundry at Richmond, work was slow on the *Virginia,* as the frigate was now named.   Her progress toward completion was, from day to day, telegraphed to the New York press, and this impelled Ericsson to action. On August 29, 1861, he wrote to President Lincoln, offering plans of the *Monitor,* plans so simple that they could be executed within ten weeks from the day they were taken in hand.   Ericsson was invited to lay these plans before the Navy Department.   Accordingly he reported himself in

Washington on September 14, 1861. Sixteen years afterward, in a letter to Captain E. P. Dorr, of Buffalo, he narrated his reception:

". . . On entering the room occupied by the Board over which Commodore Smith presided, I was very coldly received, and learned to my surprise that the Board had actually rejected my *Monitor* plan, presented by Mr. Bushnell (afterward his partner in her construction). Indignant, my first resolve was to withdraw, but a second thought prompted me to ask why the plan was rejected. Commodore Smith at once made an explanation that the vessel lacked stability. My blood being well up, I finished my demonstration by thus addressing the Board:

" 'Gentlemen, after what I have said, I deem it your duty to the country before I leave the room to give me an order to build the vessel.'

" I was asked to call again at one o'clock. Commodore Paulding invited me into his room, and in a very cordial manner asked me to report my explanation about the stability of the vessel. I complied, having in the meantime drawn a diagram presenting the question in a very simple form. My explanation lasted about twenty minutes, at the end of which the frank and generous sailor said:

" 'Sir, I have learned more about the stability of a vessel from what you have said than I ever knew before.'

" Commodore Smith then desired me to call again later in the day. On my appearance I was asked to step into Secretary Welles's room, who briefly told me that the commodores had reported favorably, and that, accordingly, he would have the contract drawn up and sent after me to New York, desiring me in the meantime to proceed with the work. I returned at once, and before the contract was completed the keel-plate of the intended vessel had already passed through the rollers of the mill. . . ."

Why the *Monitor* was so named, her designer narrates in his "Contributions to the Centennial Exhibition":

"The Navy Department at Washington having, shortly before the launch, requested me to suggest an appropriate name for the impregnable turreted steam-battery, I addressed a letter to the Assistant Secretary of the Navy, saying: ' The impregnable and aggressive character of this structure will admonish the leaders of the Southern Rebellion that the batteries on the banks of their rivers will no longer present barriers to the entrance of the Union forces. The iron-clad intruder will thus prove a severe monitor to those leaders. But there are other leaders who will also be startled and admonished by the booming of the guns from the impregnable iron turret. Downing Street will hardly view with indifference this last Yankee notion, this monitor. To the Lords of the Admiralty the new craft will be a monitor, suggesting doubts as to the propriety of completing those four steel ships at three and a half millions apiece. On these and many similar grounds I propose to name the new battery *Monitor.*'

" It will be recollected that this letter was regarded in England as possessing political significance, several members of Parliament having called for its reading in the House of Commons when the news of the result of the battle between the *Monitor* and the *Merrimac* appeared in the *Times.* Unquestionably the advent of the *Monitor* materially counteracted the pressure which the French Emperor brought to bear on the British Ministry at the time, in favor of the Southern States."

On October 25, 1861, the keel of the *Monitor* was laid; she was launched January 30, 1862, and practically completed by February 15. Her extreme length was 172 feet, her breadth 41½ feet, with 11½ feet as her depth of hold; she drew 10½ feet of water. Her turret was 9 feet in diameter and 8 inches thick; her side armor was 5 inches thick, her deck plating was one inch thick. Her two propellers were each 9 feet in diameter; her steam cylinder was 36 inches in diameter, with a stroke of 26 inches. She was a vessel of 776 tons. Her design was the slowly ripened fruit of a lifetime varied in engineering experience, rich in bold and original thought. Ericsson knew every line of the working plans carried out on the Göta Canal; he had studied artillery and its allied problems in the camps of Jemtland; for commerce and for war, he had designed ship after ship from keel to masthead.

For the daring plan of the *Monitor* he declared his in-

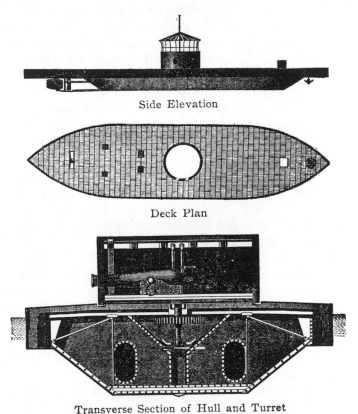

Side Elevation

Deck Plan

Transverse Section of Hull and Turret

THE "MONITOR"

Designed by John Ericsson. Built at New York, 1861.

debtedness to his observation of rafted timber on Swedish lakes. In a storm he had seen the raftsman in his elevated cabin subjected to but little motion, while waves were freely breaking over the logs around and beneath him. Above and beyond all other qualifications, Ericsson was a man to whom the rules of past practice were servants and not masters. He was convinced that all engineering feats thus far accomplished were trifles as compared with victories near at hand. In the *Monitor* he gave war a wholly new and terrible weapon. She was an impregnable floating battery, with guns of the largest caliber then produced, with a hull shotproof from stem to stern, and with her rudder and screws protected from an enemy's fire by an overhang of 13 feet. In order to navigate the shallow waters of the Southern States, her draught was but eleven feet, demanding a sunken hull from the impossibility of carrying the weight required to protect a high-sided vessel. Her cylindrical turret, revolving on a vertical axis, made feasible an all-around fire while the vessel remained stationary. Turrets, modified from Ericsson's design, appear in every modern man-of-war. The *Monitor* cost her builder $195,142.60, yielding a net profit of $79,857.40. Of this Ericsson's share was one-fourth, $19,964.35, plus $1,000 for engineering services. Happily for Ericsson and for the Union, the Assistant Secretary of the Navy, Gustavus Vasa Fox, was a man of ability and courage, who had served fourteen years in the Navy when appointed Assistant to Secretary Welles, who used his technical knowledge with daily advantage. At first Mr. Fox dissented from Ericsson's plans; he soon became their stanch supporter.

When the *Monitor* was ready for duty, it was intended to despatch her to join Farragut's expedition against New Orleans. News of the approaching completion of the *Virginia* at Norfolk changed this program: the *Monitor* was ordered to proceed to Hampton Roads on the earliest date possible. She left New York on the afternoon of March 6, 1862, in tow of a tug, and accompanied by two steamers, the *Currituck* and the *Sachem*. For twenty-four hours in a smooth sea, the *Monitor* moved evenly and comfortably. Then, with a rising wind, the sea swept her deck, entered through the hawsepipes, and choked her draft. These mishaps, and others less serious, were in part due to errors in construction easily remedied, and to lack of experience in handling so novel a craft. There was only one man on board who thoroughly understood the build of the *Monitor*. This was Chief Engineer Alban C. Stimers, the naval inspector of ironclads, who was a passenger. Years before, he had been chief engineer of the *Merrimac*. But for his skill and presence of mind, the maiden voyage of the *Monitor* might have ended in disaster. From her cabin he wrote to Ericsson on March 9, 1862:

"After a stormy passage which proved us to be the finest seaboat I was ever in, we fought the *Merrimac* for more than three hours this forenoon, and sent her back to Norfolk in a sinking condition. Ironclad against ironclad, we manœuvered about the bay here, and went at each other with mutual fairness. I consider that both ships were well fought. We were struck twenty-two times, pilot house twice, turret nine times, deck three times, sides eight times. The only vulnerable point was the pilot-house (perched above the turret). One of your great logs, nine by twelve inches thick, is almost broken in two. The *Merrimac* tried to run us down and sink us as she did the *Cumberland* yesterday, but she got the worst of it. Her horn passed over our deck, and our sharp upper-edged rail cut through the light iron shoe upon her stem and well into her oak. She will not try that again. She gave us a tremendous thump, but did not injure us in the least, we were just able to find the point of contact. The turret is a splendid structure; I don't think much of the shield, but the pendulums are fine things, though I cannot tell you how they would stand the shot, as they were not hit.

"You were correct in your estimate of the effect of shot upon the man inside of the turret when it struck near him. Three men were knocked down, of whom I was one. The other two had to be carried below, but I was not disabled at all, and the others recovered before the battle was over. Captain Worden stationed himself at the pilot-house. Greene fired the guns, and I turned the turret until the Captain was disabled, and was relieved by Greene, when I managed the turret myself, Master Stoddard having been one of the two stunned men.

"Captain Ericsson, I congratulate you upon your great success; thousands here this day bless you. I have heard whole crews cheer you; every man feels that you have saved this place to the nation by furnishing us with the means to whip an ironclad frigate that was, until our arrival, having it all her own way with our most powerful vessel."

This narrative from inside may be supplemented by a recital from outside, by a Confederate soldier, who, from a safe position, saw the fight.* He declares that had the *Monitor* concentrated her fire upon the water-line of the *Merrimac*, she would have been pierced as if paper. At a later day it was proved that the guns of the *Monitor* could safely bear charges of powder much heavier than those fired during her famous battle. In justice to her officers it should be remembered that they were forced to fight immediately upon arriving in Hampton Roads, after a fatiguing voyage, under singularly trying conditions, and with a vessel whose idiosyncrasies they had no time to learn. "All the men," wrote her chief engineer, Isaac Newton, "were nearly exhausted. I, for one, was sick on my back, with little hope of being up in a week, but a short time before the action. The *Merrimac* was entirely in our power when she hauled off, but orders were imperative to act on the defensive." The commander of the *Merrimac*, Catesby Jones, testified before a naval court that the *Monitor* ought to have sunk his vessel in fifteen minutes. Alban C. Stimers met Mr. Jones, on the last of many occasions, in 1872. Mr. Jones remarked : " The war has been over a good while now, and I think there can be no harm in saying to you that, if you had hit us twice more as well as you did the last two shots you fired, you would have sunk us."

While the contest in Hampton Roads pointed to the necessity of redesigning the naval armaments of the world, it failed to show all that a monitor might do. When Ericsson's vessel left his hands, it was beyond his control. He had created an impregnable floating battery, carrying guns powerful enough to destroy any of the enemy's ships: he could do no more. The wave of rejoicing which overswept the North was due less to the achievement of the *Monitor,* fought as she was, than to confidence that the Government had at least one vessel that could not be sunk by the *Merrimac;* and what was to prevent the rapid building of a fleet modeled on the *Monitor?* Happily the *Merrimac* was fated to give the North no further trouble. A few weeks after her most famous battle, and without firing another shot, she sank in Chesapeake Bay. A like fate befell the *Monitor,* which foundered in a gale near Cape Hatteras, on December 31, 1862.

Following the success of the *Monitor,* there flowed upon her designer a great tide of congratulation and applause. From State Legislatures, from Chambers of Commerce and Boards of Trade, from public meetings convened for the purpose, thanks and laudations were poured upon the *Monitor;* upon Ericsson, her creator; Worden, her commander; Greene, her executive officer; Newton, her chief engineer; and upon Stimers, the engineer appointed to accompany and report upon her, who worked her turret. President Lincoln, members of his Cabinet, many of the diplomatic corps, officers of the army and navy, and ladies, too, crowded to see the new ship of war, and to view its scene of conflict in Hampton Roads. On March 28, 1862, Congress passed a joint resolution acknowledging the enterprise, skill, energy, and foresight of Captain John Ericsson, displayed in his construction of the *Monitor,* which arrested the destruction then proceeding by the enemy's ironclad steamers, seemingly irresistible by any other means at command, according him thanks for his great services to the nation.

After disabling the *Merrimac,* the *Monitor* joined the ironclad *Galena* and several wooden vessels in a demonstration against Richmond. " This," says Professor Soley, " was one of the boldest and best conducted operations of the war. Had Commander Rodgers been supported by a few brigades, landed at City Point or above on the south side, Richmond would have been evacuated. The *Virginia's* crew alone barred the way to Richmond; otherwise the obstructions would not have prevented his steaming up to the city, which would have been as much at his mercy as was New Orleans before the fleet of Farragut." *

Admiral Farragut, by the way, was at first opposed to Ericsson's great invention. After the battle of Mobile Bay he changed his mind. Referring to that contest, Ericsson said: " Admiral Farragut now admits that a single monitor can sink a whole fleet of wooden vessels. He was convinced after seeing his own gun-deck covered with blood and mangled bodies by the fire from the ram, while on board the turret-vessels not so much blood was shed as a mosquito would draw."

Yet so fair-minded was Ericsson, so compelling his sense of right, that in 1875 he wrote to an inquirer: " In reply to your kind letter asking for a copy of acknowledgments received complimentary to what you are pleased to call my ' great work,' I beg to state that nothing could induce me to lay before the world the approving opinions of the monitor system without also presenting the adverse criticism of my work of which learned as well as skilful, practical men have written in great numbers."

Critics of the monitors pointed to disasters which had overtaken several of them, disasters to which warships of

* "Battles and Leaders of the Civil War," p. 761.

ordinary models would not be exposed. In comment, Ericsson wrote to his friend John Bourne, the eminent English engineer, on November 3, 1863:

" The monitors have not only proved sea boats, but they are lifeboats on a large scale, which cannot perish in any hurricane or raging sea, provided there is water under their bottoms and their deck openings are properly closed. The sinking of the original *Monitor* was caused by an inexperienced commander raising her turret before going to sea, and then putting oakum under its base. The turret, on being let down, rested on a few thick lumps, the sea washing out the rest and producing a leak of some fifty feet in extent, admitting more water than the pumps could take away. But the vessel did not go down in an instant, as reported, for it took full four hours before the stream of water under the turret overpowered the pumps. The monitor *Weehawken* went down at anchor in Charleston harbor during a gale, the forward deck-hatch having been left open and remaining so for fifteen minutes, while the sea made a clean breach over the vessel. We have positive evidence that both the seams and rivets of that vessel remained sound.

" Ordinary vessels roll because the wave on the weather side, impeded by the hull, rises to a greater altitude than on the opposite side. In the case of the *Monitor* the wave can only rise sixteen inches, after which it mounts the deck, and by force of gravity bears down the hull and checks the tendency to roll. The projecting side armor also assists powerfully in preventing rolling. The pitching, from the same cause, is less in monitors than in other vessels. As to ventilation, old sailors who have been in these vessels night and day for two years have assured me that no other vessels of war can compare with them. It must be so, since the air before entering the boiler-room sweeps through the quarters. To assume that the means of ventilation fail is to assert that the vessels have ceased to move, there being no sails and no air for the boiler furnaces except what is drawn in by centrifugal blowers through the turret, or through impregnable air-trunks on deck."

In the course of the year 1863, which saw Ericsson thus defending his monitors, his heart was cheered by news from England.   Sir Edward J. Reed, the chief constructor of the British Navy, had designed an ironclad, the *Bellerophon,* in which a revolving turret was introduced.   To this vessel succeeded the *Thunderer* and the *Inflexible,* suggested by Ericsson's *Dictator,* a ship to be presently described.   England was followed by Italy, whose citadel-ship *Duillio,* completed in 1880, embodied an Ericsson turret, with armor thicker and tougher than it had been possible to bestow upon the *Monitor.*   From her Ericsson's only profit was as one of her builders.   He did not patent the *Monitor* as an invention, nor did he patent at least two score devices which he originated in her equipment.   In 1882, Senator Orville H. Platt, of Connecticut, proposed that Congress should accord Ericsson some material recognition of his services.   He replied: " Nothing could induce me to accept any remuneration from the United States for the *Monitor* invention, once presented by me as my contribution to the glorious Union cause, the triumph of which freed four million bondmen."

The cardinal feature in the *Monitor* was its revolving turret; Ericsson's claim as its originator was disputed by Theodore R. Timby, who, in 1842, patented a cylindrical iron citadel for harbor defense, having several floors, each carrying guns fixed on radial slides.   In its original plan this structure was intended to revolve continuously, whether its guns were fired or not.   Timby exhibited his model at home and abroad, and he accused Ericsson of deliberate plagiarism, apart from unessential improvements of detail. This borrowing Ericsson denied with indignation, pointing out that revolving structures for the discharge of projectiles were two thousand years old, and affirming that he could not remember the time when he did not know of their existence.   He claimed that a ship of war provided with a turret capable of turning toward any point of the compass was original with himself.   But there was Timby's

patent for a structure of features unmistakably similar; this
patent, as reissued with broadened claims, was bought by
the partners of Ericsson, but without his consent. Their
purchase, they believed, would give them control of a harbor defense which they expected the Government to adopt
on a comprehensive scale. In Timby's design the pilot-
house was in the upper part of the turret. Ericsson put his
pilot-house at some distance from his turret, an arrangement
which Timby criticised in vain. The controversy with
Timby provoked Ericsson greatly: it plainly turned up-

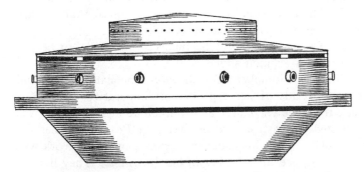

FLOATING BATTERY INVENTED BY ABRAHAM BLOODGOOD, 1807

on a case common enough in the history of inventions, where an idea occurs independently to more seekers
than one.

As long ago as 1807 there appeared in Albany, in the
Transactions of the Society for the Promotion of Useful
Arts in the State of New York, an illustrated description of
a floating battery invented by Abraham Bloodgood. It was
designed to be firmly anchored, and this is the only particular in which it essentially differed from the *Monitor*.
Its cylindrical turret for guns, strongly armored, was held to
offer new advantages in attack:

(1) Its rotary motion would bring all its cannon to bear

successively, as fast as they could be loaded, on objects in any direction.

(2) Its circular form would cause every shot that might strike it, not near the center, to glance.

(3) Its motion, as well as its want of parts on which grapplings might be fastened, would render boarding almost impossible.

(4) The steadiness with which it would lie on the water would render its fire more certain than that of a ship.

(5) The guns would be more easily worked than is common, as they would not require any lateral movement.

(6) The men would be completely sheltered from the fire of the elevated parts of an enemy's ship.

(7) The battery might be made so strong as to be impenetrable to cannon shot.

With the triumph of the *Monitor,* the national demand for armorclads of her type became imperative. Within a week from the encounter at Hampton Roads, Ericsson was requested to construct six monitors, the *Passaic* and her sister vessels. With his usual energy, as soon as the work was verbally agreed upon he began his drawings. They flew so fast from his hands that his most rapid assistant was soon left far behind; and so complete was every detail, so thorough the coördination of part with part, that he did not find it necessary to examine any work after execution. His method was to begin with the drawing which demanded most shopwork, the others following in their order of difficulty. One sheet went to this foundry, another to that machine shop, and so on. When the several parts were assembled, each fitted the others as a voussoir joins its mates in a well-planned arch.

While the *Passaic* and five similar monitors were still on the stocks, Ericsson was requested to furnish plans for four more monitors, the *Nahant, Nantucket, Weehawken,* and *Comanche.* Ericsson told his partners that he had agreed to furnish duplicate plans to the contractors for these vessels; his partners said that this would simply invite competition with firms who secured for nothing what had cost the inventor and his associates much money. He replied that he felt in duty bound to aid the Government to the full extent of his power in meeting the emergencies of war. To this sentiment his partners yielded, but the result they feared was suffered. Rivalry led to an active demand for labor and material. The firms who worked from Ericsson's matured plans, made castings from his patterns, and duplicated his wrought-iron work, had distinct advantage over him as a builder.

On June 18, 1862, the Secretary of the Navy requested Ericsson to build two large ironclads; one of them with a single revolving turret, the other with two turrets. These vessels were afterward named the *Dictator* and the *Puritan.* The *Dictator* was 312 feet in length, 50 feet in breadth, 21 2-3 feet in depth of hold, with 20 feet draught. Her turret, with an inside diameter of 24 feet, had armor 15 inches thick. Her two propellers were each 21½ feet in diameter: her displacement was 4,971 tons. Ericsson opposed the demand for two propellers as here introduced, and he objected to two turrets for the *Puritan,* but, sorely to his chagrin, he had to bow to official behests. Two years later he had his way, when it was decided that the *Puritan* should have but one turret, with two 20-inch guns, each weighing 48 tons, with solid spherical shot of 1,000 pounds. The *Dictator* sailed from New York on December 15, 1864, arriving at Fort Monroe two days afterward. The Civil War was fast approaching its close, and the *Dictator* was never tested under fire. When peace was declared, the *Puritan* was unfinished, and, there being no immediate demand for her services, unfinished she remained.

War vessels much less massive than the *Dictator* or the *Puritan* were suggested by the *Monitor.* Her success was in part due to her lightness of draught, but eleven feet, which enabled her to manœuver in shallow waters. Gunboats on the same general plan, designed to draw but six feet of water, could ply in many a Southern stream not deep enough for the *Monitor*. In response to a request from Assistant Secretary Fox, Ericsson sent the Navy Department, without charge, specifications for shallow boats of this type. Their dimensions were to be 221 by 41 feet, with flat-bottomed hulls, 168 by 31 feet, incased in solid timber, with easy lines, and extending 20 feet beyond the hull forward, and 32 feet aft. Each was to have two propellers, and carry 3-inch armor. Turrets and pilot-houses were to copy those of the *Passaic*. These designs were handed for execution to Chief Engineer Stimers, who had been associated with Ericsson in the construction of the *Monitor,* and who had rendered vital services in her fight with the *Merrimac*. Under his direction twenty boats were built, at a cost of $14,000,000. Ericsson's plans, as they left his hands, could have been carried out with success; as radically changed by Stimers, the boats, when launched, all but refused to float. An opportunity to swarm up the shallow waters of the South was therefore missed, and an immense outlay was wholly wasted. From time to time, as work progressed on his altered designs, Ericsson loudly remonstrated, and in vain. He was enraged and disgusted; but that large heart of his had no space for rancor. Though forced to condemn Stimers' work, he bore no hostility to the man. Stimers died soon afterward, and in poverty. Ericsson educated his daughter, and joined in a plea that Congress should pension Stimers' family.

Ericsson was a great engineer because he was first of all a great man. This came out in his passionate love of his native land. He had left her shores at twenty-three—never to behold them again, yet she had no son on her soil more devoted to her. He was convinced that Sweden, with her small population, could only defend herself against Russia or Germany by mechanical means. He sent to Stockholm, as a gift, a 15-inch Rodman gun, then the most effective piece of ordnance afloat. Throughout the summer of 1867 he remained in New York, busy at his drawing-board, planning means of defense for the coasts of Sweden. He proposed a fleet of vessels, each of but 140 tons, designed to fight bows on, their turrets stationary and oval in section, so as to offer the narrowest possible target to an enemy. The pilot-houses were put aft, out of the line of fire. The machinery for the first vessel he presented as a gift. Creeping along the coast from inlet to inlet, always in shallow water, these boats could not be run down, and meantime could deliver a deadly fire. Afterward Ericsson advised Sweden to adopt for her defense, gunboats as preferable to monitors. The torpedoes of that day he regarded without fear. He maintained that their removal, even in considerable numbers, involved no special difficulty or risk. His plans and counsels were accompanied by material aid. His gifts to the Swedish navy up to September, 1867, exceeded $23,000, a large sum as compared with his modest fortune.

Spain followed Sweden on Ericsson's drawing-table. In September, 1868, Queen Isabella II. was driven from her throne, and Spain entered upon a long period of civil strife. This prompted the enemies of Spain in Cuba to attempt delivering the Island from Spanish authority. The Provincial Government, representing the Spanish Monarchy, found repression to be a perplexing and perilous task. In their extremity they despatched to New York, early in 1869, two naval officers of high rank, to secure sorely needed ships of war. They called upon Delamater & Company, who immediately consulted their friend Ericsson. As he had just solved questions for Sweden such as those now presented by Cuba, he at once suggested a scheme for thirty gunboats to encircle the Cuban seaboard. Each vessel was to be 107 feet by 22½, with 6 feet depth of hold; two propellers, and a 100-pound gun were to complete each equipment. Surface-condensers were to perform double duty, returning exhaust steam as fresh water to the boilers, and supporting the engines so as to dispense with special framework.

The price for each vessel was $42,500, so that the whole fleet cost $1,275,000, or no more than a single cruiser of moderate size. The first boat was launched on June 23, 1869, thirty-four working days after laying her keel. When three months and sixteen days more had elapsed, the thirtieth and last vessel was launched, and fifteen of the fleet had taken their boilers and engines on board. Captain-General De Rodas issued a proclamation to the insurgent Cubans on March 24, 1870, pointing out that in view of the chain of war vessels on their coasts, they could not expect aid from abroad. His warning was effective. It is highly probable that the insurgents would, in 1869, have achieved independence for Cuba had Ericsson not thus strengthened the hands of Spain.

In planning his vessels of war, Ericsson devoted much thought to improving their heavy guns. This led him to a prolonged study of the strength of metals and alloys as used for guns, the effects of explosions, the wear and tear they cause, and the laws governing the paths of projectiles. Year by year, as his investigations proceeded, powders were heightened in effect, so that their use became at once more difficult and more alluring. These advances left unaffected the value of his reinforcement, originated on the *Princeton* in 1842, when he had bound her cracked gun with hoops of wrought-iron. That gun, thus strengthened, did its duty faithfully, as we have already observed. It penetrated four and a half inches of iron, and then passed through a sandbank behind it eight feet in thickness.

This gun had an auxiliary in Ericsson's wrought-iron carriage for the *Princeton,* devised in 1843, which dispensed with breeching. This invention substantiated his claim to be the pioneer of modern ordnance.

The hoops, or huge washers, with which Ericsson clasped the core of a gun were, after all, a return to the first artillery ever built. The earliest makers of heavy guns arranged in a circle longitudinal bars of wrought-iron, and surrounded them with hoops of the same material. These rude weapons were for a time superseded by guns of cast-iron, a metal which Ericsson always distrusted. He returned to the use of wrought-iron, and, well aware of the injury it might receive in large masses under a mammoth forging hammer, he had recourse to hoops, identical in form and effectiveness with those of old days. In each hoop, or ring, the iron-fiber, neither bruised nor jarred, was at its strongest. It was easy to use rings so wide that the encircled gun might safely be filled with powder from end to end. With this reinforcement at command, Ericsson designed a gun of 15-inch caliber, and he insisted that in all reinforced guns charges of powder might be much increased with perfect safety. Experiment proved him right. No 15-inch guns came to grief during the Civil War; one of them was tested with 100 pounds of powder, and at the trying elevation of 45 degrees, yet showed no distress. In 1890, guns weighing 111 tons, five times as much as the 15-inch gun, were rendering satisfactory service to foreign navies. Ericsson, during the Civil War, was constantly provoked to anger by having his guns undercharged with powder. Naval commanders, with the limits of past practice in their minds, were blind to the fact that his guns were vastly stronger than the guns built in their early days of service. He found, as many another reformer has found, that old habits are inflexible, and that new knowledge must undergo many a wearisome test, and survive many a baseless doubt, before it acquires a right of way.

One objection to Ericsson's heavy guns was the alleged impossibility of handling them aboard ship. Their designer once more came to the rescue. His wrought-iron gun-carriage, with its friction gear, checked the recoil of a 12-inch gun with a 30-pound charge in a distance of 16 inches. Yet more: on the Spanish gunboat *Tornado,* he provided a rotary gun-carriage and transit platform for heavy guns, enabling a gunner to aim at any point of the compass. Here he repeated in effect the mechanism of his revolving turret, with its sweep through a full circle.

From guns Ericsson now passed to torpedoes. He held that when stationary they had little or no value; his experiments led him to expect much from torpedoes properly directed and propelled. In 1870, he devised a torpedo driven and steered by compressed air carried through a flexible tube, paid out from a reel either on board the weapon or on shore. At intervals for five years Ericsson continued his experiments. In the spring of 1875, Commodore W. N. Jeffers, Chief of the Naval Bureau of Ordnance, reported that a model torpedo which he had received from Ericsson " worked regularly without the slightest trouble. . . . I have exhibited it to other chiefs of Bureaus, and to other naval officers, who were free in their expressions of wonder and satisfaction at the successful manner in which it operated."

Commodore Jeffers now placed at the disposal of Ericsson a smooth-bore 15-inch gun with its carriage, mounted on a Navy Yard scow. With this gun tests were conducted at Sandy Hook, proving that an elongated 15-inch shell forming a torpedo projectile 10 feet in length, designed to carry dynamite or other high explosive, could be fired in any direction from an ordinary smooth-bore gun, using a small charge of powder as the impelling agent. The plan embraced a revolving turret for projecting and directing the gun. This turret Ericsson regarded as indispensable, and when Commodore Jeffers wished it to be omitted, the experiments were discontinued. Ericsson, on his own initiative, now proceeded to plan his famous *Destroyer,* which embodied his matured ideas of torpedo warfare.

The *Destroyer* was a comparatively small, swift, armor-clad vessel, with a submarine gun to project torpedoes. All her vital parts were deeply submerged, and it was in-

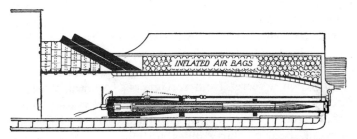

LONGITUDINAL SECTION OF "DESTROYER" SHOWING GUN AND PROJECTILE

[From "Life of John Ericsson" by W. Conant Church. Copyright, by Charles Scribner's Sons, New York, 1891.]

tended that her pace should equal or excel that of the craft she sought to destroy. Ericsson submitted his plans to the Navy Department; three years passed, and nothing was done. He decided to look elsewhere than to Washington. His experiments were so gratifying that on August 7, 1880, he announced to his friends, the Delamater Company, who built the *Destroyer*: " Ironsides are doomed. Our torpedo, with the propelling piston bolted to its aft end, went yesterday 275 feet in a direct course under water, and then floated to the surface. The torpedo was not fully loaded, hence did not go as far as it might. Enough was accomplished, however, to show that we can sink an enemy without ram, steam-launch or spar-torpedo of our navy. All these devices are gone to the dogs."

Commander Jeffers was relieved from his office on July 1, 1881. His successor did not regard the *Destroyer* with favor. He held that the projectile of the submarine gun should have more range, ignoring the fact that the range of a missile fired in so dense a medium as water is very limited. Aside from this, a longer range would demand a greater velocity, demanding a charge so heavy as to shatter a projectile of the necessary lightness. The plans were now submitted to a naval board, with Admiral Self-ridge as its chairman. They reported favorably, and re-ceived the concurrence of Admiral Porter, the head of the Navy, who sought from Congress an appropriation for the purchase of the *Destroyer*, urging Ericsson to keep her construction a secret from foreigners. Admiral Porter in formal terms recommended that twenty steel vessels be built on Ericsson's plans, with quadruple expansion engines to assure a speed of thirty miles an hour. To this proposal the new chief of the Ordnance Bureau demurred, insisting on conditions to which Ericsson would not agree. These conditions included a thorough test of the *Destroyer* at its inventor's cost, and at sea, although the vessel was not built for sea service. And, further: it was required that her guns employ high explosives. In vain Ericsson pleaded that these terms would subject him, in case of accident, to the penalties of manslaughter, or, at least, to heavy damages, as his ship did not hold a Government commission. He justly said that it was unfair to ask him to add twenty thou-sand dollars to the hundred thousand he had already ex-pended in solving a problem of national defense.

One-half the cost of the *Destroyer* had been advanced by Mr. C. H. Delamater, and he grew weary of the long de-lays in canvassing for its adoption. His interest in Erics-son prompted him to protest against his devoting to a thankless public service any more of the life of an octogenarian. To the end of his days Ericsson was warmly concerned in the *Destroyer,* though he had little hope of aid from a nation which in forty years had not found time to pay him for his work on the *Princeton.* Twice he offered to build for the Navy Department an improved *Destroyer,* with a guarantee of success, relieving the Department of all responsibility. His offers were declined. In 1886, in his eighty-fourth year, he wrote to the Hon. A. H. Cragin:

" The success of the *Destroyer* would destroy the prospects of the powerful fortification and gun interest, which looks forward to an expenditure of one hundred millions within a few years. Then we are opposed by the ironclad shipbuilding and armorplate combinations; not to mention torpedo-boat builders, submarine-boat projectors, and dynamite gun manufacturers, all against us, as their plans will be worthless if foreign ironclads can be shattered and our harbors defended without guns and fortifications, by the employment of the simple and cheap submarine artillery system."

The cost of the British *Inflexible,* with its turret and armament, was $3,250,000. For this sum a fleet of thirty *Destroyers* could be built, and one-half of the three hundred and fifty men forming the crew of the *Inflexible* could man them all. To the four heavy guns of the larger vessel they would oppose thirty submarine cannon, each having the huge bulk of the armorclad as a target for its 500 pounds of high explosive. Was it not better, Ericsson argued, to distribute the risks of war among thirty vessels than to center them in a single huge craft? And could there be any doubt that the advantage would rest with the navy which chose the superior weight of metal,— or, in this case, of explosive?

On April 27, 1887, Ericsson wrote to the Secretary of the Navy, the Hon. William C. Whitney, stating that he had just completed the plan of a vessel for harbor defense: she was of the *Destroyer* type, 24 feet beam, 13 feet deep, and carried a projecting belt of steel armor 3 inches thick and 30 inches deep, extending around to her outer hull. This armor, backed by oak planking, 3½ inches thick, was sufficient protection against the fire of machine guns, and the vessel, when trimmed for conflict, would be nearly submerged. The portion of the cabin, projecting 3½ feet above the main deck, was similarly protected. The breast armor for protection against heavy guns in fighting, bow on, was of inclined compound steel plates 30 inches thick, backed by 6 feet of oak timber. Ericsson asked $275,000 as the price of this vessel. His offer to build it was not accepted.

In 1876, Ericsson justly described himself to an intimate friend, as " the man who has done more to promote marine engineering, mechanical motors, and implements of naval warfare than any other ten persons together during the last thirty years." Let us review his improvements in the steam engine, which, as a prime-mover, he vainly endeavored to supersede. His steam engines, from those built for the little tug *Stockton,* in 1839, to those of 4,500 horsepower for the *Dictator* in 1882, all had one feature in common, original with him. They brought the power of two engines to bear at right angles upon one crank-pin. In another invention he gave effect to a suggestion of James Watt, by making a piston vibrate within a semi-cylinder. Ericsson introduced this design in the *Princeton,* and applied it with modification in the *Edith* and the *Massachusetts.* In 1859, the United States Navy sought an engine specially adapted to screw propulsion. Ericsson responded with a semi-cylinder of qualified type. He divided a cylinder midway by a steam-tight partition, forming two short cylinders, each with a piston: the two pistons moved in opposite directions, and were attached to the same crank on the propeller-shaft by levers, rockshafts, and connecting rods. These, and other inventions of a high order, Ericsson described and pictured in his "Contributions to the Centennial Exhibition," published in Philadelphia, in 1876.

During his sixty years of professional activity, the efficiency of steam engines was increased about tenfold. Toward this advance he contributed the surface-condenser, a feed-water heater, and a superheater. In addition to these original devices, wherever he came upon good practice he carried it a step further. He adopted and improved artificial draft, the expansion of steam in two cylinders instead of one; and, well aware of the great economy of high pressures, he employed steam at 225 pounds per square inch when 100 pounds were deemed the limit of safe working. With metals and alloys of new strength, with machine-tools of heightened power and precision, he saw that new gifts were proffered to engine builders. He grasped them with boldness and success.

From Ericsson, the engineer, let us turn to Ericsson, the Swede. Once, in writing to the Royal Librarian at Stockholm, he said: "I know but one fatherland: I would rather that my ashes reposed under a heap of cinders there, than under the stateliest monument in America."

And Sweden requited his fealty with every honor in her gift. In 1852, he was made a Knight of the Order of Vasa. In 1866, an industrial exhibition was held in Stockholm, to which the great inventor was invited in the most cordial terms by the Crown Prince, afterward King Oscar II. His invitation, with equal cordiality, Ericsson declined on the score of pressing engagements from which he could not free himself. The next year his old neighbors of Filipstad paid him a compliment which touched him to the heart. On September 3d they unveiled at Langbanshyttan, a superb shaft of granite, pyramidal in form, 18 feet high, and 8 feet square at the base, inscribed:

JOHN ERICSSON
was born here
on the 31st of July, 1803.

There was a characteristic word in the letter of acknowledgment which he sent through his friend, Commander A. Aldersparre:

". . . It is with great pleasure I find that, at the dedication of the monument at Langbanshyttan, my former playfellow, Jonas Olsson, now foreman at the iron foundry, was present. This honorable man must have a souvenir from me. Will you excuse me troubling you again? I inclose a check for five hundred crowns ($140), and would you please for that sum buy a gold watch and have engraved on the inside, ' To Jonas Olsson from his playmate, John Ericsson,' and then have it delivered to the honest workman. Could this be done through my friend Gustaf Ekman and with a little ceremony, I would be pleased."

In 1867, when a terrible famine prevailed in large areas of his native land, Ericsson sent $5,600 to Norrland, for the purchase of grain best adapted to its soil. Says his biographer, Mr. Church: " A Swedish traveler, who visited him at this time, tells how his voice choked, and tears filled his eyes as he spoke of the distress in his native land. He said: ' Let us not be content with assurances that life can be sustained on herbs not intended by Nature for the food of human beings. Bags of meal will be more welcome among the unfortunates than good advice as to gathering coral-moss for winter food.' "

Until his mother's death, in 1853, news from Sweden came to Ericsson chiefly through her letters. He loved his mother with all his heart. When nothing else could tempt him from his drawing-board he would turn aside long enough to respond to a word from her; and his responses usually included remittances for her comfort. To his sister in Sweden, Mrs. Odner, Ericsson gave a commodious house, and the proceeds of his Swedish patent for the caloric engine, yielding a considerable yearly income. On October 25, 1870, in a letter to his nephew, John, he said: "The news that I no longer have a brother was, indeed, a severe blow; it pained me all the more as I had received only a fortnight before information that my sister had been laid in her grave. The thought of their sufferings presents itself constantly to me, and is in the highest degree painful." Ericsson gave largely and constantly to impoverished relations and friends, and to public objects. Yet his bestowals did not denote mere pecuniary incontinence: he carefully considered the justice of each claim, and his gifts were bestowed with sound judgment.

In 1868, the University of Lund, in celebrating its second centenary, extended a hearty invitation to Ericsson. He could not attend, but he honored the occasion by sending a thesis on solar heat as a source of motive-power. His paper recounted experiments in which solar rays falling upon a surface ten feet square had been concentrated by reflectors, so as to evaporate 69 cubic inches of water in an hour, and generate by steam one horse-power. The University, in acknowledgment, gave him a degree as Doctor of Philosophy.

He constructed his first solar motor in 1870, and intended it to be a gift to the Academy of Sciences in France. As incidentally it registered the amount of steam generated, friction was minimized to the utmost in its design. The sun's rays were focused upon a cylindrical heater, placed lengthwise above a reflector shaped like a trough. Ericsson believed that motors on this model would have great value in regions where solar heat is intense, and where sunshine is seldom obscured by clouds. He said:

"Experiments show that my mechanism abstracts on an average, during nine hours a day, for all latitudes between the equator and 45 degrees, fully 3.5 units of heat per minute for each square foot presented perpendicularly to the sun's rays.   A unit of heat equals 772 foot-pounds, so that,

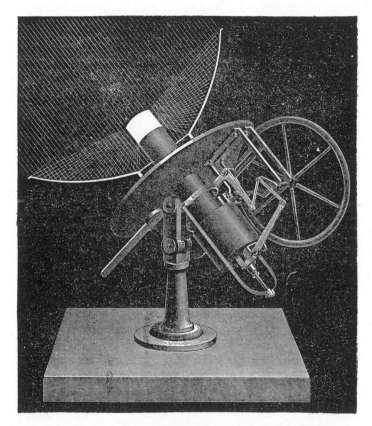

SOLAR ENGINE, OPERATED BY THE INTERVENTION OF ATMOSPHERIC AIR
Designed by John Ericsson.   Built at New York, 1872.

theoretically, energy of 2,702 foot-pounds is transmitted by the radiant heat per minute for each square foot, or 270,200 foot-pounds for ten feet square, or 8.2 horse-power.   But engineers are well aware that the whole dynamic energy of heat cannot be utilized in any engine whatever. Hence I assume that but one horse-power will be developed by the solar heat falling upon an area ten feet square within the latitudes mentioned."

From time to time during the remainder of his life he busied himself with this motor and with the storage of its motive-power. When he compressed air for this purpose, he found that he had to employ a reservoir of undue bulk. It may be that the electrical storage battery will prove to be the desideratum here. But before the sun in its direct beams replaces fuels in which its rays are indirectly stored, coal, peat, and wood will have to be much dearer than they are to-day. Heat engines of modern types not only show a high economy, but that economy is steadily rising, while their exhausts are now much more widely utilized for heating and manufacturing than ever before. But Ericsson's labor, as he improved his solar engine, was not barren. It brought him to principles of construction which, adapted to his hot-air engine, conferred a new effectiveness upon that motor. In its improved design it was built by thousands by the Delamaters for a profitable sale. Strange to say, Ericsson never patented this engine, his most lucrative invention. For sixteen years Mr. Alfred W. Raynal was superintendent of the Delamater Works. He has said: " The chief characteristic of Ericsson was nobility of soul. He had genius of the first order, and under a grim exterior he had a heart of gold. A workman, Bernard Sweeney, whom he liked, fell ill and died. Ericsson ordered the Works to be closed on the day of the funeral, that all who wished might attend. He cheerfully paid more than a thousand dollars as the wages involved in this tribute of respect."

And now it is fitting, as this sketch draws to a close, that a word be said about the homes of Ericsson in New York. In 1843, he removed from the Astor House, where he had lived for about two years, to 95 Franklin Street. Here he remained until 1864, when he bought a house at 36 Beach Street for $20,000, and made it his home until his death. Beach Street runs toward the Hudson River, a few blocks below Canal Street. At the time of his purchase it was the southern boundary of St. John's Park, an inclosure much resembling Gramercy Park to-day. Ericsson's front windows at first enjoyed a full view of beautiful trees and flowers. To oblige a friend, Ericsson joined in transferring the Park to the Hudson River Railroad Company: he sent the cash consideration paid him to Sweden, in relief of famine there. His neighborhood soon lost character when an ugly freight-house, with its heavy and noisy traffic, took the place of the grass and quiet of the Park. All this was uncomfortable and disagreeable to a man so sensitive as Ericsson. But there he remained, through an unconquerable dread of removal.

During the final years of his life, Ericsson was assisted in his engineering work by Mr. F. V. Lassoe, a native of Denmark. His private secretary for twenty-five years was Mr. Samuel W. Taylor, whose compliance with his idiosyncrasies made him indispensable. Ericsson grew so accustomed to his secretary's clear handwriting that when, in his later years, he received a typewritten letter, he read it only when copied by Mr. Taylor's pen. Indeed, this champion of mechanical progress, in his hostility to innovation in personal matters, illustrated anew that a strong brain may be built in water-tight compartments. Objections urged against the copying-press on its original introduction were, in Ericsson's mind, never silenced. He would have only manuscript copies of his letters, and, of course, this rule created much unnecessary labor. In account-keeping he went no further than to scribble memoranda in his checkbooks. For more than fifty years he kept diaries, professional and personal in their entries. These he destroyed on the appearance of Froude's "Life of Carlyle." A contributing reason probably was, too, that he wished to be judged by his mature work, with no record of the gropings and fumblings which, of necessity, had gone before.

When he had a difficult problem to solve he would lean back in his chair, with his head resting against the wall, and sink into a quiescent state, approaching unconsciousness. Then, he was accustomed to say, his best thoughts came to him. Once, indeed, a puzzling combination in his solar engine was worked out in a dream. He felt that it was only by sheer disregard of precedent and example that he could free his mind from restraint, and fulfil his destiny as an original worker. And yet the habit of solitary toil thus acquired became at last too strong. When mechanical and engineering practice was forging ahead with quickened pace, he ignored its new horizons, and thus missed what he might otherwise have accomplished. It must be plainly said that there was in him, with all his high virtues, a streak of downright perversity. He never took a trip on the elevated railroad of New York. He never saw Central Park, and would have never seen Brooklyn Bridge, had not his secretary once driven upon its roadway when they were out together, without saying where they were going. It was long before he believed in the telephone, and, as his secretary listened to a voice which he recognized, Ericsson exclaimed: "You are deceived."

Joined to traits such as these, were rules of regimen simple and sensible. His plain food and drink were carefully chosen and exactly measured. After his fiftieth year he drank no alcohol. His usual beverage was water, in summer cooled with ice to a temperature about twenty degrees below that of the air. He was fond of strong tea: he never used tobacco in any form. His sleeping-room had its windows slightly open the year round. For two hours every morning he practised the calisthenics he had learned

as a youth; this was followed by a sponge-bath and a vigorous rubbing.   As plumbing was one of his aversions, there
was no bathroom in his house.   In his eighty-third year he
wrote: " I have important work before me, and hence live
like a man training for a fight. My reward is unbroken
health.   I digest my food now as well as I did at thirty.
Nor is my muscle less tough and elastic than at that age."
This was a somewhat rosy statement, but in the main it
was true.

For many years his cook and housekeeper was Ann Cas-
sidy, a tidy little Irishwoman.   She knew just how long to
keep loaves on the dining-room mantel until they became
stale enough for the Captain's palate.   She knew in what
order to dispose the two hundred and forty pins which kept
smooth the sheet upon his mattress.   She faithfully stood
guard over his privacy.   Yet more: she pretermitted the
wieldings of her broom and duster in strict deference to his
desire to be undisturbed.   A devout Roman Catholic, she
set up an altar in her quarters on the third floor.   Never
by word or sign did Captain Ericsson, a stanch Free-
thinker, show disrespect to her faith or her devotions.

With advancing years he became a recluse.   Those who
had business with him, and understood his ways, could
always gain access to him; but he allowed no visits of mere
curiosity.   Beneath his indifference to social usages, his
heart throbbed as warmly as of old.   On his last birthday
the Swedish societies of New York honored him with a
serenade.   As he heard the melodies of his native land, his
eyes filled with tears.   When, at twenty-three, he sailed from
Sweden, there he left his heart.

When Ericsson entered his eighty-sixth year, his powers
of mind and body plainly fell into declension.   In December of that year, 1888, he drew the plans for a small solar
engine.   On the 1st of the following February he received this engine from a workshop.   This, his final task,

completed the cycle which began with the flame engine he had built in Jemtland, seventy years before. On February 7th he was profoundly distressed by the death of his beloved friend, Cornelius H. Delamater, who passed away at the comparatively early age of sixty-seven. Depression of mind now aggravated feebleness of body. On February 23d the iron courage of Ericsson gave way. His heart action was now so irregular that he consented, although with reluctance, to submit to medical treatment. His superb physique battled with disease until early in the morning of March 8, 1889, when he breathed his last.

He had lived so long in solitude, and so far outlived the eras of the *Princeton* and the *Monitor,* that few were aware how great an engineer had for fifty years lived in New York, until they read the long and weighty record of his achievements. On March 11th, his personal friends, with representatives of Swedish and other leagues, assembled at his house in Beach Street. Thence a funeral cortège proceeded to Trinity Church, where the burial service was read. The remains were then borne to a receiving vault in the Marble Cemetery, in Second Street.

Through the sympathetic offices of the Secretary of State, the Hon. James G. Blaine, and the acting Secretary of the Navy, the Hon. James R. Soley, it was arranged that, in response to a desire expressed by the Swedish nation, the ashes of her famous son be sent to his native land. The *Baltimore,* a cruiser commanded by the late Admiral Winfield Scott Schley, then Captain, was accordingly commissioned to transport the remains to Stockholm, sailing from New York, August 26, 1889. Nineteen days thereafter, on September 14, the *Baltimore* dropped anchor in the Swedish capital. With honor and reverence the funeral train was greeted all the way from Stockholm to Filipstad, where the interment took place in the cemetery of the Lutheran Church.

CYRUS H. McCORMICK

A CENTURY ago Virginia in population and wealth stood third in the sisterhood of States, closely following New York and Pennsylvania. So rich was her soil that her yield of wheat led the Union. In Virginia, then, one might reasonably expect a reaping-machine to appear. Let it prove itself to be worth while, and it would find acceptance not only at home, but in the regions west of Virginia, fast filling with newcomers, who were earning more as farmers than farmers ever earned before. It might further be expected that a practical reaper would be built by a man as dexterous before an anvil as behind a plow, and withal a man forceful enough to create a market among folk distrustful of any contrivance more complicated than a fanning-mill or a grindstone. This man duly appeared in the person of Cyrus Hall McCormick, who is commonly supposed to have invented the reaper. That supposition is wrong. And yet, after all subtraction of undue credit, he stands head and shoulders above everybody else concerned in bidding engines and machines take drudgery from the nerves and muscles of farmers the world over.

Cyrus Hall McCormick came of the hardy stock which, in the reign of James I., left Scotland for Ireland. Taxation, unjustly heavy, followed them to Ulster. To escape its burdens, they came to America. Many of the hardier spirits passed from Philadelphia, and other seaports, to frontier settlements west of the Susquehanna River, before the Indians ceded that territory to the Penns. Among these immigrants was Thomas McCormick, the great-grandfather of our hero, who, with his wife, Elizabeth Carruth, landed in America in 1735, and took up a farm near Har-

[Engraved from a photograph and finished under the personal criticisms of Mrs. McCormick, by G. F. C. Smillie.]

risburg, Pennsylvania. Seven years later he received from the Penns a large tract in Paxtang Township, Cumberland County, in the same State, and removed thither. Robert, the youngest of his five sons, in 1779 emigrated to Rockbridge County, Virginia. He fought bravely in the revolutionary war, and was wounded in the battle of Guilford Court House. In 1780 a son was born to him, baptized as Robert, who became the father of Cyrus Hall McCormick. This second Robert McCormick, like many of his neighbors, joined a handicraft to his tillage of land. He was a weaver as well as a farmer. His skill with cogwheels and ratchets, no less than with hoes and harrows, spurred and fed the ingenuity of a man who sorely needed new machinery, and patiently wrought his plans into wood and iron with such tools as he could command.

Robert McCormick on February 11, 1808, married Mary Anna Hall, the daughter of Patrick Hall, a farmer of Scottish-Irish blood. Their first child, Cyrus Hall, was born on February 15, 1809, at their homestead near the village of Midvale. Seven brothers and sisters followed him; of the eight children, he was much the most sturdy and energetic, with clear promise of winning any prize he set his heart upon. He attended the common schools of the district, and at fifteen swung a scythe in line with his father's reapers. To lighten his toil he built a cradle, so that he readily kept pace with his sinewy companions of full age. Like many another Virginian lad from George Washington down, he took up land-surveying. A quadrant which he fashioned for this task was accurate and neatly finished. He afterward built a hillside plow, and a self-sharpening plow which he patented in 1831. But his horizon stretched itself far beyond his father's lands, wide though they were. Many years afterward, his sister Caroline said: " Cyrus was a smart boy and always very much indulged by my mother. She thought his opinion on every subject was just right, and if she differed from him on any point he never rested until he had convinced her that he was right. If Cyrus ever failed in getting his way with father, then he went to mother, and through her, he was generally successful. Cyrus never liked to work on the farm. I remember when I was about twelve his saying that he had a great desire to be rich, not liking the life of a farmer." An amusing bit of testimony as to the standing of Cyrus in the family comes out in a letter from Isaac Irvine Hite, a neighbor, who says: " In 1842 my father by my request purchased for me of C. H. McCormick and Father, a reaper at $110. . . ." That suffix " and Father " is significant of much!

Robert McCormick added farm to farm until at last he owned 1,800 acres, a considerable estate, even in Virginia a hundred years ago. A river with a goodly fall swept through his land, so that he had plenty of water-power for his saw and grist mills, enterprises which still further drew out his talents as a maker and mender of machines. A good deal of hemp was then planted in the South. For its treatment when harvested Robert McCormick invented a brake and a horse-power for its actuation. Cyrus offered this brake for sale in Kentucky, where more hemp was grown than in Virginia. But he found no customers. This taught him a lesson he never forgot, to wit, that it is one thing to invent and build a machine, and quite another and more difficult feat to sell that machine.

Long before he began to devise his hemp-brake Robert McCormick had busied himself modeling a reaper, for which his design went back as far as 1809, the year of Cyrus' birth. As this machine left his hands in 1831 its cutters were rotary saws eight to ten inches in diameter, revolving like shears past the edge of a stationary knife. They were driven by bands revolving around a cylinder turned by the main wheel of the reaper. Vertical reels pressed the grain against the cutters, and delivered the cut grain on a rear platform, where an endless apron carried it across the platform and delivered it beside the machine. In a later design he employed stationary curved sickles as cutters, upon which the grain was forced by vertical reels having pins on their rims.

This crude machine became the starting-point for the life-work of his son Cyrus. There has been a bitter controversy as to the parts played by the father and son respectively in devising the McCormick reaper. This is what Cyrus McCormick wrote to Philip Pusey, a leading member of Parliament, who was a judge at the Great Exhibition in London, 1851:

" My father was a farmer in the county of Rockbridge, State of Virginia, United States. He made an experiment in cutting grain in the year 1816, by a number of cylinders standing perpendicularly. Another experiment of the same kind was made by my father in the harvest of 1831, which satisfied my father to abandon it. Thereupon my attention was directed to the subject, and the same harvest I invented and put in operation in cutting late oats on the farm of John Steele, adjoining my father's, those parts of my present reaper called the platform for receiving the grain, a straight blade taking effect on the grain, supported by stationary fingers over the edge, and a reel to gather the grain, which last, however, I found had been used before, though not in the same combination.

" Although these parts constituted the foundation of the present machine, I found in practice innumerable difficulties, being limited also to a few weeks each year, during the harvest, for experimenting, so that my first patent for the reaper was granted in June, 1834.

" During this interval I was often advised by my father and family to abandon it, and pursue my regular business, as likely to be more profitable, he having given me a farm.

" No machines were sold until 1840, and I may say they were not of much practical value until the improvements of my second patent in 1845.

" These improvements consist in reversing the angle of the sickle teeth alternately—the improved form of the fingers to hold up the grain, etc.—an iron case to preserve the sickles from clogging, and a better mode of separating the grain to be cut. Up to this period nothing but loss of time and money resulted from my efforts. The sale now steadily increased, and is now more than a thousand yearly."

McCormick, neither on this occasion nor on any other, acknowledged how much he owed to preceding inventors. Let us trace that indebtedness in a brief outline:

At the beginning of the nineteenth century Great Britain in mechanical invention led the world. For many generations her soil had never been trodden by an invader; her silver seas had protected her from the strife and pillage suffered by Germany, Italy, and France. Her mines were rich in iron for the building of engines, machines, and railways, and equally rich in coal for their motive-power. Following the triumph of Watt in devising his steam engine, her spinning-jennies had ousted her spinning-wheels; steam-looms in Lancashire and Yorkshire had sent hand-looms by the thousand to the dust-bin. Why should British inventors stay indoors, why not invade farms and fields with machines to replace sickles and scythes? At harvest tide the weather was often wet, so that quick reaping machines would save many a thousand bushels of grain otherwise ruined by rain and wind. Then, too, such machines would save wages, always higher in Great Britain than in continental Europe. Thus it came about that mechanical reapers were again and again attempted a hundred years ago in England and Scotland. Most of them never went beyond the stage of models for experiment. A few were built in working dimensions, only to be cast aside as utter failures. Two or three types had merit enough to stay hard at work for years, and transmit their strong points to modern apparatus. Let us take up the chief elements in reapers as they were successively brought out and united:

First came the reel, somewhat like the frame on which

fishermen dry their nets. This presses the grain against its cutters. A " rippling cylinder " in the machine invented by William Pitt, of Pendeford, England, in 1786, was a reel of a crude kind. It took off the heads of grain and delivered them in a box behind the strippers. The reel in an improved form was introduced by Henry Ogle in 1822, and independently by Patrick Bell in 1826.

A reel presses grain upon cutters. Originally these were mere scythes, mounted radically on a spindle, and whirled through a crop. Joseph Boyce, who patented this rough-and-ready appliance in 1799, was succeeded by an implement maker in London, Thomas J. Plucknett, who used a circular saw instead. This cut grain fast enough, but it acted merely as a mower. What was wanted was a reaper, a device much more difficult to produce. It was Robert Salmon, of Wo-

PITT'S RIPPLING CYLINDER, 1786

burn, who, in 1808, abandoned saws and hit upon the mechanism which, duly bettered, is the core of every harvester to-day. He bade a long sharp knife glide to and fro across finger-like blades which firmly held the grain to be cut. All these machines at first were shoved in front of an ox, or a horse, as were the headers of ancient Gaul. Gladstone, a millwright of Castle Douglas, Kirkcudbrightshire, in 1808 invented the side-draught, as a much more convenient mode of propulsion. His reaper had a circular table, with strong wooden teeth notched below it all around, fixed immediately above the cutter and parallel with it. These teeth collected the grain and held it to be cut. After being cut, the grain was received upon the table and taken away by a rake, or sweeper, and laid upon the ground. Gladstone included in his machine a small wheel covered with emery, applied to the cutter, so as to keep it always sharp. Joseph Mann, of Raby, in 1820, took the important step of gathering the grain when duly cut. He invented rakes which revolved on a vertical axis whose teeth, six inches long, carried off the grain in swaths. And now, says Robert L. Ardrey, in " American Agricultural Implements," * we come to the most original, the cleanest, simplest, and greatest single invention ever made in harvesting machinery, that of Henry Ogle, a schoolmaster in Rennington, England, in 1822, aided by Thomas and Joseph Brown, founders at Alnwick, near by. Ogle says: " I made a model, but not being a workman myself, and being on very friendly terms with Thomas Brown, a founder, and his son Joseph, I presented it to them." Reciting their first efforts, which were unsatisfactory, he continues:

" They then made the teeth, or guards, shorter, and tried it again, in a field of wheat. It then cut to greater perfection, but still not laying the grain into sheaves, the farmers did not think that I lessened the expense much. Mr. Brown took it home again, and added the part for collecting the grain into a sheaf (G, G, the platform), when he tried it once more in a field of barley, which it cut down into sheaves remarkably well. Messrs. Brown then advertised, at the beginning of 1823, that they would furnish machines complete for sheaving grain. But farmers hesitated at the expense, and some working-people at last threatened to kill Mr. Brown if he persevered any further, and it has never been tried more."

From the cutting it did it was estimated to have an average capacity of fourteen acres per day. The illustration shows that this machine had the elements of the modern hand-raking reaper and dropper. It was drawn from the front side; it was supported on two driving-wheels, and had an ordinary reel. It had a projecting bar with guard teeth, and a grain platform attached to the bar and behind it.

* Published by the author, Chicago, 1894.

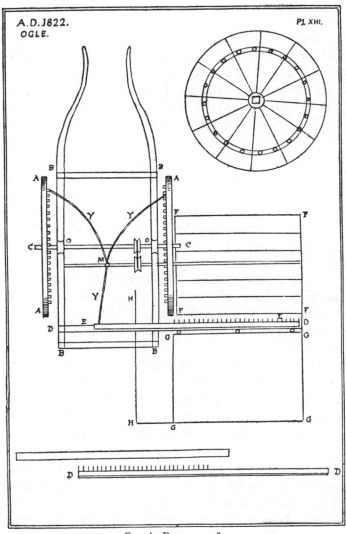

A.D. 1822.
OGLE.

Pl. XIII.

OGLE'S REAPER, 1822

A, A, wheels, giving motion to all parts of reaper. B, B, B, frame of machine. C, C, axle. D, D, frame of knife. E, E, knife. F, F, F, F, reel. G, G, G, G, platform. H, H, lever. M, center on which Y turns. Y, rod connecting wheels with knife.

[From the *Mechanics' Magazine*, London, 1826.]

Hinged, it was used as a dropper; rigid, the grain was put
off in gavels to one side. "Its frame or platform, G, G,
when hinged," said Mr. Ogle, "is lifted till as much grain
is collected as will be a sheaf, and let fall by a lever, H, H,
over a fulcrum upon the frame, B, B, when the grain slides
off. It was found, however, better when the grain was put
off by a man with a fork toward the horse, as it is easier
bound and leaves the stubble clear for the horse to go
upon."

From the position of the lever it is certain that a seat was
provided for the operator. As the grain "was put off by a
man and a horse,"—not raked,—the forker probably stood
on the machine; unquestionably as the machine was made
for use in the field, it had a grain-wheel, or shoe, a divider
and inside gatherer, as these had been previously invented,
described, and publicly used. It doubtless had other parts
to make it fully practical, for in closing his description, Mr.
Ogle says: "I have given only a part of the framing, as
most mechanics have their own way of fixing the main
principle."

Another source of information and help to all concerned
arose in Scotland. In 1826, on quite independent lines,
Patrick Bell, afterward a Presbyterian minister at Carmylie
in Argyllshire, invented a reaper with a row of clipping
shears as cutters. He brought it before the Highland and
Agricultural Society, who appointed a committee to examine the machine at work. Their report was favorable,
so the Society awarded Mr. Bell fifty pounds as a premium
for his invention, a model being placed in the Society's
museum. Many years afterward, in 1867, the Rev. Mr.
Bell gave the British Association at Aberdeen an account
of his invention. The principal part of his paper appeared
in the *North British Agriculturist,* of Edinburgh, on July
10, 1907:

BELL'S REAPER, 1826

a, upper part of frame. *b*, driving-wheel, nearly 4 feet in diameter. *c*, brace for cutter-bar *k*. *z*, lower part of frame. *e*, bevel-wheel, 20 inches in diameter. *f*, bevel-pinion. *g*, sloping shaft. *h, i*, short crank. *k*, vibrating cutter-tail bar. *l*, small sloping shaft. *m*, shaft for horses. *n, n*, two rollers. *o*, canvas web rolling to left or right, as desired. *p, p*, holder for reel. *p'*, three bevel-wheels and clutch. *q*, horizontal shaft. *r, r*, cutter-bar, six feet long. *s*, reel. *t*, twelve movable and thirteen immovable blades of shears.

[From "Transactions Highland and Agricultural Society," Edinburgh. 1851-52.]

". . . From my earliest days I had a liking and turn for the study and practice of mechanics. I am the son of a farmer, and was accustomed from my early youth to witness all the operations of the farm performed, and in most of them I engaged with my own hands. I was not a Presbyterian minister during the time in which I invented the reaping machine, as is currently stated, but an alumnus of one of our national Universities—the University of St. Andrews. A farmer's son, in my days at least, although an academic, would not have been allowed to study undisturbed in his sanctum, and was liable, especially in the harvest season, to be summoned to wield the fork or some other implement of toil. At a very early period of my life I was most painfully struck with the very severe nature of the toil to which the harvest workers were subjected—a toil made doubly oppressive sometimes by the heat of the weather, and always by the very awkward position in which they were obliged to stoop when engaged in their work. It may sound as an empty sentimentalism, but it is nevertheless true, that a desire to mitigate such excessive toil led me to inquire whether there might not be a possibility of transferring part of it at least to beams of wood and bars of iron, supplemented by the bones and sinews of the horse. Sure I am that I had no intention of taking the people's bread from them; and had I been so taunted I believe that even then I could have demonstrated that the multiplication and employment of machinery in agricultural work immediately promotes the increase of the people's bread, and does not ultimately tend to diminish the means of the people to obtain that bread. For years I had thought of the matter, and had diligently searched for some principle; and, taking one after another, I duly weighed the possibilities of their application to the object in view, and abandoned them all as worthless.

" One evening after tea, while walking in my father's garden, my eyes caught a pair of gardener's shears sticking in the hedge. I seized them by the handles, which protruded, and I proceeded to snap at the twigs of the thorns. My mind was full of mechanics at the time, and many hours were spent in my workshop; and, contemplating the shears attentively, I insensibly said to myself, Here is a principle, and is there any reason why it should not be applied to the cutting down of grain? Not altogether satisfied with my performance on the hedge, I brushed through it, with the shears in my hand, to a field of young oats adjoining, and commenced cutting them right and left. It was well that no neighboring gossip saw me at the unwonted employment, else the rumor might have been readily circulated that the poor student had gone crazed. For weeks, and for months, by night and by day, those shears were uppermost in my thoughts, and I searched anxiously and indefatigably for the mode in which they should be employed. Plan after plan presented itself to me, and was put upon paper. The merits of each, and the likelihood of its success, were carefully scrutinized and pondered, and eventually I fixed upon the plan, now successfully in operation. This took place in the summer of 1827. The next step was to construct a model, and to ascertain how thoughts would look when transferred to steel and iron. This was done, and it was during the process of making the little wooden frame and my puny cutters that the idea of a sloping canvas for conveying the cut grain to the side occurred to me. My first idea was to place the canvas level with the ground, and it was merely because it was more conveniently situated in the model, and pleased the eye better, that the angular position was adopted, so that in reality the position and the angle of the canvas were more matters of accident than the result of consideration. Were the truth always known, I believe that much more important improvements in mechanical science would be found to have a similar origin. Having finished my model and speculated as accurately and deeply as I was able upon the possibilities and probabilities of the actual results, I determined to have a machine constructed upon the large scale. For this purpose I had to pass out of my character of inventor into that of engineer and workman. The plan I took was this. After making my calculations as to size, etc., I joined a quantity of rough sticks together, and called them a frame. Then I made cutters of wood of every part that required to be made of iron and steel. I sent these, piece by piece, as I required them, to the blacksmith, with the instructions to make a thing of iron as like the wooden ones sent as possible. When I got a few of the pieces from the smith, I finished them with the file, and secured each to its proper place. I remember the cutters gave me a world of trouble and vexation. When they came into my hands they were in a very rude state, and required much filing, grinding, and fitting. By dint of patient application I got the whole into a sufficiently perfect state, as I thought, for trial.

" It may amuse you, perhaps, if I give you some account of the first field I cut. That you may understand this, imagine an empty outhouse, rather long and narrow, having in one end a wright's bench, and in the other a rude-looking piece of mechanism, an embryo reaping machine. For my subsequent operations I chose a quiet day, that is, a day when there were few people about the place. On that day an eavesdropper might have seen me busily but stealthily engaged in conveying earth in a common wheelbarrow into the workshop. When the place between the bench and the rude but ambitious candidate for the honors of the harvest field was covered to the depth of some six inches, I proceeded to compress the loose mold with my feet. I next went to an old stack that happened to be in the barnyard, and, drawing a sheaf of oats out of it, and carrying it to the workshop, I planted it stalk by stalk at about the same thickness I knew it would have grown in the field. This done, I shut and barred the door, and then, going behind the machine, I pushed it forward with all my might through my planted oats. As soon as I recovered my breath, I anxiously examined how the work had been done. I found that it had been all very well cut, but was lying higgledy-piggledy, in such a mess as would have utterly disgraced me in the harvest field. Upon the whole, however, I was not discouraged, but rather encouraged by this first experiment. The cutting was perfect, and that was the first great point I then aimed at.

"Although by this experiment I had proved my new invention to be a cutting machine, it certainly little deserved to be dignified with the name of reaping machine, and yet it was a reaping machine I had set my heart upon constructing. Had I at this stage been content to summon a man with a rake to do the work of wheels and pinions, my machine was complete; and had I been contented with a combination, I would have saved myself a host of trouble, and what to me at the time was no small expenditure of money. My workshop was again speedily cleared of earth and loam, and made

ready for the jack-plane and piles. I proceeded forthwith
to put the canvas in order. One might naturally suppose
that this would be an easy matter, but I did not find it so.
After the rollers were put in position, the wheels for driving
them adjusted, and the canvas stretched and fixed upon
the rollers the proper tightness, I conceived in my simplicity
that the work was done, and my object secured. The result
was otherwise; for, on pushing the machine forward only
the length of the house, I found that it twisted, and would
have been torn in pieces if it had proceeded many yards
forward. I proceeded now to make grooves at the end of
the rollers, in which I placed a small rope. To these ropes,
one at the top and the other at the bottom of the rollers, I
sewed the canvas, expecting that the ropes and canvas
would move together in uniformity, and that my object
would thus be obtained; but, upon trial, I was a second
time disappointed. The ropes, from inequality in the
grooves, moved irregularly, and the canvas became twisted
as before. For a time I was nonplused and dispirited, but,
plucking up courage, and ruminating over mechanical appliances, I thought of the pitched chains. Having made
some six inches of such a chain out of a piece of old iron
hoop, I sent the same as a pattern to the blacksmith, with an
order to make for me so many feet of chain like the model
sent. Having received the chains, and put them in their
place, the canvas was speedily attached, and the machine
was prepared to meet the third trial of its construction
which had now been made. The wheelbarrow was again in
requisition, and another visit made to the old stack in the
barnyard, and the process of dibbling another sheaf gone
through. The door was again shut, and, palpitating with
expectation, I pushed the machine forward. To my un-
speakable satisfaction the oats were not only nicely cut, but
were lying almost unanimously by the side of the machine
in one even continuous row, as I had confidently expected.
You may smile, but I complimented myself sensibly, I think,
on my success, being convinced that I had converted the implement from a cutting to a reaping machine. All this took
place in 1828. Until the crops were ripe nothing more
could be done. I was in high excitement and hope, and I
waited patiently for the ripening of the grain. In the meantime I revolved in my mind, with anxious and provident

hope, everything that was likely to happen when the actual trial in the open field should come to be made. I was fearful that there should happen to me what I knew had happened to many an experimenter before who performs his experience to a wish in the laboratory or workshop, but who utterly fails when he actually adjourns to the actual domain of nature or art. I had observed in my experiment upon the pigmy and artificial field in the workshop that while the oats upon the whole came to the canvas, and were regularly removed to its side, nevertheless some seeds straggled away capriciously in different and adverse directions. And yet I could not forget that in the workshop all was calm, and that I had the elements greatly under my own control, but that in the open field the blowing wind might multiply the capricious stragglers and fan the flame of disunion, and damage the success of the operation. It was an anticipation of this kind that induced me to think of the reel or collector. Having plenty of time before harvest, I constructed this part of the implement, and laid it past, to be used or not as the emergencies of the field might require.

"The period now approached that was to decide the merits of the machine. That night I will never forget. Before the corn was perfectly ripe (I had not patience to wait for that), a young brother of mine and I resolved to have a quiet and unobserved start by ourselves. That could not be got while the sun was in the heavens, nor for a considerable time after he was set; and, accordingly, about eleven o'clock at night, in a dark autumn evening, when every man, woman, and child were in their beds, the machine was quietly taken from its quarters, and the good horse Jock was yoked to it, and we trio wended our way through a field of lea to one of standing wheat beyond it,— my brother and I the meanwhile speaking to one another in whispers. We reached our destination, and the machine was put in position right in the end of a ridge. My duty was to look ahead, and my brother's to guide the horse. I gave the word of command to go on, and on the implement went; but it had not proceeded above five or six yards when I called upon my brother to stop. Upon examining the work we found it far from satisfactory. The wheat was well enough cut, but it was lying in a bundle before the machine. For a moment we were both downcast; but, recollecting myself, I had yet great hope, and said so, the whole of the machine not being used, the reel or collector having been left behind. I ran across the field and brought the reel, and everything connected with it, upon my shoulders, and adjusted it as well as the darkness of the night would permit, and we were soon ready for a second start. Taking our positions respectively as before, the machine moved forward, and now all was right. The wheat was lying by the side of the machine as prettily as any that has been ever cut by it since. After this we merely took it back again to the end of the ridge, and made a cut with the open edge to ascertain how the swathes would lie upon the stubble, with which being well pleased, we, after some pardonable congratulations, moved the machine back to its old quarters as quickly and quietly as possible."

In Loudon's "Cyclopedia of Agriculture," published in London in 1831, the Bell reaper was depicted and described with the utmost clearness. Similar machines were also presented, but not with the same fulness, because of much less promise. At that time Great Britain far surpassed America in her forges, foundries, and machine shops, turning out models incomparably better. Hence it was that in America the builders of reapers, as well as the builders of steam engines, locomotives, and looms, at first did little else than copy British designs. The earliest American patent for a reaper having a vibrating cutter was granted on May 3, 1831, to William Manning, of Plainfield, New Jersey. As we shall see, the patents to Cyrus Hall McCormick and to his chief rival, Obed Hussey, were issued respectively two and three years later.

When the Bell machine underwent its original test, James Slight was curator of the Highland and Agricultural Society, under whose auspices the test took place. In its "Transactions," published in 1852 in Edinburgh, he said: "This reaper soon worked its way to a considerable success in Forfarshire. In the harvest of 1834 I saw several

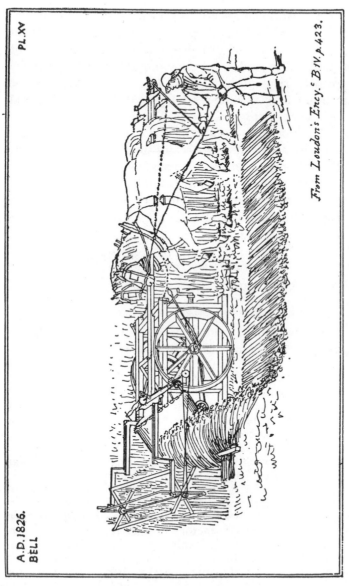

PL. XV

A.D. 1826.
BELL

From Loudon's Ency.ᵃ B.IV, p. 423.

BELL'S REAPER AT WORK

[From "Loudon's Encyclopedia of Agriculture," London, 1831.]

of them at work, all giving satisfaction.   They were manufactured in Dundee, and thence found their way throughout
the country.   Four of them went to the United States of
America.   This renders it highly probable that they became
the models from which the many so-called inventions of the
American reaper have since sprung.   At the Exhibition held
in New York, in 1851, six reapers were shown, each claiming to be an original invention.   Yet in all of them the principal feature, the cutting apparatus, bears the strongest evidence of having been copied from Bell's machine.   There
are slight variations, as might naturally be expected, in the
cutters, but the original Bell type is evident throughout.   It
is remarkable, too, that in Hussey's reaper, which appears

HUSSEY'S HARVESTER-FINGER

to have been brought out first in the Union, there is the
closest possible resemblance to the Bell reaper."

    " In a few cases," says Mr. Slight, in these pages of 1852,
"the Bell reaper has been kept in operation up to the present
time.   One of the most interesting of these cases is that of
George Bell, of Inch-Michael in the Carse of Gowrie, a
brother of the inventor.   Mr. Bell has a strong natural bias
toward mechanics, and during fourteen years in which he
has regularly worked his reaper he has taken particular
pleasure in seeing it put in proper working order at the
commencement of the harvest; so prepared, it is then managed with perfect success by any plowman of ordinary intelligence.   By these simple precautions Mr. Bell has been
enabled in the most satisfactory manner to reap on an average four-fifths of all his grain crops every year; the remaining fifth, more or less, according to the season, being
too much laid for the machine, has been reaped by the
scythe.   The expense of machine-reaping has in this case

been found not to exceed 3 shillings and 6 pence (85 cents) per imperial acre. Under these favorable views of the efficiency and economy of Bell's reaper, a question naturally arises, What has been the cause of such a machine falling so much into disuse? One obvious reason is that all the best reaping machines herein referred to may very appropriately be said to have appeared before their time—that is to say, before the soil on which they were to act had been prepared for their reception. In the first quarter of the nineteenth century, furrow draining, leveling high ridges, and filling up the old intervening furrows, were only beginning to assume their due prominence in the practice of agriculture. So long as these improvements remained in abeyance, the surface of the land was ill suited for such operations as those of a reaping machine. Hence serious obstacles presented themselves; as these are fast being removed, there is a prospect of a more successful application of machinery of all kinds being brought to bear upon the the operations of the farm.

" In the process of working this machine, Mr. Bell's practice is to employ one man to drive and conduct the machine; eight women are required to collect the cut grain into sheaves and make bands for them; four men to close and bind the sheaves, and two men to set them up in stocks —in all fourteen pairs of hands, besides the driver, will traverse 12 imperial acres per day. . . .

" McCormick's machine, which on its first appearance in England had its cutters nearly identical with those of Bell, has latterly been fitted with one long straight-edged and finely serrated cutter, giving, apparently, a new character to the machine, though, in fact, it is no more than engrafting a new idea upon the original Bell machine. Mr. McCormick has also gone a step beyond his neighbor, Mr. Hussey, by taking from our original also the revolving vanes [reel] in front for collecting and holding the grain to the cutter. By these means the machine is made more effective, and operates with the assistance of but one man upon the machine besides the driver."

Nearly twenty years after Mr. Slight thus discussed the indebtedness of McCormick to the Rev. Patrick Bell, the friends of that inventor bestirred themselves, though tardily, to do him honor. In January, 1868, the Highland and Agricultural Society in Edinburgh presented the Rev. Mr. Bell with one thousand pounds sterling subscribed by his friends and admirers throughout the United Kingdom. In acknowledgment, the inventor said:

"My feelings are very different this day from what they were forty years ago—when I left my father's house on a cold winter morning, and took my seat upon the top of the Edinburgh coach, for the purpose of making my first bow to this honorable Society. On that occasion I was full of fears and trembling, afraid that my invention would turn out a mere chimera, and trembling when I thought of coming before learned and scientific men. I had a small wooden model of the machine under my arm, which looked like anything rather than a design for cutting grain. As my friends advised me before I started, I waited upon the Secretary of the Society, Sir Charles Gordon, to hear what he would say about it. Sir Charles examined my model attentively, declared he was no mechanic, and, consequently, would give no opinion upon the matter, but added, he would be glad to introduce me to a celebrated mechanic who lived in the town, Sir John Graham Dalyell. I went, accordingly, to Sir John's house, and explained my model to him,— it looked more like a rat-trap than anything else I know of. Sir John looked at it, and said it was a very difficult thing to give a decided opinion upon the model of any contrivance that would be able to cut a standing crop of grain in an efficient manner. But, so far as he was able to judge, the model looked like a thing that would do so, and he recommended me to get a machine constructed upon a large scale after the pattern of my model, and try it next harvest. This was the first encouragement to prosecute my idea that I had received. The horizon of my imaginings grew brighter, and I was able to speak, even to Sir John, in more confident terms. When I got home a large machine was immediately set about being constructed; it was finished before harvest, started amongst the standing grain before it was ripe, and it worked very well, and I was obliged to Sir John for the friendly advice he gave me. Had he condemned the principle of my reaper, it might never have gone a step further."

McCormick always kept his lips firmly closed as to the sources of his successive models. Whatever they were, he gave them diligent study, careful experiment, and such changes in detail as work in the field demanded. He built his first machine, he tells us, in 1831, testing and improving it for nearly three years. Only on June 21, 1834, did he obtain a patent,—the first in a long series covering his

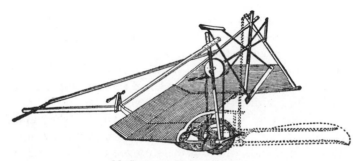

McCORMICK REAPER, 1834
[From "Who Invented the Reaper?" by R. B. Swift, Chicago, McCormick Harvesting Machine Co., 1897.]

reaper in its later developments. Almost incredibly loose was the management of the Patent Office in the early decades of the nineteenth century. "At that time," said Edmund Burke, Commissioner in 1852, "the Patent Office made no examination upon the points of originality and priority of invention, but granted all patents applied for, as a matter of course." As already stated, a reaper with a vibrating cutter, plainly of British origin, was patented by William Manning, of Plainfield, New Jersey, on May 3, 1831. A cutter, much the same, was patented by Obed Hussey on December 31, 1833. On June 21, 1834, McCormick's first patent was issued, including a vibrating cutter.

That Manning's claim was prior to that of Hussey, and of McCormick, was promptly pointed out in the *Journal of the Franklin Institute,* Philadelphia.* Manning, for some un-recorded reason, dropped out of the running and was heard from no more. Hussey, who proved to be an inventor of mark, remained in the field, and for many years stoutly op-posed McCormick. His improvements survive to this day.

A few months before the issue of his patent, McCormick offered reapers at thirty dollars each in the columns of the *Union,* of Lexington, Virginia. Thus early did he show his ability as an advertiser: his offer was supplemented by four testimonials from neighboring farmers who had used the machine with success. Next year, 1834, the attention of the McCormicks, father and son, was withdrawn from reapers and riveted upon a smelting enterprise. In part-nership with John Black, they bought the Cotopaxi Fur-nace on the South River, about two miles from their home-stead. Robert McCormick supplied nearly all the capital invested, opening an account for the firm with a leading bank in Richmond. The business proved a failure, and the panic of 1837 dealt it a mortal blow. Black withdrew from the bank all the cash there deposited, about $12,000 in all, and put his property beyond the grasp of his creditors. Robert McCormick lost about $18,000 in this venture, which threatened him with bankruptcy. His lawyer sug-gested that he divest himself of his farms, to evade pressing claims. " No," said he, " I would rather die and leave my children without a cent, than that it should ever be said that their father had been a dishonest man! " Eventually, by dint of hard work and close economy, he paid off every dollar of his debts, as became a man of scrupulous honor.

When the Cotopaxi Furnace, empty and cold, had become

* Manning's patent is briefly described in the *Journal of the Frank-lin Institute,* Vol. VIII.: p. 195, 1831. Hussey's is given, Vol. XIV.: p. 37, 1834; and McCormick's, Vol. XV.: p. 44, 1835.

dusty with neglect, Cyrus McCormick reverted to his reaper, which he felt might lift him out of his financial slough. First of all, he must bring the machine before the public. In the fall of 1839, accordingly, on the farm of Joshua Smith, near Staunton, Virginia, he gave the first of many thousand public exhibitions. With two men and a team of horses he cut wheat at the rate of two acres an hour. Wonderful! There was loud applause and no buying. Why?

Farm tools in that day were few and simple, so that they could be easily made by a country blacksmith and kept in repair at home. It was plain that McCormick's reaper did the work of ten men, but its intricate mechanism was guided by a dexterous man, familiar for months with its cogs, levers, and blades. Onlookers said with united breath: " It is a marvel, sure enough, but we are running farms and not circuses." McCormick had to wait until 1840 for his first customer, Abraham Smith, of Egypt, in Rockingham County, Virginia, who had seen the reaper at work near Staunton. He highly resolved to part with thirty dollars and take home a machine. In 1841, the next year, McCormick did not effect a single sale, so he took occasion to improve the build of his reaper. He was now convinced that he had a machine which deserved a market, and that market he was determined to create there and then. Fortified with an indorsement from Abraham Smith, he decided on $100 as his price, and became a salesman at that figure. By dint of a persistence that never took no for an answer, he sold seven reapers in 1842, twenty-nine in 1843, and fifty in 1844. Thus, after thirteen years of struggle and defeat, he came to victory. It was now time to relinquish farming for good and all, and restrict himself to manufacturing and selling his reaper. Instead of tilling one farm, he was to take a hand in reaping a million farms the world over.

His beginnings were slow. But soon from the West came messages of cheer,—orders in quick succession for

seven reapers. Two farmers in Tennessee, one each in Wisconsin, Missouri, Iowa, Illinois, and Ohio, wanted machines. McCormick now clearly saw that his farmstead
was not the place for a reaper factory. It was too far East,
for one reason. Through delays in transit four of the seven
ordered reapers arrived too late for that season's harvest.
A friend said to him : " Cyrus, why don't you go West with
your reaper, where land is level and labor scarce? " His
mind was ripe for that golden hint. His reaper should
henceforth be built and sold in the West, where it was
most needed. One morning, soon afterward, he put three
hundred dollars into his belt and set out on a jaunt of
three thousand miles. He went by stage through Pennsylvania to Lake Erie, thence to the leading ports of Lake
Ontario. Next he proceeded through Ohio, Michigan, Illinois, Wisconsin, Iowa, and Missouri, shrewdly comparing
town with town, port with port, State with State. He now
saw prairies for the first time, so flat and fertile that they
seemed to have been specially created to give play to his
reaper. The fields visibly beckoned for machinery faster
than the scythes and sickles imported from Eastern hills
and dales. Virginia, with her rolling, irregular land, might
possibly be persuaded to use the reaper ; the West, smooth,
treeless, and stoneless, simply must have the reaper at
once. As McCormick drove through Illinois he saw hogs
and cattle feeding on broad stretches of ripe grain, because
laborers were lacking for scythes and cradles. Illinois
that year grew five million bushels of wheat, vastly more
than her farmhands could cut. The shortness of time for
harvesting, but four to ten days, offered McCormick his
supreme opportunity. His rapid machine, forestalling bad
weather, would save millions of bushels which otherwise
would rot on the ground.

McCormick returned home with broadened views and
quickened pulse. He would forthwith patent his reaper in

an improved design, and press its sale far and wide, especially in the prairie country he had just explored. His drawings and specifications were soon in his satchel, for he was always the soul of despatch, and the next week found him in Washington, where his second patent was granted on January 31, 1845. McCormick's reaper, as now improved, had its blade serrated like a sickle, with the angle reversed at each alternate tooth; the blade had its supporters screwed on the front of the platform, bent in such wise as to let straw freely escape. The fingers, or guards, to hold the grain while being cut, were spear-shaped. The lower end of his reel post was placed behind the blade, and curved forward at its top, where it was securely braced.

McCormick, while in Washington, not only obtained a patent for distinct and important improvements on his reaper, he took a long stride toward success as a manufacturer. Among the public men whom he met at the capital was the Honorable E. B. Holmes, of Brockport, New York, who told him that Seymour & Morgan had just established in Brockport a factory of farm implements, where reapers of good quality could be produced at low cost. He pointed out that Brockport was halfway betwixt the Eastern and Western markets, which McCormick was about to invade. McCormick at once proceeded to Brockport. Says Robert L. Ardrey, in "American Agricultural Implements":

"The machine McCormick brought with him was very crude. There was no driver's seat, and the man who raked off walked alongside the platform. The gearing was imperfect, and the sickle was but a thin, straight strip of steel, on the front edge serrated reversely every four or five inches of its length, and liable to be clogged at the slightest provocation. Yet, though so coarse, immature, and imperfect, it was a machine with which it was possible to cut grain when all the conditions were favorable. Trials suggested improvements. It was cut down a little here,

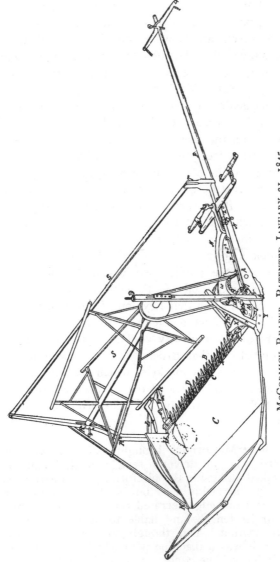

McCormick Reaper, Patented January 31, 1845

A, blade case. B, blade. C, platform. D, twenty-seven fingers. F, driver or connecting-rod. H, flywheel. I, crank. J, lever. J2, loose pin. K, divider, a scantling 3 feet square. M, pinion of nine teeth. N N, hounds, main wheel pieces. P, tongue. R, reel post. S, reel. T, tongue post. U, brace. V, bolt. W, W, sand-board. Y and Z, bolts. X, straw-board.

strengthened a little there, and generally brought into better form. The raker sat astride a saddle provided for him in the rear of the gearing, and used an ordinary hand-rake, but the driver rode a horse, or walked, for still there was no seat. It was arranged that Seymour & Morgan build a quantity of McCormick reapers, as improved, for the following season's harvest. Accordingly, for the harvest of 1846, one hundred of these machines were made and sold, the first large quantity of reapers ever manufactured. As an example of the primitive methods then usual, a portion of the spear-shaped guard-fingers of these machines were let out to country blacksmiths, to be forged at 24 cents each, as well as the machine bolts at 4½ cents. For each piece the iron, cut in proper lengths, was furnished by Seymour & Morgan. Next year, by using swages, the guard-fingers were made at their shops for less than half the price paid to blacksmiths. A little later they were made of cast-iron. In 1848, the original McCormick patent expired, and the manufacture of McCormick reapers ceased at the Brockport factory."

On October 23, 1847, shortly before he ceased to have his reapers produced in Brockport, McCormick obtained a third patent. It included for the first time a seat for the raker; such a seat had been provided by Hussey on his machine as far back as 1833, and in all likelihood it appeared in Ogle's reaper of 1822. To balance this seat and its occupant, McCormick now placed his driving-wheel further back than in his former machines, rearranging the gearing with a new compactness.

McCormick sagaciously noted that the railroads were fast stretching westward, and his keen gaze saw the broad zones of arable land thus brought within the swing of his reaper. He felt that the time had come to build machines in a factory of his own. But where? Its site should be at the center of these rich prairies, preferably at a port on a great lake. With painstaking diligence he studied a map of the Western States, and ended by placing his forefinger on Chicago, then a raw town of about 10,000 population. This choice was one of the master strokes of his career. At that time Milwaukee, Cleveland, and St. Louis were more thriving than Chicago, but to this discerning judge they were cities of less promise. He saw that Chicago, for all its mud and shabbiness, stood at the very focus of Western trade. Here he could best assemble steel and iron from Scotland and Pennsylvania, and lumber from the forests of Michigan, and hence he could ship his bulky machines, eastward or westward, at minimum charges for freight.

When McCormick voted for Chicago, he did so with empty hands. It behooved him to cast about for a backer who would advance capital for the execution of his projects. He found him in William B. Ogden, who had been the first mayor of the city, and was still its civic leader and arbiter. Said he to the Virginian: " You are the man we want. I will give you $25,000 for a half-interest in this reaper business. Let us build the factory at once." Thereupon the firm of McCormick, Ogden & Company was born, soon to rear its premises on the site where, in 1804, John Kinzie had built the first house in Chicago. Here five hundred reapers were manufactured for the harvest of 1848, and the business fast prophesied the stupendous expansions since recorded. But if two men ride a horse, one must ride behind. Neither McCormick nor Ogden could long occupy a back seat, for both men by temper and habit were imperious and unyielding. In 1849 their partnership came to an end, McCormick paying Ogden $25,000 for profits and interest.

McCormick soon realized that his business was to take on dimensions which would forbid his handling anything more than the rudder. He thereafter confined himself to sketching the broad outlines of his campaigns, committing the details to his brothers, Leander and William, whom he admitted to partnership. Before long he laid down rules of action from which he never swerved, and which contributed as much as his great executive ability to his success. First of all, he produced a machine of high merit, from year to year embodying every improvement worthy of inclusion. He gave his reapers the widest possible publicity, through an army of tactful and tireless agents, and by means of field contests sustained for years. His newspaper advertisements were liberal to prodigality. His customers once at-

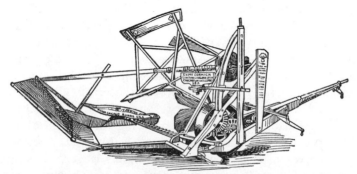

McCORMICK REAPER SHOWN AT THE GREAT EXHIBITION, LONDON, 1851
[From "The Illustrated Exhibitor," London, 1851.]

tracted, he made them his friends. He sold at invariable prices, giving a written guarantee with each machine. A dissatisfied buyer had his cash returned without parley. A responsible agent in every town worth while gave instruction to inexperienced buyers, while he sold and fitted repair parts on moderate terms. This energy, sagacity, and integrity were amply rewarded. Soon McCormick's business had become so prosperous that he cast wistful glances across the sea. Why not add markets in Europe to markets in America? For this a door opened with the inaugural of World's Fairs by the Great Exhibition held in London in 1851. Thither McCormick sent an array of reapers, as did

Obed Hussey, his chief rival at home. Hussey faced the
McCormick machine in a competition witnessed by thousands of farmers and farmhands. Hussey's reaper was in
charge of a raw recruit, who mismanaged it, so that the
medal went to McCormick. At Ormesby, near Middles-
borough-on-Tees, a second contest took place, in which the
palm went to Hussey.

These tests, following, as they did, the daily inspection
of the American reapers by thousands of visitors to the
Crystal Palace, deeply stirred the British public. The local
press declared that every essential feature of these machines
had long been devised in England and Scotland, and approved itself in years of constant use. It was the vast
breadths of level land in America that had given the reaper
an opportunity for which British farms could offer no
parallel. So far as McCormick was concerned, his exhibits
in London had two permanent results. He received an advertisement of immense value, assuring the success of the
branches he established throughout Europe. The second
item appeared on the opposite side of his ledger. His opponents at home, always numerous and troublesome, were
greatly heartened by the onslaughts of his foreign critics.
His patents were attacked in court and out of court, and,
in the main, with success. When he sought renewals of
these patents, his basic claims were decided to be unfounded.
He was wont to aver that his income had been derived
not from royalties as an inventor, but from profits as a
manufacturer. One of his suits has a place in history. In
1856 McCormick sued Talcott, Emerson & Company for infringement of patents. The counsel in defense were
George Harding, of Philadelphia, the eminent patent lawyer,
Edwin M. Stanton, and Abraham Lincoln, whose retaining
fee was $1,000. Mr. Lincoln did not argue the case, but
he closely followed its proceedings, forming a high opinion
of the acumen of Stanton, whom he afterward chose as his

Secretary of War. To Stanton went the decision against McCormick.

And now let us return to the reaper which, undoubtedly British in its creation, has been developed in America, step by step, until it has become the self-binding harvester. In each successive stride of this evolution McCormick was, of course, vitally interested as the leading manufacturer in the world. In 1849 a McCormick reaper had been furnished by J. J. and H. F. Mann, of Indiana, with a moving platform, which carried the cut grain to a wagon alongside. This was good, but why should good stand in the way of better? In 1858, Charles W. and William W. Marsh, two brothers of Canadian nativity, residing in De Kalb, Illinois, were using a Mann machine, when Charles asked William: "Why should this grain be carried up to a wagon? Why not put a footboard on this machine, where two men can stand while they bind the grain as fast as it is carried up?" This idea proved sound when, a few weeks afterward, it was tested in the first Marsh harvester. That machine held the field for ten years or more. It did not dismiss the human binder, but, as he could now stand up straight, he worked twice as fast as before, and with comparative ease. While the Marsh harvester in itself scored a decided advance, it put inventors on the track of the self-binder, that climax of mechanical ingenuity. For this the chief requirement was a knotter. This came first from Charles B. Withington; a later and better device was invented by John F. Appleby.*

Charles B. Withington, like Ottmar Mergenthaler, entered the arena of invention through a watchmaker's shop. As a youth, at Janesville, Wisconsin, to earn a little pocket money, he went into the fields near home to bind grain. He was so slight in build that the toil was unendurably

*Charles W. Marsh's "Recollections 1837—1910," were published in 1910, by the Farm Implement News Co., Chicago.

severe. This impelled him to devise a machine to abolish
the fell drudgery of binding by hand. His first self-binder
was put together in 1872, to be manufactured and sold by
Walter A. Wood, at Hoosick Falls, New York. Two
years later the inventor struck a bargain with McCormick,
who thereafter produced the machine. Its design was
highly ingenious. Two steel arms caught each bundle of
grain, whirled a wire around it, fastened the ends of that
wire with a twist, then cut the bundle loose and cast it
to the ground. A Withington machine was tested for Mc-
Cormick on the Sherwood Farm, near Elgin, Illinois. It
cut and bound fifty acres of wheat without a slip. Harvesting had at last dismissed all hands but a driver for the
horses. Sicklers and cradlers, rakers and binders, were at
a stroke paid off.

Withington was not the only inventor in his field. The
brothers James F. and John H. Gordon, of Rochester, New
York, devised a self-binder manufactured by D. M. Os-
borne & Company, of Auburn, in the same State. In its
latest form this machine afforded means of shifting the
binder to accommodate various lengths of grain. This
feature survives in all modern machines. But the Withington and Gordon binders, with all other machines of the
same class, harbored a fatal defect in their use of wire.
This wire fell into straw and killed cattle: it became mixed
with wheat to strike fire in flour mills and burn them down.
It lacerated the fingers of grain handlers at docks, elevators,
and railroad stations. Deering, a formidable rival to Mc-
Cormick, came into the market with a binder which used
twine instead of wire. This competition had to be met, so
McCormick engaged Marquis L. Gorham to devise a binder
of distinct pattern which should use twine. This was duly
accomplished, and the Gorham machine was at once placed
on sale by the vast round of McCormick agencies. Twine-
binders gave a strong impulse to every harvester factory in

America, supplying, as they did, the one link which had been lacking in a machine otherwise perfect. In 1860 about 60,000 reapers were sold in America; by 1885 the figure had reached 250,000, more than four times as many. Most of these machines were the " Appleby." Just here a word of comment by Robert L. Ardrey is worth repeating: " Appleby's success was not due to the newness of the devices he applied, or to the surpassing character of Appleby's genius, although he has been a persistent and clearheaded inventor; but it would seem that the ingenuity of a number of inventors, running in the same direction, had become massed or dammed before certain common obstructions, beyond which they could not flow. It was reserved for him to combine in his binder, built upon the Marsh harvester, the most practical of these principles, directing the best efforts of many predecessors into one channel, and by adding devices of his own to remove the obstructions, thus opening the way for the flood that followed."

While twine-binders were fast broadening the tilled areas of the West and the Northwest, with equal step went a remarkable change in the manufacturing world. Year by year, while the sale of self-binders swept steadily upward, the number of producers became fewer and fewer: the era of big production had dawned, the " Harvester trust," with its nation-wide grasp, was not far away. Many firms were squeezed out of business through lack of capital. Small shops, with comparatively simple outfits, could not furnish an intricate machine, of standard quality, at the low price then current. Yet that price, on the prodigious turnover of McCormick, netted him a huge fortune.

Striking is the contrast between the first reaper that McCormick made and the self-binding harvester he was now manufacturing. In its elaborate mechanism its inventors had repeated their own nerves and muscles, and even their brains. It cut its grain, carried it on a canvas elevator to steel bands which shaped it into bundles, neatly tied a cord around each bundle, and then cut the cord. This bound sheaf was then pushed into a basket and held until five sheaves were collected, when they were dropped to the ground. Since 1884, the year of McCormick's death, there has been no essential change in the self-binder. Within his span of seventy-five years he saw the reaper born and gradually flower into this wonderful self-acting machine.

Machines, as they have taken the place of tools on American farms, have wrought an advance comparable with that ushered in when tillers of the soil first equipped themselves with picks and spades, plows and scythes. In 1904, Mr. H. W. Quaintance published "The Influence of Farm Machinery on Production and Labor," in the series of the American Economic Association. In contrasting 1896 with 1830, he found that the cost of producing wheat had in sixty years fallen as much as 72 per cent. In this result harvesting machinery had played the chief part. Figures much more striking are recorded in the Far West, where headers are employed to gather the crops:

"On California and Oregon farms, fifty horse-power traction engines are at work. Each one drags sixteen ten-inch plows, four six-feet harrows, and a press-drill for planting seed-wheat. One engine thus performs the triple labor of plowing, harrowing, and planting at once. One machine plants with wheat fifty to seventy-five acres in a day, mounting hilly and rough ground as easily as it traverses a dead level. When the grain is ripe, a harvester is, by the same means, pulled across the fields. Its cutters are twenty to twenty-six feet wide. When they have finished their task, automatic rakers gather the grain stalks and carry them to rows of knives, where they are at once headed. Then, in the same operation, the wheat, hard and dry, in that climate, is threshed out, cleaned, and sacked, leaving behind the huge machine a trail of sacked wheat ready for the market. Another traction engine, with a train of a dozen cars, follows along, gathering up the sacks and taking them to the granary. Seventy or more acres of wheat are thus harvested in one day. All the work on a farm of a thousand acres may be thus accomplished by six men in much less time than by sixty men on a farm of half the area without these modern machines."

A great invention, such as the header of the Far West, or the self-binding harvester of the Mississippi Valley, may be regarded as a target. Its bull's-eye is reached, zone by zone, only by those marksmen who have the skill and patience to practise all the way from circumference to center. Over and over again inventors strove to design self-raking devices before a practical cutter was born. And long before a successful reaper had taken its path through a field of wheat, there were half a dozen attempts to build automatic binders. As long ago as June 28, 1836, H. Moore and J. Hascall, of Kalamazoo, Michigan, patented a machine for harvesting, threshing, cleaning, and bagging grain at once!

The marvelous economy of modern farming machinery explains the drift of rural populations to cities, a movement which has given rise to so much comment, wise and unwise. Mr. Quaintance, in the monograph already cited, says:

" The transfer of occupations from the country to the town is still going on, and will go on until division of labor and labor-saving devices shall have served their purpose. It is in the nature of things that this should be so, since thus work can be done most economically; and it is equally in the nature of things that people should compete for the better conditions thus offered. It is in vain to try to keep the boy upon the farm where the work is slipping from his grasp. He must follow his work. The zeal which some townspeople manifest in their efforts to persuade the farmers' boys to remain upon the farm, betrays a fear that the advent of vigorous blood may diminish the profit which now arises by reason of the somewhat restricted number of competitors."

McCormick's vast scale of production was not always as economical as it might have been. One morning, in the seventies, Edward K. Butler, at the head of the sales department, said to the chieftain: "If I had control of this factory I could double its output with but little extra expense." "Go ahead," replied McCormick. Butler made good. By the end of a twelvemonth he doubled the production of machines without hiring a single additional hand. So much for "scientific management" long before its rules were codified by Frederick Winslow Taylor.

McCormick late in the sixties removed his home to New York, where he resided at 40 Fifth Avenue, near Tenth Street. During the great fire in Chicago in 1871, he was in that city, transacting business of importance. When, in response to a despatch, his wife came to him two days afterward, he met her wearing a hat and waistcoat half burned. His factory, which had been building ten thousand harvesters a year, lay in ashes. He asked his wife: " Shall I rebuild, or retire from business? " She, with her son in mind, said: " Rebuild." At once McCormick became energy incarnate. He bought every stick of timber he could lay his hands on. He bade all his out-of-town agents remit him every dollar in their tills. Before the cinders in his cellar were cool, he planned bigger and better premises than those destroyed. And he decided to return to Chicago as his home. He had seen her census multiplied thirty-fold: she had earned for him the bulk of his fortune: in her distress he came loyally to her rescue. His example was catching. Many a neighbor took heart as McCormick led the way to refound a new metropolis on the shores of Lake Michigan. In 1879, eight years afterward, his firm became the McCormick Harvesting Machine Company, with Cyrus Hall McCormick as its president and guiding spirit.

McCormick was a great deal more than a strong and thriving man of business; he was a good citizen, who all his life long took a keen interest in politics. He was a Democrat of the school of Jefferson; while several times nominated for office, he never won an election. These contests culminated in 1877 by his seeking admission to the National Senate. When news of his defeat came to him, he did not waste a moment in complaint or regret, he simply said: "Well, that's over. What's next?"

In the months of turmoil and anxiety which preceded the storming of Fort Sumter, in April, 1861, he was deeply moved. As a Southerner born and bred, who had lived in the North since early manhood, he clearly saw both sides of a quarrel which threatened the nation's life. He attended the Democratic Convention of 1860, in Baltimore, as a supporter of Stephen A. Douglas for the Presidency. McCormick strove with all his might for compromise and peace. To that end he wrote editorials, delivered speeches, and interviewed the leaders in all camps. When he returned home he continued his labors, equally in vain. He bought the Chicago *Times* to explain to his fellow-citizens the circumstances and arguments of the South. During the war he poured into the Democratic press a large part of his income from the reaper. That machine was every whit as effective in the Union cause as if McCormick had bestowed upon its army a rifle of lengthened range, or an explosive of doubled penetration. Said Edwin M. Stanton, the Secretary of War: "The reaper is to the North what slavery is to the South. By taking the place of regiments of young men in the Western harvest fields, it releases them to do battle for the Union at the front, and at the same time keeps up the supply of bread for the nation and its armies.

Without McCormick's invention I fear the North could not win, and the Union would be dismembered."

Appomattox, the scene of the surrender of Lee to Grant, is in the same State as the McCormick homestead. That surrender at once kindled in McCormick's heart an earnest desire for amity and good will between the reunited halves of the nation. On behalf of church unity he said: " Now that the great conflict is past and its issues settled, religion and patriotism alike require the exercise of forbearance all round, and the pursuit of those things which tend to peace." His interest in church affairs had begun many years before that morning. In 1834, when twenty-five years of age, he joined the Presbyterian Church, and was ever one of its stanch supporters, deeming himself of its " old school." After his first visit to New York, he summed up his impressions thus: " It is a desirable place, with regular and good Presbyterian preaching." In 1859 he gave $100,000 to found the Northwestern Theological Seminary of Chicago, which replaced a decaying college in New Albany, Indiana. He afterward added gifts of nearly $400,000. His last public speech, read for him by his son Cyrus because of his own serious illness, was on the occasion of adding a building to this Seminary. After his death it received his name, and his widow and children added more than a million dollars to its resources. McCormick was a faithful son of Virginia. At the close of the Civil War her institutions of learning were sorely in need of help. He gave $30,000 in 1866 to her Union Theological Seminary. To the Washington and Lee University of Lexington, near his first home, he gave $20,000. Of this University he was a trustee during the last fifteen years of his life. After his death his heirs established its McCormick professorship of natural philosophy by an additional gift of $20,000.

What of Cyrus Hall McCormick as a man? His biographer, Herbert N. Casson, tells us:

"Cyrus Hall McCormick was a great commercial Thor. He was six feet tall, weighed two hundred pounds, and had the massive shoulders of a wrestler. His body was well proportioned, with small hands and feet. His hair, even in old age, was very dark and waving. His bearing was erect, his manner often imperious, and his general appearance that of a man built on large lines and for large affairs. Men of lesser caliber regarded him with fear, not for any definite reason, but because, as Seneca has said: ' In him that has power, all men consider not what he has done, but what he may do.' He was so strong, so dominating, so ready to crush through obstacles by sheer bulk of will power, that smaller men could never quite subdue a feeling of alarm while they were in his presence. He was impatient of small talk, small criticisms, and small objections. He had no tact at retail, and he saw no differences in little-minded people. All his life he had been plagued and obstructed by the Lilliputians of the world, and he had no patience to listen to their chattering. He was often as rude as Carlyle to those who tied their little threads of pessimism across his path. At fashionable gatherings he would now and then be seen —a dignified figure; but his mind was almost too ponderous an engine to do good service in a light conversation. If a subject did not interest him, he had nothing to say. What gave him, perhaps, the highest degree of social pleasure was the entertaining, at his house, of such men as Horace Greeley, William H. Seward, Peter Cooper, Abram S. Hewitt, George Peabody, Junius Morgan, Cyrus W. Field, or some old friend from Virginia.

" His long years of pioneering had made him a self-sufficient man, and a man who lived from within. He did not pick up his opinions on the streets. His mind was not open to any chance idea. He had certain clear, definite convictions, logical and consistent. What he knew, he knew. There were no hazy imaginings in his brain. The main secret of his ability lay in his power to focus all his energies upon a few subjects. Once, in 1848, he mentioned the French Revolution in one of his letters. ' It is a mighty affair,' he wrote, ' and will be likely to stand.' But usually he paid little attention to the world-dramas that were being enacted. He was too busy—too devoted to affairs which, if he did not attend to them, would not be attended to at all." *

In 1858, at the mature age of forty-nine, McCormick married Miss Nettie Fowler, of New York. She was a wife worthy of him. As he grew older he leaned on her judgment more and more. To their union four sons and two daughters were born. Cyrus, the eldest, is president of the International Harvesting Company, lineally descended from his grandfather's little foundry business in Virginia. As the hand of time was placed on the stalwart shoulders of Cyrus Hall McCormick, his health became impaired, so that for weeks together he was unable to cross his threshold. At such times his memory would return to his earliest years. One morning, looking at a bunch of beautiful flowers, he said: " I love the old-fashioned pinks : they used to grow in my mother's garden." Often the tears rose to his eyes when he saw mountains like those of his native Virginia. " Oh, Charlie," he said one day to his valet, " how I wish I could get on a horse and ride through those mountains once again ! " As the end approached, he found more and more solace in music. As a youth he had sung in the New Providence Church in Rockbridge County, and ever since he had never failed to hear the best musicians of his day. He was wont to recall with enthusiasm the performances of Jenny Lind and Ole Bull, Scandinavians both, as he was wont to remark. The winter of 1883-1884 brought his strength to a low ebb. The warmth of spring brought him no restoration. On the 13th of May, 1884, he died at his home in Rush Street, Chicago. His parting words were: " Work, work ! "

*"Cyrus Hall McCormick: his life and work," by Herbert N. Casson, copyright by A. C. McClurg & Co., Chicago, 1909.

INVENTOR OF THE REMINGTON STANDARD TYPEWRITER

CHRISTOPHER LATHAM SHOLES

My niece, seven years of age, picked up, an hour ago, a few acorns under an oak of October. From one of these nuts she has pulled away the cup. This cup, dipped in water and pressed upon paper, makes a dozen much better circles than Jessie could draw with either her pencil or pen. And why? Because now she has simply to press one object on another, an acorn cup on a bit of paper, to leave an impression. Without knowing it, she is a Printer. When her forbears long ago came to this art of printing they proved themselves to be human in skill and faculty, and gave token of an immeasurable advance beyond their lowly kindred of the forest and the glade. At first, in all likelihood, they imprinted upon mud and clay the outlines of nuts and leaves, feathers and shells, more in simple sport than from any other impulse. When the arts of making weapons and tools arose, we may be sure that swords and knives, arrow-heads and hammers, were bidden to impress their contours upon clay, wax, and other yielding surfaces. By and by stamps and brands for cattle and horses were produced,—a new step in the art of printing. More important still was the carving of seals. These gradually became larger and more intricate, so as to set forth a tribal record, a deed of sale, a mortgage, or a military proclamation. The point to be remarked is that a printer, wholly devoid of skill, can impress a complicated outline from a crystal or a metal plate every whit as well as its carver or engraver. In the labor of depiction it is this artist who does the chief part of the work; when he has finished, a mere copier, with slight exertion, can reproduce his outlines rapidly and easily. Such is the marvel of printing.

Second only to articulate speech is the art of writing; and the slowness of writing, its laboriousness, its frequent illegibility, have for centuries prompted men of ingenuity to modes of printing instead of writing. Years ago, near Rome, a brass plate was found bearing the name:

> CIACAECILI
> HERMIAE. SN.

It is about two inches long and nearly an inch wide. This plate could be used either as a seal to save its owner writing his name, or as an engraving from which to print with ink. To keep clean its user's fingers, it had a convenient handle. Ancient, to be sure, is the lineage of like stamps, to-day cast in rubber, and sold for a few cents each throughout America.

Beyond this making of name-plates, a noteworthy step was taken by Italian copyists as long ago as the twelfth century. They engraved elaborate initials upon metal stamps, and impressed these upon their pages. They may have lacked skill enough to execute these letters with pens, or they may have simply wished to save time as they copied a Bible or a Psalter. Long before their time, linen and silk had been printed with intricate patterns from engraved blocks, and this effective plan they applied to the production of books and manuscripts. So gainful was this ingenuity that soon not only initials, but every other character on a page, was printed from stamps, so that whole books were produced from just such simple tools as book-binders use to impress titles on their volumes. Of books printed with hand stamps, the most famous is the Silvered Book of Upsala, in Sweden. It is so called because its letters are in silver; occasionally these letters are found turned upside down, an error possible to a hand printer, but not a penman. This work contains the four gospels in the Mœso-Gothic language, and is deemed a relic of the Gothic Bible of about A. D. 360.

And now a leap was taken, memorable for all time, and quite without forecast as to the wings it would bestow upon human faculty. Hand stamps, such as were employed in Italy for centuries, were taken to the Netherlands, where they shrank into nothing less than the first movable types. Donatus, an eminent teacher who flourished about 350, wrote for boys a Latin Grammar which bore his name. For centuries after his death it was reprinted from engraved wooden blocks. In Holland, during the fifteenth century, new editions appeared in which movable types were, for the first time, in service. They were rudely cut or cast, so that they stood together somewhat unevenly. But, poor as they were, they built the bridge which led from ancient copying to modern printing. It would seem that Gutenberg only perfected a casting of types, which, in their original manufacture by his predecessors, were faulty both in shape and size. When movable types were cast in uniform molds, carefully cut, hand stamps were ousted from all but a mere corner of their field. In America hand stamps bearing numerals remained in use for paging account books, for numbering tickets, and the like, as recently as 1866, when their slowness of pace suggested the invention of a machine to do their work better and cheaper. Its designer, successful in this modest venture, was thus led to devising the modern typewriter. In this achievement he bade slight blows replace the delineations of the pen, slow and faulty at best. And from the typewriter has sprung a machine more ingenious still, the linotype, in which a lettered keyboard is the initial feature.

Christopher Latham Sholes, the inventor in question, was born in Mooresburg, Montour County, Pennsylvania, on February 14, 1819. The blood of John Alden ran in his veins, and so did that of New England soldiers who had borne a brave part in the revolutionary war. Both by nature and nurture he was a man of brains, character, and courage. At fourteen he was apprenticed to the art and craft of printing in the office of the *Intelligencer*, at Danville, six miles from his birthplace. At eighteen he was a proficient compositor, with a mastery of his trade much more thorough than would have been feasible in a city printing office, with its departments narrowly subdivided. His familiarity with types, with the mechanism of presses, with the details of printing, was indispensable to him, at a later day, as an inventor.

His elder brother, Charles, a printer like himself, some years before this had gone to Wisconsin, where he was thriving as the owner and editor of the *Democrat*, in Green Bay. Christopher promptly accepted his offer of a post on its staff, and went West for good and all. In his new field he displayed unusual ability, and a trustiness more uncommon still. Within a year he was sent to Philadelphia, then a formidable journey, there to have printed in book form the Journal of the Wisconsin Legislature. He punctually brought home the volumes; they were executed in a style and with a correctness which at once gave him promotion. He was given charge of the *Inquirer*, at Madison, a newspaper owned by his brother. While he held its rudder, he supervised the public printing, a less onerous task in 1839 than now. But his activities, manifold though they were, left him wishing to be still more busy. In partnership with a friend, Michael Frank, he established the *Telegraph*, at Southport, now Kenosha, a journal which maintains its prosperity to this day. Sholes, through his public spirit and transparent honesty, soon became a trusted leader in his new home. This was recognized by his being appointed postmaster in 1843, by President Polk. Then and always he was a man of clear convictions which he honored by use.

He saw an exclusiveness in the churches, a drifting of the lettered few from the unlettered plain people, which he deplored; by way of remedy he took a hand in founding the Excelsior Church, with pure democracy as its corner-stone. Men and women of all shades of belief, and disbelief, were invited to take part in its free discussions of life here and hereafter. For two years this little band of come-outers held together, making a deep mark on the community; then it fell apart like a sand heap, never again to unite.

In politics, Sholes was equally the servant of ideas. He joined the Barnburners' wing of the Democratic party, and fought hard against the growth of slave-holding influences in national lawmaking. As a member of the State Senate, in 1853, he introduced a bill to allow negroes claimed as fugitive slaves the right of habeas corpus and trial by jury. This measure was defeated. Next year a mob in Milwaukee rescued from jail Joseph Glover, a runaway slave, enabling him to escape to Canada. Then came a clash between the State and Federal Courts on the question as to how far a State could protect its citizens from arrest and imprisonment at the hands of national authority. Meanwhile the Chief Justice of the Supreme Court of Wisconsin declared the Fugitive Slave Law to be unconstitutional and void. On the strength of this decision, the State openly nullified pro-slavery laws of Federal enactment, with the outspoken approval of its people. When the inevitable conflict between Slavery and Freedom burst into flame, no State of the Union sent braver troops to the front, year after year, than did Wisconsin. Every fifth male in her population became a soldier, and her death list in the field was no less than 10,752. In all that preceded an appeal to arms, in all that went to bestow victory upon the soldiers of the North, Sholes took an unwavering part, exerting an influence as wide as the State. While a member of the Wisconsin Assembly for Kenosha County, he witnessed a tragedy which moved him profoundly. This was the shooting of Charles C. D. Arndt, the Representative of Brown County, by James H. Vineyard, of Grant County. Their quarrel had turned on a nomination for a post as sheriff, Vineyard advocating his brother for the place. Sholes published a recital of this murder in the Southport *Telegraph*, where it caught the eye of Charles Dickens, who transcribed it in his "American Notes," with an array of other acts of violence, all due, he maintained, to the brutalizing influences of slavery.

Errands of business often took Sholes to Milwaukee, where he saw with what rapid strides that city was leaving behind every other in Wisconsin. To Milwaukee, accordingly, he removed, to become editor of the *Sentinel,* and later of the *News*. In Milwaukee, with its comparatively large population, his ability and straightforwardness gave him a wider group of friends than ever. In token of popular regard he was chosen Commissioner of Public Works, and afterward Collector of Customs. Yet it is not as a legislator, an editor, or a public official, that he is remembered. His fame was destined to take its rise from the trade he had acquired as a lad, that of printing. In those days it was usual for newspapers, even in cities, to conduct a department of job printing, as a rule at considerable profit. A strike by Sholes' compositors so angered him that he seriously took up the notion of typesetting by machinery. He built models in which types impressed themselves on wax, but this wax bulged in provoking ridges that spelt utter failure, so he cast his models aside and made peace with his staff. On quite another path of printing he was to win a great triumph, beginning with hand stamps, such as those wielded by Italian copyists centuries before. Sholes, at this time, manufactured a good many blankbooks, tickets, coupons, and so on, all numbered by metal stamps of the old-fashioned kind. One day it occurred to him that he could devise a machine to perform this work much more neatly and quickly. He discussed this project with a friend, Samuel W. Soule, like himself a printer, and a man of decided ingenuity. They began work at once in a small room on an upper floor of a mill owned by Henry Smith, an old friend. This two-and-a-half story building, in simple ashlar, stood on a narrow strip of land between the Milwaukee River and the Rock River Canal. Here, day by day, Sholes drew his plans with Soule's aid, and here their model gradually took form, proving to be a thorough success in a final test. On the same floor of the mill was the workshop of another tenant, Carlos Glidden, the well-to-do son of a retired ironmonger. Glidden was an inventor, too, and he was developing a spader which he believed would outdo the work of any plow on the market. Naturally, there arose many a colloquy betwixt the three inventors regarding their plans, with much debate of the weak points disclosed as their experiments followed one another.

Sholes and Soule duly patented their numbering machine on November 13, 1866. Shortly afterward they showed it to Glidden, as it turned out capital work at a pace far outstripping that of manual labor at its best, and with infallible correctness. Glidden exclaimed: " Sholes, why cannot you build a machine to print letters and words as perfectly as these figures are struck off here?" This query had doubtless often been put to other inventors, but now it was asked of the man who was to give it a triumphant response. But not at once, although the idea took firm root in Sholes' mind, and kept him on the lookout for any information that would serve his turn. He who seeks, shall find. In July, 1867, Sholes came upon a description, in the *Scientific American*, of a writing machine for which a great deal was claimed. It had been exhibited in London by its inventor, John Pratt, of Centre, Alabama. Its description was accompanied by an editorial prophecy since fulfilled in all but its closing words: " A machine by which it is assumed that a man may print his thoughts twice as fast as he can write them, and with the advantage of the legibility, compactness, and neatness of print, has lately been exhibited before the London Society of Arts, by the inventor, Mr. Pratt, of Alabama. The subject of typewriting is one of the interesting aspects of the near future. Its manifest feasibility and advantage indicate that the laborious and unsatisfactory performance of the pen must, sooner or later, become obsolete for general purposes. Legal copying, and the writing and delivering of sermons and lectures, not to speak of letters and editorials, will undergo a revolution as remarkable as that effected in books by the invention of printing, and the weary process of learning penmanship in schools will be reduced to the acquirement of the art of writing one's own signature, and playing on the literary piano above described, or, rather, on its improved successors."

Pratt's machine struck Sholes as complicated and liable to get out of order. He believed that he could devise mechanism more simple, and at least as efficient. Soule had been a helpful partner in the numbering machine, a success from the start; would Soule embark with him in this second project? Yes. Glidden, who had given Sholes his first push from the shore, was received as a third partner: he was to contribute the necessary funds. A conference was held as to plans, which were sketched in a preliminary way. First of all a writing machine must write, but how was its paper to be imprinted? Soule suggested the scheme, never excelled, of placing convergent typebars on the rim of a circle, so that each might strike the center. Whether this design was original with him, or borrowed, is not to be ascertained at this distant day. It first appeared in the writing machine of Xavier Progin, in 1833; it presented itself again in the embossing machine of Alfred E. Beach, in 1856. Other inventors had gone astray in sliding their typebars through a horizontal circle, rotated on a vertical axis, as Charles Thurber did, in 1845. When an operator wished to print " A " he turned the ring until " A " stood over the printing point. He then depressed the " A " typerod so as to leave " A " printed on the paper beneath. This mechanism, much too slow for business, survives in toy machines.

And yet the Thurber design, faulty in the disposal of its typerods, displayed a feature of cardinal value; its paper was borne on a cylindrical carriage, or platen, and this Sholes adopted in his second model. It remains to this hour an indispensable part of every standard machine. Sholes devised the letters, all capitals, a spacer, and other details equally important. But no one of the three partners undertook any systematic inquiry as to what their predecessors had done, so they troubled themselves to devise novelties which worked badly, when they might have laid hands on old contrivances that worked well. In their first model Sholes built a keyboard resembling that of a piano, with two rows of keys:

3 5 7 9 N O P Q R S T U V W X Y Z
2 4 6 8 . A B C D E F G H I J K L M

He did not know that Dr. William Francis, of New York, in his remarkable machine of 1857, had introduced keys of the peg form now universal, and arranged them in four rows so as greatly to shorten the journeys taken by an operator's fingers. Sholes at length abandoned his piano keyboard at the instance of his model-maker, Matthias Schwalbach, a builder of tower-clocks in Milwaukee. As we have just seen, Sholes in his first keyboard gave his characters a strictly alphabetical and numerical order. He soon changed this for the present order of disposal which, like the compartments of a printer's case, places the characters oftenest used nearest to the working center. As patented on July 14, 1868, the claims of Sholes, Glidden, and Soule were: (1) A circular annular disc, with radial grooves and slots to receive and guide the typebars so that they struck the center. (2) Radial typebars to correspond with this disc. (3) A ratchet to move the paper-carriage by the breadth of a tooth when a key was struck. (4) A hinged clamp to hold the paper firmly on its carriage.

Frederick Heath, of Milwaukee, as a lad was employed as a messenger by Mr. Sholes as he began to devise his typewriter. On the wall of Mr. Heath's office he has framed a rough, uncouth model of the first machine invented by Mr. Sholes. " His original idea," says Mr. Heath, " was to have his keyboard fashioned after that of a piano, and there you have it. The first row is of ivory, duly lettered; the second row is of ebony; and then, as you see, a third row, made up of letters and characters that are little used, is in the form of pegs. The framework is of wood, with the leverage below, and the basket form of typebars above closely resembles those of some machines in use to-day. The original model was very clumsy and weighty. The writing was on a tape of tissue paper, and the platen was fastened to the body of the boxlike affair. The writing could not be seen till it was completed, and when the document was once removed from the machine there was no way by which it could be replaced with any degree of certainty that the lines would correspond with those previously written.

" Mr. Sholes was collector of customs of the port of Milwaukee during most of the time that he was engaged in devising his typewriter, and later he was Comptroller of the city of Milwaukee. While acting in this latter capacity, it fell to his lot to enter into a contract, on behalf of the city, for the paving of certain streets. He had the contract

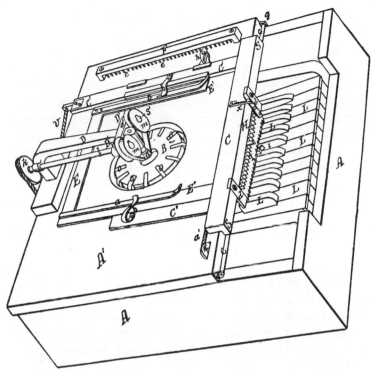

FIRST PATENT, SHOLES, GLIDDEN, AND SOULE, JUNE 23, 1868

Key-levers, L, vibrating on the fulcrum, M, with the inner fingers, *u*, reaching under the typebars, so that the keys act directly on the types.

The spacer or ratchet, I, combined with the bifurcated lever, H, connected with the bar, T, pivoted at *s* and resting across the arms of the keys, L, so that striking the key-faces will work the teeth of lever-forks up and down and into the notches of the spaces, so as duly to move the paper-carriage.

The pins, *e*, fastened to the table A', combined with the pawl, *h*, and the spring, *l'*, to give the paper-carriage a certain and regular cross-line movement at a right angle to the space movement from line to line.

The spring-clasps, *b*, attached to the bars, C and C', on a line through the middle of the platen, G, combined with the springs, *a*, attached to the bar, E, hold the paper on its carriage smoothly and tightly.

The spools, *m*, combined with the gudgeon, *s'*, the shaft, *l*, the pulleys, *k* and R, the band, *v'*, the cord, *v*, the weight, W, the ratchet-wheel, V, the pawl, *t*, and the bar, P, pivoted to the back of the case, A², feed a fresh part of inking ribbon to each type successively.

written on one of his machines, and this is claimed to have
been the first official document ever produced on a typewriter. In that machine, only capitals appeared; lower-
case letters came later as an addition. For his first model
Mr. Sholes used an old kitchen table which he found in a
garret." *

It has often been asked, why did inventors so ingenious
as Foucault in 1849, and Beach in 1856, limit their machines to mere embossing, so that their services were restricted to the blind? Simply because they were unable
to contrive a simple and trustworthy inker. This was contributed by Dr. Francis in 1857, as he produced the inked
ribbon now in general use. Such a ribbon is virtually dry
under a light touch; under the sharp stroke of a typebar
it readily parts with its color. Sholes employed this ribbon
in his first machine, and was ready to use carbon paper as
an alternative. To-day carbon paper is employed solely for
duplication; ribbons are the chief source of ink. One or
two popular typewriters use inkpads, and find them satisfactory.

In that grimy old mill on the Rock River Canal there were
interludes to lighten and brighten the toil of experiment.
All three partners were chess players of more than common skill, and they often turned from ratchets and pinions
to moves with knights and pawns. Ever and anon a friend
would drop in, and the talk would drift from writing by
machinery to Reconstruction in South Carolina, or to the
quiet absorption by farms and mills of the brigades mus-
tered out after Appomattox. Then, with zest renewed, the
model was taken up once more, to be carried another stage
toward completion. One morning it printed in capitals line
after line both legibly and rapidly. Sholes, Soule, and Glidden were frankly delighted. They determined to let their
friends see at once what they had achieved, so they wrote

* "Typewriter Topics," New York, April, 1909.

hundreds of letters on their typewriter to correspondents far and near. Just one of these letters hit the bull's eye. It went to James Densmore, of Meadville, Pennsylvania, who

FOUCAULT'S PRINTING KEY FRAME, BY WHICH THE BLIND MAY WRITE

Shown at the Great Exhibition, London, 1851. All the letters of the alphabet, in high relief, are fixed on the upper end of a metallic rod, made to slide longitudinally in a channel of its own. They are disposed like the ribs of a fan, each rod showing its letter both at the upper and lower ends. All the letters converge to a center. When a letter is embossed, the paper moves sidewise by the breadth of a letter. At the end of a line, the paper moves perpendicularly by the breadth of a line.

took fire at this demonstration that a writing machine was about to supplant the pen. He was sagacious enough to foresee a wide and profitable acceptance for the typewriter, so he asked the price of a share in its patent. The partners were greatly cheered by this proof that their invention already had a cash value. They held a hurried conference, and agreed to offer Densmore one-fourth of their patent on his paying all expenses to date. He said " Yes," without a day's delay, and this before he knew what the expenses were. It was the following March when he first saw the machine, and he examined it with no indulgent eye. Its creators had meanwhile embodied vital improvements on their original design, and they were rather proud of the machine as it stood. Densmore bluntly declared that it was good for nothing except to show that its underlying principles were sound. He urged the trio to proceed with further improvements, and promptly, for which he would advance all needed funds. At this stage of affairs, Soule and Glidden retired from the scene, leaving Sholes and Densmore in sole possession of the patent, and whatever harvest it might yield in time coming.

They manfully attacked the defects of their model, and patiently built other models, about thirty in all, each with some change, usually intended to reduce friction and heighten speed. Both Sholes and Densmore expected that stenographers would be among the first and best buyers, so they sent experimental machines to a leading reporter in Washington, James Ogilvie Clephane, who afterward greatly helped Ottmar Mergenthaler, inventor of the linotype. Clephane was so unsparing in his tests that not seldom he reduced a machine to ruin. His judgments, too, were so caustic that Sholes, forbearing though he was, lost his temper at last. Said he to Densmore: " I am through with Clephane! " Densmore's comment was: " This candid fault-finding is just what we need. We had better have it now than after we begin manufacturing. Where Clephane points out a weak lever or rod let us make it strong. Where a spacer or an inker works stiffly, let us make it

SHOLES TYPEWRITER, 1873

[Museum, Buffalo Historical Society.]

KIRBY HOUSE, MILWAUKEE, WISCONSIN, SEPTEMBER 2, 1872.

MR. INGERSOLL,---YOUR LAST LETTER CAME THIS MOR

-NING.

I WILL BE READY TO PROSECUTE THE CONTINUATION
OF THE EXAMINATION AT THE TIME YOU SET.---MONDAY, THE 16T
OF THIS MONTH, AT CORRY.

I WILL BE THERE ON THE MID-DAY TRAIN.

I EXPECT TO BE ABLE TO DO AS YOU WISH ABOUT CON

-TINUING IT TILL WE ARE BOTH THROUGH.

RESPECTFULLY,

JAMES DENSMORE.

A NOTE TO EDWIN D. INGERSOLL ON AN EARLY SHOLES MACHINE

work smoothly. Then, depend upon Clephane for all the praise we deserve."

This counsel was heeded, and Sholes further improved his models in the light of objections from Washington. When the total output of machines had risen to fifty or so, produced at an average cost of $250, Sholes and Densmore concluded that they had learned from Clephane as much as he could teach them, for the present at least. They were convinced that the time had come when their typewriter could challenge examination by an expert mechanic of the first rank, who would look at their machine with a fresh eye, and advise them as to its manufacture for the markets of the world. Their choice fell upon George W. N. Yost, whom they at once invited to Milwaukee.

He subjected their latest model to a thorough inspection and to repeated tests. He suggested several changes in matters of detail; and he declared that what the machine now required was precision in manufacture. He recommended Sholes and Densmore to take their typewriter to Eliphalet Remington & Sons, at Ilion, New York, where it could be produced and constantly improved. The Remingtons were then manufacturing firearms, sewing machines, and farm tools, all of the highest merit. Their plant included lathes, drop forges, and other machinery of the latest and best patterns. Every part of each of their pistols or rifles was accurately copied from a model to the one-thousandth part of an inch. This system, applied to typewriters, would minimize friction to the utmost, while rendering it easy to renew parts broken, or worn out of true. More important than its admirable plant was the staff in charge of its experimental work. This staff was the prototype of many such staffs now busy throughout America. At such electrical centers as Schenectady and Niagara Falls, at the headquarters of oil, steel, paper, and sugar manufacture, groups of experts to-day coöperate in attacking new and difficult problems, developing a team-play which earns golden rewards.

To such a group of organized constructors Sholes and Densmore displayed their typewriter, early in 1873. It was agreed that the machine should remain at Ilion to be improved, tested, and, in all likelihood, manufactured on a large scale for home and foreign markets. Thus, at last, the typewriter ceased to be a mere experimental model among other such models, and took its place as a practical and vendible article, like a sewing machine or a harvester. It had been put together by amateur mechanics; it had been developed under the fire of an unrelenting critic; it had been examined and amended by a distinguished inventor; it was now to undergo standardization in a great modern factory, to be produced with the utmost strength of material, the least possible liability to derangement, and the highest feasible speed.

The Remingtons took hold of the typewriter with both hands. They saw its possibilities, and brought these into actualities, step by step. They felt sure, that the patent was well worth buying, so they bought it, Sholes and Densmore consenting that the machine be called the " Remington." Sholes for his interest accepted a lump sum, which tradition places at $12,000.00. Densmore wisely preferred a royalty, which yielded him a million and a half. Sholes continued to reside in Milwaukee, where, with the assistance of his sons, Louis and Zalmon, he built new models of typewriters, constantly simplified in design and lightened in touch. The latest and best of these machines, " The Sholes Visible," displays not only the line being written, but all that is written. Its typebars are each in a single unjointed piece, L-shaped, and operate in a guide from the instant of pressing a key until its type impresses the paper. In fewness of parts, perfection of alignment, and durability, this machine is distinctly superior to any predecessor from its inventor's hands.

Never stalwart in frame, Sholes had hardly passed his prime when his weak lungs became infected by tuberculosis. He fought this fell disease most bravely for nine years. Then, on February 19, 1890, he succumbed, leaving six sons and four daughters to mourn him.

Good reasons, we have seen, attracted Sholes and Densmore to the Remingtons. The same good reasons brought to that firm James H. Hammond, with a model of his typewriter, embodying not typebars, but a typewheel, against which his paper was rapped to be printed. While the Sholes and Densmore machine was preferred by the Ilion manufacturers, the Hammond typewriter has found favor with a large public, chiefly through the perfection of its alignment. Its types are arranged on a rotating cylinder. Sister machines employ only a segment of a cylinder, and find that enough. These three plans,—convergent typebars, a typewheel, and type on the segment of a wheel— are the only successful modes of construction thus far devised.

Upon these three well seasoned plans, hundreds of different typewriters have been invented: most of them now obsolete and forgotten. Less than twenty machines supply ninety-nine per cent. of the market. Each of these survivors is suitable for some particular field of work. Most of them are adapted to ordinary duty in offices, where hundreds of letters, bills, or reports must be despatched every day, asking only a fair quality of output. Other machines execute the precise and neat work which commends itself to teachers, scholars, and editors, to ladies who write their own letters. One or two machines appeal to travelers who insist upon a light and simple mechanism, unaffected by the jars and hazards of journeys by land and sea. But the designers of such machines work within limitations, and are thoroughly aware that their models cannot be placed in the front rank.

The typewriter, as it left Sholes' hands, simply provided (1) means for hitting the paper with types at due intervals; (2) moving the paper a suitable space after a stroke; (3) moving the paper lengthwise at the end of a line; (4) striking a bell near the end of a line. To these facilities have since been added: (5) means of retracing a line in correcting an error; (6) varying the distances apart at which lines may be written; (7) using a shift-key so that at will one of two characters may be written by each key. An upper case "B" and a lower case "b" are, let us say, engraved on a block attached to the "b" key. When that key is struck "b" will print, as "B" is too far off to impress itself. Lowering the shift-key moves the carriage into such a position that "B" imprints itself when the key is struck.

To know the typewriter at its best we must use a standard machine built for office work. We will find it admirable in its accuracy and beauty of characters, its range and speed. It writes in every language of the world, including the Jewish, which proceeds from right to left, a direction opposite to that of ordinary script. Typewriters have been adapted to producing musical scores. In machines whose product is to be read by blind folk, Braille and other codes replace the usual characters. In an ingenious machine a stenographer is provided with shorthand symbols instead of ordinary letters. Last of all, electricity has been invoked to lessen the toil of manipulation which, continued hour after hour, becomes fatiguing.

No penman, however skilful, can match the legibility and compactness of a typewriter. When he writes a letter with a pen, he can take a single copy, and no more, on a wet sheet of tissue paper in a letter press. A typewriter with a brass platen affords as many as sixty copies from carbon paper. With similar carbon sheets a bookkeeper can at one operation write an entry in a sales-book, and duplicate its lines for a bill. A tabulator, controlled by a touch, keeps all the figures of an account in their proper columns. Yet more: an attachment, smaller than a lady's watch, adds and subtracts these figures with precision, so that they may be printed as totals or remainders. This recalls that Sholes first of all invented a numbering machine, which feat, as we have seen, led him to devising his typewriter. His successors in one instrument unite computation with writing.

Long ago typewriters entered into rivalry with printers as well as with penmen. A circular, or a program, was transferred from a typewritten sheet to a gelatine mold from which forty to fifty copies could be neatly struck off. To-day a better method yields as many as two thousand copies, and with more despatch: the types of the writing machine are used to cut a stencil in a film of stiff wax from which, on a small rotary press, copies are rapidly printed in ink. These and many another golden harvest are to-day reaped from machines derived from Sholes' great invention. In all machines, heavy or light, simple or intricate, elegant or solid, certain principles of design are indispensable for success. Let a few of these principles be reviewed:

The carriage must be strong and move firmly in its slide, and the typebars should have a leverage as simple and rigid as possible. These features insure good alignment, always in evidence. Nobody can tell from a glance at a page at what pace it was typewritten; but a glance at once detects any irregularity of line. When a machine is solidly built, both quick operation and heavy manifolding are borne for years with little wear and tear. Operators usually demand speed, and speed requires a rapid escapement. However rapid an escapement may be, it is never instantaneous, so that, with a swift pace, good alignment is difficult. This shows how two wants may oppose each other, so that no machine whatever can satisfy in the highest degree every want. Perfect alignment must be paid for in a slight reduction of speed. At very quick paces there is an unavoidable loss of neatness, and an increase in errors.

Next to speed, an operator desires ease of working. He does not always get it. Some machines are more than twice as resistant as others. In stiff machines, with a long play or dip of the keys, fatigue sets in early in the day, to be registered in lapses due to no other cause. Ball-bearing carriages were introduced about 1896, easing the labor of operation in a remarkable degree. Where these bearings are placed in V-shaped runways, there is at times a liability to uneven wear, causing sluggish movement of a carriage. Most machines of the best grade are now fitted with roller-bearings, which wear uniformly and give no trouble.

Operators like a quick and easy machine: their next preference is for a machine with its writing in plain sight. Blind machines came first, and many typists became so accustomed to them that they cling to them still. These operators, through sheer force of habit, when they work a visible machine, are apt to lose somewhat of their self-confidence, and refer too often to their notes. With blind machines they keep their eyes on these notes, except at odd moments when they glance at their keys. But to-day the majority of beginners adopt visible machines, and with advantage. They are thus enabled to note an error, and correct it, with the minimum of trouble and delay. Visible machines are steadily gaining ground, and will in a few years, in all probability, hold the field.

Shift-key machines ask shorter trips from an operator's fingers than machines without a shift-key. Here another case of force of habit comes to view. A typist brought up on a " Yost," or a " Smith-Premier " machine, with its double keyboard, may be induced to adopt a shift-key machine. But in a few weeks or months the operator is apt to return to the old machine. Yet these instances grow fewer year by year. For most purposes shift-key machines econ-omize time and energy, and with this advantage they are driving their competitors from the market. In some minor tasks, cataloguing and directory work, for example, where there are frequent changes from small letters to capitals, and vice versa, an old-fashioned machine may turn out more work in an hour than any other.

A machine as radically novel as the typewriter, discovers, or creates, as you please, a round of aptitudes unimagined before its advent. When the Sholes machines first appeared their operators were perforce clumsy and slow. Practice soon heightened their speed, and operators to whom speed was impossible simply dropped out of the running. From that time to the present hour, the pace of working has gradually increased. This is due, in part, to better ma-chines,—of easier touch, of keyboards not only more com-pact, but so arranged that an operator's fingers take the shortest paths possible. To-day, also, more fingers of each hand are brought into play, and are better taught their busi-ness, than when typing was a novelty.

Thirty years ago beginners seldom used more than one or two fingers of the right hand, employing the left hand scarcely at all. To-day touch-systems teach the use of all the fingers of both hands, instructing the thumbs to move the space-bars and shift-keys. These systems, when mas-tered, greatly promote speed. An expert operator of the first rank keeps his eyes fixed on his " copy," never glanc-ing at his keys, which, indeed, may be blank. In ac-quiring this remarkable facility the first step is to cover two or three characters with paper, so that the learner must feel for them. When the places of these characters have become familiar, two or three more characters are hidden from view, and so on, until the whole keyboard is blank. At exhibitions, a pace may rise to 200 words a minute, so as to advertise the " Speedwell," let us say, as the conqueror.

But words thus shot on paper may have been committed to memory, or may be so familiar as to be written with much greater ease than the words of an ordinary dictation or copy. What means most to an employer, day by day, is the net amount of really good work that a typist turns out. A lightning pace is bought too dear at the cost of many errors. Employers agree that the typists who serve best are men and women of education and culture, who are never in doubt about spelling or syntax, or the best form to give a sentence. A typist of this class may strike the keys with but one or two fingers, and yet leave far behind an operator who is master of the touch system, but who lacks training and the literary sense.

"It is well," says Arthur G. Seal, of New York, " for every beginner to learn under a competent teacher, so as to form only good habits, and understand, from the start, all that may be done with a machine. Pupils at first are apt to strike keys too hard. A light, firm touch is best. Operators who keep time with their keys find their toil distinctly lightened, just as in telegraphy."

ELIAS HOWE

Dr. Oliver Wendell Holmes used to say that the Discovery of America, in 1492, astonished him less than the Forgetting of America, thousands of years before. Columbus arose ages after the day when explorers from Asia were able to find their way to America; century by century their descendants fell away in skill and nerve as navigators, until America faded out from the legends of every other continent of the seas. Almost within our own time there have been parallel cases where not a great discovery, but a great invention, has had its birth and a forgetting. Of this we have a striking example in the mechanism for stitching. In 1790, Thomas Saint patented in England a chain-stitch sewing machine of capital design. With the insight of genius he created features which appear in good machines to-day,—an overhanging arm of goodly girth, and a horizontal cloth-plate. His intermittent feed was effective; his continuous thread had tighteners above and below its needle. And yet this machine was virtually forgotten for sixty years. One inventor after another followed Saint in planning sewing machines, only to miss points of excellence which Saint had included in his model. Why was this stitcher, so ingenious and efficient, allowed to fall into this neglect? Simply because its inventor offered people a good thing before they were ready for it.

Let us be just to the British folk of the time of Thomas Saint. They lived in what was still the day of tools, while we live in the era of machines. To-day we are surrounded and served by uncounted contrivances, all invented within the past century or so, and pressed upon public acceptance by systems of advertisement and can-

[From the painting by Joseph Eliot, owned by the late Mrs. Jane R. Caldwell, New York, daughter of Elias Howe.]

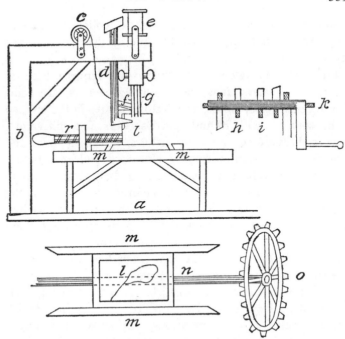

SAINT'S SEWING MACHINE, 1790

It possessed (1) a horizontal cloth-plate; (2) an overhanging arm, on the end of which was (3) a vertically reciprocating straight needle, and on the top of which was (4) a thread spool, giving out its thread continuously; (5) an intermittent automatic feed between stitches; made the chain-stitch; and had thread tighteners above and below.

The machine consisted of a bed-plate, *a*, with a post, *b*, having a projecting arm on which was the thread spool, *c*; a shaft, rotated by a hand-crank and carrying cams by which all the motions of the machine were obtained; the same overhanging arm carried a spindle, *d*, for tightening the stitch, and a needle and awl-carrier, *e*, into which a needle, *f*, and awl, *g*, were secured by set-screws, and moved by cams, *h i*, on the shaft, *k*. The needle was notched at its lower end to push the thread through the hole made by the awl, and thus form a loop. The work was supported on a box, *l*, sliding between guides *m, m*, and advanced by a screw, *n*, turned by a toothed wheel, *o*, which was engaged by a projection from an arm depending from the shaft, *k*, at each revolution of the latter. A looper was operated by the bent point of the spindle, *d*, in a manner still employed in some of the chain-stitch machines. The screw, *r*, served to adjust the box, *l*, on the guide-plate, and provision was made for varying stitches for different kinds of work.

[From *Knight's American Mechanical Dictionary.* Copyright by Hurd & Houghton, Boston, 1876.]

vassing which have become arts taught in colleges. To-day every American family above the line of dire poverty has machines for sewing and washing, in many cases impelled by the electricity aglow in millions of our lamps. Electric motors and heaters, fans and vacuum sweepers, are common in households, offices, and factories. As in the city, so in the country, with its multiplied seeders and cultivators, mowers, harvesters, and corn shellers. Both in town and country we constantly employ elevators and motor-cars, trolleys, telegraph, and telephones, so that, from dawn to bedtime, we are as familiar with elaborate machinery as the neighbors of Thomas Saint were with pins and needles, hammers, gimlets, and chisels. Four generations ago there were probably fewer than a thousand power-looms in all England. Little marvel that Saint's stitcher was looked at askance in a world that felt no need of it, whose peace and quiet it threatened to disturb. Saint's drawing, evidently taken from a model, gathered dust in the British Patent Office for two generations, during which it might have rendered inestimable service to designers. But these designers neglected the rule which bids an inventor begin his work by a thorough survey of what other inventors have already done.

Next in rank to Thomas Saint in time and in talents is Barthelemi Thimonnier, who, in 1830, patented his sewing machine in France. Eleven years later he had eighty of them at work on army uniforms. He used a crochet needle, whose barbed point formed two hundred chain-stitches a minute; his feed included a presser-foot, reinvented long afterward. The tailors and seamstresses who saw this quick machine at work were afraid it would throw them into idleness; so they mobbed Thimonnier's workroom, and smashed his machines in pieces. Seven years afterward he resumed their manufacture, but without financial success: he died in 1857.

To-day a toy which executes chain-stitches like those of Thimonnier may be bought for a dollar. Its mechanism, which may be understood at a glance, involves much the same principles as sister machines more elaborate and costly. Its one thread is carried in an eye-pointed needle which descends below the cloth. As this needle rises it throws out a loop of thread, which is seized and opened by a rotary hook. Through this loop the needle passes in its next descent, when the operation is repeated until stitch after stitch forms a neat chain. Here, reduced to their utmost simplicity, are the essentials of a sewing mechanism. First, a needle to take a thread through cloth, with a hook to form a stitch. Next, a spring to keep the thread at proper tension; with a holding surface to keep the cloth motionless at the moment of stitching, and then move it forward by a stitch-length.

A chain-stitch has two drawbacks: it unravels when a break in the thread is followed by a slight pull; and much more thread is required than in lock-stitching, an item of importance, especially when the thread is costly silk. The chain-stitch machines of Saint, of Thimonnier, and their successors, have been far outdone by the lock-stitch machines of a later day. Their two threads interlace in the middle of the sewn fabric, so as to form a neat line of stitches on each side. For some purposes, as in sewing garments which are to be taken apart after a season's wear, a chain-stitch machine is often preferred. Chain-stitches, too, are employed to ornament dresses, gloves, cushions, and so on. Particularly pretty are the double chain-stitches formed by the Grover and Baker machine, which uses two threads. The first machine of this kind was invented by John Fisher, of Nottingham, England, when he was only nineteen years of age. He patented it on December 7, 1844. Gloves, with linings, were stitched by this machine. It was only the ornamental effect that Fisher and his customers looked at. They missed the vastly more important fact that the machine had sewn together the leather of a glove and its lining. One would suppose that an inventor of Fisher's talent could easily have devised and added suitable feed and tension mechanisms, such as were designed by many other ingenious men both in America and England.

The first lock-stitch machine was devised and built by Walter Hunt in New York, between 1832 and 1834. At the end of a vibrating arm it held a curved needle with an eye at its point, through which passed the upper thread. Its lower thread was borne in a shuttle thrown within a loop formed by the needle and beneath it. Whether this machine worked well or ill is not recorded. It does not seem to have satisfied its inventor, as he did not apply for a patent. He took many steps toward his goal, and then omitted the one final step which would have brought him to the winning post. Hunt was a man of restless versatility, and soon busied himself with inventions vastly less important than the sewing machine,—one of these was a mill which turned out paper collars, bearing stitches in a capital imitation. After the amazing victory of the Howe machine, Hunt sought a patent. It was refused on the score of abandonment twenty years before.

Now we come to Elias Howe, and to the question, Why did he succeed where others failed, and by what steps did he arrive at his great triumph? Elias Howe was born in Spencer, Massachusetts, about twenty miles from Worcester, on July 9, 1819, in a family of sturdy New England stock, endowed with an extra share of Yankee ingenuity and gumption. An uncle, William Howe, devised a truss for roofs and bridges which enjoys vogue to this day. Another uncle, Tyler Howe, was an inventor on a less ambitious plane: he designed a spring bed and other simple aids to household comfort. These two worthies, and their famous nephew, Elias Howe, are commemorated in their native village by a handsome monument. Elias Howe, senior, who gave his son the same name as his own, had eight children; so, with all his hard work, he remained poor. He was first of all a farmer, but, with the reluctant soil of Worcester County, his harvests were scant, and he eked out a livelihood by grinding meal for his neighbors, by sawing and planing lumber, by splitting shingles.

Early in the last century such a family as the Howes carried on some simple handicraft, in which their children could take part. At six years of age, Elias worked with his brothers and sisters at stitching wire teeth into cards for cotton mills. Later on he attended the village school in winter, and in summer took a hand in farm work and his father's mills. Day by day this observing boy saw what machinery did to lighten toil and multiply its fruit. And, besides this, he received a cultivation of hand and eye, of good sense and resourcefulness, which made his training, unsystematic though it was, a capital preparation for his labors as an inventor. One day he trued a grindstone, glazed a window, and soldered a tea-kettle, next morning he nailed shingles on a leaky roof; the week afterward saw him building a corn crib, rearing a well sweep, and bringing from the wood lot a new prop for his mother's clothesline. And meantime he was acquiring, too, more than mere handiness; he received the sterling discipline of sticking to a task, whether he liked it or not, until that task was finished. From boyhood, as long as he lived, Elias Howe had the unrelaxing grip of a bulldog; when once his mind was made up, he was deaf to dissuasion and proof against discouragement. He had other traits which smoothed his path for purposes firmly maintained. As a boy he was lively and play-loving, with chums a-plenty. As a man he was kind and sociable, so that, in his darkest days, he never lacked a friend to proffer him aid and comfort.

In his twelfth year he went to live with a farmer in the neighborhood, intending to remain with him until he had thoroughly mastered the routine of planting, tilling, and reaping. But young Howe suffered from a lameness which, though slight, was disabling; this made farm drudgery a distress to him, so that, within a year, he returned home to resume work in his father's mills. This continued till he was sixteen. At that critical age, with new ambition astir, a friend told him how bright and busy a place Lowell was, where Elias could earn much more than at Spencer, and have a much better time. So to Lowell he went, taking a learner's place in a large factory of cotton machinery. Here he remained for two years, when the panic of 1837 closed every mill in town and sent him adrift. He went to Cambridge, and there found work in a machine shop, taking charge of a hemp-carder invented by Professor Treadwell, of Harvard College. As a shopmate and roommate, Howe had his cousin, Nathaniel P. Banks, who became a Major-General of the United States Army, and Speaker of the House of Representatives. After a few months of hemp-carding, a task not to his mind, Howe heard of pleasant work in Boston at better wages. Thither he proceeded, engaging himself to Ari Davis, on Cornhill, a manufacturer and repairer of chronometers, surveying instruments, and the like. Davis had invented a dovetailing machine which had brought him some profit, and his head was brimful of plans for other machines, from which he expected profits much larger. He was eccentric in manner, and peculiar in dress, so that he did not seem to be as shrewd as he really was. Often his judgment was in request by inventors who brought him their experimental models, or who wished his opinion on their schemes. What place beneath the sky could have been better for our young mechanic from Spencer than this shop of Ari Davis?

One morning Davis had a caller who was trying to invent a knitting machine. When his model had been duly inspected, Davis said: " Why do you bother with a knitting machine; why don't you make a sewing machine?" " I wish I could," replied his visitor, " but it can't be done." " Oh, yes, it can," said Davis; " I can make a sewing machine myself." " Well," responded his caller, "you do it, and you will have an independent fortune." Howe overheard this as he sat nearby, and from that moment the current of his life was changed. As he brooded over what Davis had carelessly said, he thought: " I may be the man to invent that sewing machine and win a fortune."

He built upon solid ground as he thus quietly resolved upon his great task. He had shown ingenuity in adapting and improving instruments for Davis's customers. From Davis himself, sanguine as to the future, disrespectful as to the past, he had caught the conviction that most tools and machines are faulty and slow, and should be improved or supplanted, the sooner the better. In skill and quickness Howe was surpassed by more than one of his shopmates, and he always said that he never studied the abstract principles which underlie mechanical construction. But if he was ignorant of mechanical philosophy, he had mechanical practice at his fingers' ends, at work every day, as he was, on time-pieces, theodolites, and binnacles. From the time he had played as a boy in his father's mills he had observed the uses of pawls and ratchets, levers and cams, springs and weights, as they actuated clockwork and other simple machinery. In the workshops of Lowell and Cambridge he had for years together seen lathes, spinning-frames, and power-looms at work and under repair, so that his memory was a storehouse from which to draw the elements of a sewing machine. And these elements he must now carefully choose, and skilfully combine as a compact and effective unit.*

In physique Howe was not robust: his strength was of the brain rather than of the body. Yet this man with a soft eye, and a placid Quakerly face, had a sagacity that served him much better than mere shrewdness would have done. His comrades were wont to say that he disliked unnecessary toil, or, indeed, toil of any kind. Supposing this to be true, the fact was all in his favor, for what is Invention but the wise abridging or abolishing of toil? And we must remember that Davis paid him only nine dollars a week, and this had to support himself, his wife, and three children. It was uncushioned poverty that pressed him to turn to all possible account such ingenuity as in him lay. His labor at that time, says James Parton, was so tiring that when he reached home he was sometimes too exhausted to eat, and went to bed longing to stay there for ever and ever.

After brooding four years on the talk he had overheard at Davis's shop, Howe, in 1843, began to build his sewing machine. At first he took a wrong track; as he watched his wife plying her needle on a seam, he imitated her motions, one after another. Long before this, in 1829, Heilmann had pierced an eye in the middle of a needle, so that it could be worked to and fro without reversal, in his embroidering machine. Howe made such a needle which, duly threaded, he passed by pincers through two thicknesses of cloth. The stitches were so irregular that his attempt was an utter failure. One day, in 1844, the question flashed upon him: " Is it necessary that a machine should sew with

*The tailor-bird of India uses its bill in sewing leaf to leaf for a nest. Shreds of wool or silk, vegetable fibers or even the spinnings of spiders serve as thread. Dr. Jerdan once saw a tailor-bird watch a garment-sewer until for a moment he rose from his bench. At once it seized a few bits of cotton thread from the floor, and flew off with them in triumph. Mr. Layard describes a nest sewn from a dozen oleander leaves with cocoa-nut fiber.

the same motions as a human hand? No; there may be another kind of stitch than that wrought by a seamstress, quite as serviceable, though sewn by sinews of brass and steel." This thought was the turning-point which divided failure from success. It is likely that he had seen chain-stitch machines, for they were not uncommon, but he wished to build something better. There is no reason to believe that Hunt's contrivances ever came under his notice. On lines wholly original, Howe imagined a lock-stitch machine, and embarked on the labor of giving it form and substance.

Long before he was born, thatchers and lacemakers had pierced their needles with eyes near their points, so as to shorten their paths, and save thread from undue friction. Such needles had been adopted by Walter Hunt in 1840, and had been patented in England by Newton and Archbold, in 1841, for their chain-stitch machine. Howe adopted this eye-pointed needle, and united with it a shuttle such as had clacked around him in looms all his life. He was wise in thus choosing a loom-stitch where one thread interweaves itself firmly with another; and yet, when he turned his back on chain-stitch machines it was only after they had taught him two golden lessons. First, how a needle, fixed in a holder which it never leaves, may vibrate at a pace duly varied. Second, how a simple mechanism may be timed so that a needle, when below its cloth, expands one loop of thread for the admission of a second such loop. The new devices he had to invent were chiefly a shuttle duly laden with a lower thread, and the means to throw this shuttle at proper intervals through loops of an upper thread. Howe at this time was no longer in the employ of Davis: he was at work on his own account, giving every moment he could spare to his model. He completed it toward the close of 1844, and it sewed a fairly good seam, with promise of sewing still better when improved in plan and workmanship.

Howe's father at this time was living in Cambridge, where he was cutting palm leaves into strips for hats on a machine invented by his brother William. Elias, junior, with a view to economy, went to live at his father's house, setting up a lathe so as to execute any odd jobs that might be offered him. During the next few months he worked at little else than his sewing machine, exciting his neighbors to remark that he was simply wasting his time. His odd jobs were so few that often the inventor was without a dollar in his pocket. His father was anxious to help him, but could do nothing, as a fire had destroyed the palm-leaf machine and swept away all his earnings. As Elias Howe from day to day proceeded with his model, he clearly saw that his design would miss a fair test if his model were not built with the same precision as a clock. And where were the means for such an outlay to come from, when money for bread was frequently lacking?

Just then a friend came to his rescue, George Fisher, a fuel dealer. He had recently come into a legacy, and as this windfall was still warm in his pocket, he was in the humor to take up any promising speculation. Many a time had he heard Howe's confident hopes of triumph and fortune, and now Fisher was prevailed upon to become a partner with Howe in his great project of a sewing machine. Fisher was to receive the Howe family into his house as guests; and while Howe was perfecting his model, Fisher was to advance $500 toward buying materials and tools. If the machine proved worthy of a patent, a half share therein was to be Fisher's property. Early in 1844, Howe took up his quarters with Fisher, installing his lathe in a low-studded attic. For a long time nobody but Fisher shared Howe's hopes of victory. Fisher once testified in court: " I was the only one of his neighbors and friends who had any confidence in the success of his invention. Howe was generally regarded as visionary in undertaking anything of the kind, and I was thought foolish to assist him."

During the winter of 1844-45, Howe labored steadily at his machine. So clear and vivid was his imagination that he seemed to be copying a model as it stood before him, instead of giving form to conceptions which were as yet conceptions only. This picturing faculty had the happy effect that Howe was not delayed by a single misfit as part joined part week after week. By April, 1845, the stitch-forming mechanism was advanced to the point where it sewed with evenness and smoothness. Within less than a month Howe finished his model, and his invention, in every essential feature, was complete. In July it sewed a suit of clothes for Fisher, and another suit for himself. These garments were of strong material, yet their stitches outlasted the cloth. Every contrivance in Howe's original model has since his day been bettered or transmuted, for what is one inventor as compared with all other inventors? And many new devices which never entered the head of Elias Howe have been added to his model during the past sixty years. But at this hour no successful sewing machine plies in freedom from debt to Howe's design of 1845. Let us look at its construction:

A firm base, A, carries an overhanging arm, B. Through the side and extremity of this arm works a shaft, C, to which is attached the fly-wheel, D, driven by hand at E. The thread for the top stitch is taken continuously from the spool, F, and fed to the curved needle, a, through a spring, b. The needle works through the cloth at c. The cloth is carried upon pins, d. The needle arm, G, and the baster or feed-plate, H, work so that the plate moves the cloth forward one stage at the completion of every stitch. The shuttle is driven by a rod, J, which is caused to vibrate backwards and forwards by means of the cam, L. The cam l, screwed upon the sleeve, Q, actuates the lever, P, which action gives a rocking motion to the short shaft, O, and the needle arm, on being connected with this, vibrates,

THE FIRST HOWE SEWING MACHINE

carrying the needle into and out of the cloth at each revolution of the hand-wheel. The cloth to be sewn is suspended vertically by pins on the edge of its baster plate, H, which has holes engaging with the teeth of a small pinion which moves intermittently.

This feed was the least happy element in Howe's machine. A superior feed, in wheel form, was invented by John J. Greenough in 1842, and was included in his through-and-through sewing machine patented in that year. Greenough's wheel-feed allowed cloth to be sewn in any direction whatever, Howe's feed was restricted to a straight line. This limitation was soon overcome by the inventors who took up Howe's machine where he left it, and improved it in every feature.

To Howe let us return. When he had improved his devices for tension, so as to stitch with neatness and uniformity, he invited a tailor from Boston to Cambridge to use the machine, and pass upon its merits and faults. The tailor declined his invitation: he believed that if Howe's expectations were fulfilled, the tailoring brotherhood would soon be reduced to beggary. Howe then canvassed other tailors, whom he besought to test his invention. No, said they, with united breath. Their objections were manifold; they were certain that no machine work could be so strong and even as hand stitching. " To the proof," quoth Howe. Bringing his machine to the Quincy Hall Clothing Factory, he sat in front of it and sewed seams in any garment handed to him. Visitors were astonished to watch him sew 250 perfect stitches in a minute, a pace at least sevenfold that of handwork. For two weeks Howe sewed for all comers, and responded to queries with his May morning smile. There was a vein of sport in him, and it came out as he pitted his stitcher against a united band of five young seamstresses, chosen for their speed. He was ungallant enough to win; and not only in pace did he surpass his competitors; they acknowledged his seam to be the best of the six. Yet for all this repeated triumph of brass and steel over fingers of flesh and blood, nobody took any real interest in Howe's invention. To borrow a phrase from the economists, no effective demand was in evidence. Howe heard a great many Ah's and Oh's as he shot his needle swiftly through its cloth; but when his visitors departed, they never gave his machine another thought, so far as he could see.

Its most serious fault was often pointed out; its baster plate limited seams to straight lines, so that only part of a coat or waistcoat could be stitched. Howe's machine saved most labor, therefore, in manufacturing shirts and skirts, sheets and quilts, having straight sewing. Then this very fact of dispensing with much labor was turned against Howe by employers, who feared trouble with their work people if they adopted his sewing machine. One candid objector said: " We are doing well enough as we are. Your machine is costly to buy and to keep in order. There is no good reason why we should bother with it." This man, in alluding to the high cost of the machine, $300, pointed to Howe's chief obstacle. A shirt manufacturer on a large scale might need thirty to forty machines, entailing an outlay of $9,000 to $12,000, a good deal of money in those days. Since then, while the sewing machine has been immensely improved, its price has steadily fallen. At the outset of his experiments, Howe rejoiced when he could sew 250 stitches a minute. To-day the pace may be fourteen times faster, and the one check on still higher speed is the undue heating of needles.

Howe was not disheartened by the cool reception accorded his machine. He saw what its economy meant, if nobody else did, and he was unshaken in his faith that it would yet bring him fame and fortune. He forthwith began to build a second model, to be lodged in the Patent Office at Washington, as the law then required. For three months he toiled at this machine, putting aside all other tasks. By the following spring, that of 1846, his new model was finished, but he had no cash for a journey to Washington, or to pay the fees at the Patent Office. To earn a little money, he ran a locomotive on the Boston and Albany Railroad. A few weeks of this drudgery and exposure prostrated him. He bade good-by to the footboard, retaining to the end of his days a lively recollection of its exhausting demands. In the following August, Fisher agreed to pay all expenses of securing a patent, including the cost of a visit to Washington. Without a day's delay, Howe and Fisher went to the national capital, where, on September 10th, a patent for the sewing machine was duly sealed. Its issue was a piece of quiet and unmarked routine, with no augury of the prolonged legal battles its claims were to provoke. At Washington, Howe displayed his stitcher at a fair, eliciting the usual expressions of wonder. But nobody wanted to buy the machine, or even hire a machine, so that, beyond vocal encouragement, Howe went empty away. At home once more in Cambridge, Fisher's disappointment was outspoken. Not the remotest possibility did he see of being repaid advances which to him were large, amounting to $2,000. In Fisher's despair Howe refused to join. For the time being he again took shelter under the roof of his good old father.

But something must be done. England had larger factories than America: why not offer the machine in England? Howe decided to send a machine to London, in charge of his brother, Amasa, who embarked for London in October, 1846, as a steerage passenger in a sailing packet. Soon after his arrival, he found in Cheapside the shop of William Thomas, who manufactured, on a large scale, corsets, shoes, and umbrellas, wares for the most part stitched in straight lines. As Amasa clicked out his seams at a swift pace, Thomas candidly expressed his admiration. He bought the machine for £250 ($1,217), including permission to use as many more machines as he pleased.

Thomas, furthermore, was at liberty to patent the invention in England. He gave a verbal promise, which he never fulfilled, to pay the inventor three pounds ($14.60) for every machine sold in England. For years Thomas received royalties up to ten pounds on the machines he sold: on these he never paid Howe a penny. The main branch of Thomas's business was corset-making, and for this work he desired that Elias Howe should specially adapt a machine, offering a salary of three pounds a week if he would come to London for the purpose. Amasa posted to Cambridge with this offer, taking Elias his £250, a sum which soon vanished in the payment of debts long standing. As America still had its back turned to his invention, Howe accepted Thomas's proposal. In February, 1847, the brothers embarked for London, setting up in their quarters a small cookstove, so as to leave their few dollars unbroached.

When they reached London, Thomas installed them in a workshop, fully equipped with materials and tools. He did more: he advanced Howe enough cash to bring his wife and children to England, where they arrived ten weeks afterward. At the end of eight months' diligent labor, Howe handed Thomas a machine perfectly adapted to corset-making. If the sewing machine entered no other field than this, it was certain here to win its buyer a handsome fortune. When Howe asked Thomas, " What next? " Thomas replied: " You are to execute miscellaneous repairs." His tone was so haughty that the sensitive Yankee resented it, only to be dismissed on the spot.

Howe was in a distressing plight: he was penniless in a strange city: his wife was out of health, while three children needed her constant care. But now, as in every other dark hour of his life, he had a friend to help him, although this man, Charles Inglis, was almost as poor as himself. Inglis was a coachmaker, who had become acquainted with

Howe at Thomas's factory, and had taken a warm liking to him. He enabled the unfortunate inventor to hire a small room as a workshop, where, with a few borrowed tools, he began to build his fourth machine. As the task went forward day by day, improvements suggested themselves, so that Howe found his task prolonged far beyond the term he had at first assigned it. He had to choose between bringing his expenses to the lowest notch or abandoning his work. From his little flat of three rooms he removed to one room in the cheapest district of Surrey. Even this saving did not suffice, so he managed to send his family to America, where they could live at less cost than in London. For his own fare across the Atlantic, Howe looked to the sale of his machine, now fast approaching completion. This machine, at the end of four months' labor, stood finished at last. Although Howe priced it at fifty pounds ($243), he received little more than fifty shillings for it. His only customer was a poor workman who offered him five pounds in the form of a promissory note. This wretched proffer Howe was obliged to accept, selling the note for four pounds. To pay his debts, and his fare to New York, he had to pawn his letters patent and his precious first machine. To save sixpence, he drew his baggage on a hand cart to the ship. Again he descended to the steerage, with his partner in distress, Charles Inglis, in the next bunk.

It was a sunshiny morning in early April when Elias Howe landed in New York and walked up Broadway from the Battery. He had only sixty cents in his pocket, but what of that? On his homeward voyage he had heard that work was a-plenty in New York: and so it proved. He found employment at once in a machine shop and at good wages. He had barely settled down at his bench when he received sad news from his wife. For two years past she had suffered from consumption, and was now dying. A few days later Howe received ten dollars from his father; this enabled him to reach his wife's bedside in time to say farewell. At her funeral the stricken husband appeared in decent garments of black which he had borrowed from his brother-in-law: his own wardrobe held nothing beyond a frayed working-suit. Howe's natural cheeriness was now quenched. He was heartbroken, with a face as wrinkled and haggard as if ten years had passed since his return to America. To his great affliction a minor misfortune added itself. The ship bearing his household furniture was wrecked, on its way from England, on a reef of Cape Cod. Howe's utter misery moved his old friends to compassion; they took charge of his motherless children and bade him be of good cheer. While his neighbors poohpoohed his inventiveness, they highly esteemed his skill as a mechanic. He was soon at work again as a journeyman machinist, with no immediate prospects of ever being anything else.

At his bench one day he learned, to his astonishment, that his sewing machine had become famous, but not under his name. During his absence in London, pirates had stolen his invention, masking its essential features so as, if possible, to hide their theft. Howe, poor though he was, resolved to make these thieves drop their plunder. He taught them, to their cost, that for all his mild and easy-going ways, he was one of the most formidable suitors who ever entered a courtroom. Although he had then hardly a dollar of his own, he was able to command the dollars of a friend who believed in him and in his machine. At the outset of his legal battles, Howe was a journeyman, with his original model and his patent pledged for debt 3,000 miles away. When his battles were at an end, his patent was acknowledged as basic, and a great national industry was paying him a fortune every year as royalty.

But in the meantime he underwent a struggle that all but

overwhelmed him. First came the pang when his friend Fisher bade him good-by, and sold his half interest in the sewing machine to George W. Bliss. This new partner felt certain that, if the sewing machine proved a success, it would yield a vast income to its owner. As a promising speculation he advanced the cash necessary to pursue the infringers of Howe's patent, and advised the best line of attack upon them. But Bliss, with all his faith and enterprise, was a man of extreme caution. He required his loan to be secured by a mortgage on the farm of Howe, senior. This was granted. It was because Howe's father had unfaltering confidence in his son, and came gallantly to his rescue again and again, that Elias Howe came to victory at last. His suits went forward slowly from stage to stage, after the manner of suits then and now, so that the inventor had abundant leisure to exhibit his machine when he pleased, and to promote its sale where he could.

New York, he felt sure, offered him the best base for his operations, so thither he removed, to open a small shop in Gold Street. There, in the closing months of 1850, he built fourteen machines. In the following autumn one of them was shown at the Castle Garden Fair: it sewed gaiters, pantaloons, and waistcoats as fast as they were proffered. Other machines went to Worcester, Massachusetts, where they sewed bootlegs,—a severe test of their strength and precision. Two machines at a Broadway clothier's gave equal satisfaction. Thus Howe was not only the inventor of the modern sewing machine, he was the first to introduce it to manufacturers, and break ground for the legion of demonstrators and canvassers who soon entered the field.

Of Howe's opponents in and out of court, much the ablest and most formidable was a man who began his career as an actor and theatrical manager. This was Isaac Morton Singer, who patented, in 1851, improvements on Howe's original model. Singer's needle moved vertically instead of horizontally: he replaced a hand-wheel by a treadle: he adopted Greenough's roughened wheel-feed, extended through a slot of his table, a device distinctly better than Howe's baster-plate. He revived Thimonnier's presser-foot to hold down cloth, to which he added a yielding spring. But it was neither as an inventor nor a borrower of inventions that Singer shone: it was as a business organizer. To him incomparably more than to anybody else is due the awakening of the civilized world to the immense value of sewing machines. His experience on the stage and in the box office had taught him how to use brass bands, limelights, and printer's ink. He knew how many lessons the management and transportation of circuses could teach the chieftains of war and industry. He advertised and placarded; he canvassed and exhibited; he arranged exciting contests widely reported in the press. And more: he established agencies under central control, where buyers were instructed, where repairs could be promptly executed at small expense. He thus abolished the cost and risk of selling to merchants on credit; he made it feasible to present the whole world at a stroke with a new type of machine, with any new accessory of real merit. He was a man cordially hated by his rivals, but in their hearts they had to respect him. He was wise in choosing associates, mechanical, commercial, legal. On lines many years ago projected by Singer, the principal sewing machine factories of the globe are to-day united at one center in New York. Each factory makes what it can make to advantage, exchanging part of its output with sister concerns. The largest of these factories, located at Singer, Clydebank, Scotland, employs 12,000 hands. A corps of inventors are kept busy the year round in adapting machines to new duties. One year, special attention may be bestowed upon embroidering, and the next year upon lining the hats of men and women. In the factory at Bridgeport,

Connecticut, is a museum of sewing machines which is the most complete in existence.

Singer, the original mainspring of this vast system, from his first sight of a Howe machine was convinced of its immense value. In seeking to invade Howe's patent he came, one evening, upon news that cheered him greatly. He heard, what we already know, that in 1834 Walter Hunt, of New York, had invented a machine which produced a lock-stitch by means of an eye-pointed needle and a reciprocating shuttle. " Then," said Singer, " Howe was second in the field, and his patent is worthless." But where was

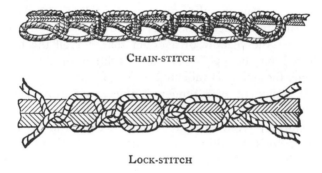

CHAIN-STITCH

LOCK-STITCH

Hunt's machine to be found, so as to be producible in court? It lay as rubbish in a workshop in that very Gold Street where stood Howe's premises. Hunt's machine was carefully cleaned and repaired, but neither its inventor nor any one else could sew a stitch with it. Hunt, in his time, had taken out scores of patents, and why he had never applied for a patent on this machine was plain. While its mechanism came near to efficiency, it just missed efficiency. Its unfortunate creator was a Mr. Ready-to-halt, and his want of a little courage and persistence had lost him one of the great prizes of the nineteenth century. In 1854, Hunt applied for a patent on his sewing machine; it was refused

on the ground of abandonment.   Court after court listened
impartially to his plea, always deciding in favor of Howe.
Theirs was a remarkable case of the same invention occurring independently to more than one mind.   Both Hunt
and Howe were familiar with eye-pointed needles, and with
shuttles which interwove one thread with another.   Each
inventor joined these cardinal elements in a machine which,
with him, was original.   To the man who took the trouble
to bring his invention to a practical success, was awarded
the palm.   In 1854, after a long trial against an infringer,
in which all the adducible evidence was presented, Judge
Sprague, of Massachusetts, decided that " The plaintiff's
(Howe's) patent is valid, and the defendant's machine is
an infringement. . . . There is no evidence in the case
that leaves the shadow of a doubt that, for all the benefit
conferred on the public by the invention of the sewing
machine, the public is indebted to Mr. Howe."

This judgment was rendered nine years after Howe's
first machine was built, and when eight years of his patent
had expired.   Even with all judicial decisions in his favor,
the inventor's royalties were small.   This cloud had a
golden lining.   Mr. Bliss, who owned half the patent, about
this time passed away, and Howe was able to buy his share
at a low figure, and thus, for the first time, become sole
owner of his patent.   This purchase was effected just as
public indifference was thawing, and when, for the time being, Howe's rivals had dropped their arms.   Fortune now
arose in a floodtide which soon swept Howe safely out of
the shoals and shallows, where he had been buffeted so
long.   His income mounted by leaps and bounds from a
few hundreds a year to more than $200,000, as much as a
million would be to-day.

But the peace then ruling the sewing machine industry
could not last long in the presence of so broad a stream of
gold pouring into Howe's coffers.   Leading manufacturers

rebelled against paying him further "tribute," and among themselves they had endless quarrels as to alleged infringements. Early in 1856, the suits of these complainants were to be tried at Albany, New York, and loud were the threats of disaster hurled by each camp in succession. In hotel-lobbies, in the ante-chambers of justice itself, faces were flushed with anger, and imprecations issued from unguarded lips. One party to the fray was an eminent lawyer of New York, George Gifford, who kept his head cool and his mind clear. His professional experience had taught him that the demands of clients are not always free from humbug. Without knowing it, he was a forerunner of the modern trust magnates, who have remodeled American industry. Said he: " In Albany to-day are assembled the men who control the sewing machine manufacture of the globe. Let them join hands instead of shutting their fists, and they will find vastly more profit in peace than in war." A survivor of that conference remembers one cause which contributed to the success of this sagacious plea. Even the most just man of them all did not wish his record unveiled and attacked in open court. Many a new patent bore an unmistakable filial resemblance to an old patent still in force. No accuser of others, however vehement, felt himself to be wholly blameless. The peacemaker was blessed with success. The threatened battle never came off, Howe's patent being recognized as fundamental by the twenty-four assembled licensees. Every machine sold in America was to pay Howe $5; every exported machine, $1. In 1861, Howe's patent was renewed: thenceforward his royalty for machines, wherever sold, was one dollar. All licensees taxed themselves heavily to prosecute infringers. These gentry raised an outcry about " combination " and " extortion," but they soon grew weary of its hollow and un-echoed sound.

Howe was now a rich man at last, and he frankly en-

joyed·his good fortune. His generous soul was rejoiced
in bestowing goodly gifts upon his kindred and friends.
More than aught else his heart was gladdened by an opportunity to render a service to the nation. He had seen, with
quickened pulse, his machine provide Union troops with
millions of uniforms and haversacks, tents and sails,
cartridge-boxes and shoes, which, within the time-limits of
battle could not possibly have been sewn by hand. Let an
example of this despatch be cited: One afternoon, at three
o'clock, a telegram reached New York from the War Department at Washington, requiring 50,000 sandbags for field
defenses. Within twenty-three hours the bags were cut
from their cloth, sewn, baled, and shipped on an express
train southward bound. With many a service like this to
his credit, Elias Howe might well have excused himself
from enlisting as a soldier, especially in view of his lameness. But he was not a man who dealt in excuses, or who
loved his country with anything less than his whole heart.
He organized the Seventeenth Regiment of Connecticut, and
presented each officer with a horse. He was elected Colonel,
and, sensible man that he was, he declined the honor, taking a place in the ranks as a private, serving faithfully
until his health gave way. For some weeks, in camp near
Baltimore, he was regimental postmaster, riding to and
from the city every day with mail bags sewn, we may be
sure, on a Howe machine.

That machine was destined soon to be radically improved,
and in some features wholly supplanted, by other inventors.
Of these men the most remarkable was Allen B. Wilson,
who was born in Willet, Cortlandt County, New York, on
October 18, 1824. It was in 1847, during a brief stay at
Adrian, Michigan, where he was a journeyman cabinet-
maker, that he conceived the idea of a sewing machine. He
had never seen such a thing, even in a picture or a diagram.
A few months later he removed to Pittsfield, Massachusetts,

where, toward the close of 1848, he completed his drawings. Next came the task of carrying out his plans in wood, iron, and brass. He found a friend in his employer, who allowed him the free run of his shop at night, so that his model might be built when the day's work was over. Wilson was not a machinist, and he had none of a machinist's tools. But by the end of the following March he had built every part of his model with his own hands. It was, of course, rough in its workmanship, but it neatly stitched several dress waists, to the delight of their owners and all Pittsfield. Wilson's design included an eye-pointed needle, and a two-pointed shuttle which made a stitch at every motion forward and backward. He included a two-motion feed, which led him to devise afterward his four-motion feed, an invention of prime importance. Wilson's original feed had the great merit of permitting a seam to take any line whatever, straight, curved, or crooked, at an operator's pleasure. This was effected by a toothed bar moved to and fro horizontally in constant contact with the cloth, which it moved onward at proper intervals by the forward inclination of its teeth. It receded while its cloth was held in position by the needle, during the brief time before the needle was withdrawn.

The following May, that of 1849, found Wilson at North Adams, Massachusetts, where he built a second machine on the same general plan as the first, and with better construction. This served as his model in obtaining a patent on November 12, 1850. Wilson was an acute critic of his own contrivances, and, as his shuttle gave him much trouble, he resolved to replace it, if possible, with a rotating hook suggested in chain-stitch machines. Next, he replaced his two-motion feed with a segmental screw device. His new machine, thus improved, was patented on August 12, 1851, the day on which Isaac M. Singer received a patent for his first sewing machine. Wilson experimented constantly with a new stitch-forming mechanism, and at last perfected a rotary hook, which he patented on June 15, 1852. This latest machine displayed a device which became quite as famous as the rotary hook; yet, strange to say, although Wilson described it promptly enough, he did not patent it until December 19, 1854. This was his four-motion feed, which for many years had all but universal vogue, and earned fortunes for its inventor and his assigns. In its

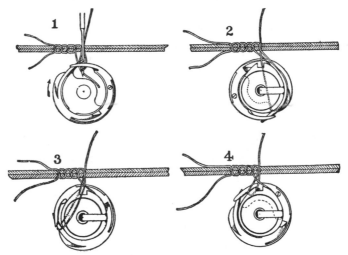

WILSON'S ROTARY HOOK IN FOUR PHASES OF FORMING A STITCH

original model it consisted of a serrated bar which, by means of cams, had a horizontal to-and-fro movement, and a vertical up-and-down motion. The serrated upper surface of this bar worked through an opening in the table upon which was laid the cloth to be sewn. Above the cloth moved a yielding presser-plate. The feeding-bar first rose so as to bring its roughened surface in contact with the underside of the cloth; it then moved horizontally forward a stitch-length, and carried the cloth along; then it descended below the level of the table, so as to leave the cloth free from contact. Finally, it returned to its original position, completing its cycle. This four-motion feed supplied the keystone for the arch of sewing mechanism, assuring its acceptance for households throughout the civilized world.

In devising a rotary hook to take the place of a shuttle driven to and fro, Wilson brought stitching machines from the second rank to the first, taking the step which divides continuous motion from motion interrupted and reversed. The advances in which his revolving hook marked a stride, doubtless began with the very dawn of human ingenuity. At first, we may imagine, burdens too heavy for human shoulders were dragged on the ground. It was an inestimable saving of toil when a round log, by way of a roller, was placed between the burden and the earth, in clear prophecy and promise of a wheel. Of kin to that early triumph, and almost as useful, are the circular saw, the rotary planer, and the milling cutter with its wonderful offspring, the Blanchard lathe. Early dynamos and motors were reciprocating; soon rotary designs took the field, to hold it forever. Oars dipped into water, throb after throb, were the first crude imitations of the galley-slave; they have disappeared even from museums, in favor of rotary screws and revolving paddle-wheels. And the engine which actuates a huge propeller is more and more frequently a steam turbine, the steadiest of steam motors, which lightens the floors not only of steamships, but of factories and central power stations, while it everywhere yields smooth running instead of a wasteful and damaging vibration. It is the rotary hook which to-day makes feasible a speed of 3,500 stitches in a minute, so that the only limit to further celerity is the heat created by friction on needles as smooth as glass.

Wilson formed a partnership with Nathaniel Wheeler, a

man of ability and integrity, who manufactured hardware at
Watertown, Connecticut. There, Wheeler & Wilson first
produced their sewing machines. Shortly afterward they
removed to Bridgeport, in the same State. Their premises,
small at first, have been repeatedly enlarged. They now accommodate 1,500 hands as Factory Number Ten of the
Singer circuit. Mr. Wilson's talents lay solely in the field
of invention; business had little attraction for him. He retired from the firm of Wheeler & Wilson in 1853, with a
goodly income as the reward of his unique devices. He
died in Woodmont, Connecticut, on April 29, 1888.

Only once has a sewing machine been born in America
outside the New England States. This was in 1855, when
James A. E. Gibbs, a farmer of Millpoint, Virginia, one
evening noticed in the *Scientific American* a picture of a
sewing machine. All that the illustration showed was the
upper mechanism, and Gibbs puzzled his brains to imagine
the unpictured devices which formed the stitch. He kept
asking himself: " What takes place after the needle punc-
tures its cloth?" For months this question weighed him
down. At last light glimmered in his brain, and he thought
out the revolving hook which enchains the stitches in a
Wilcox & Gibbs machine. But this hook had to be partnered with Howe's eye-pointed needle, and with Wilson's
four-motion feed, so that Gibbs had, at first, to pay seven
dollars in tribute as he equipped each of his machines.

It would take a very big book to recite the achievements
of other inventors in this broad and fruitful field of sewing
devices. Flying the temptation, let us return to the man
who led the procession, Elias Howe. While he still enjoyed
a fair measure of health and activity, he was gratified by
seeing his machine adapted to many diverse tasks, all executed as speedily as plain sewing. Soon a Howe machine
could not only stitch, but hem and gather, fold and braid,
embroider, and make buttonholes. To-day the successors

of his machines darn and mend with astonishing neatness, and, in the manufacture of shoes and much else, a knife trims away the superfluous edge of leather or lining as fast as its seam is sewn.

Many labor-savers have of late years found their way into American homes, to take places beside the sewing machine, yet that machine remains the most important of them all. In those sensible households where clothing and table linen, drapery for windows and the like, continue plain and simple, this machine despatches their seams in one-tenth the time required of old. For a good many years its motion was imparted by treadles; this was fatiguing, and gave rise to serious maladies. In factories, treadles were abolished as soon as it was found that, with dependence on steam-power, an operator could turn out one-fourth more work.

The sewing machine, in its quick output of garments for men, women, and children, has created the ready-made clothing business, which now offers as carefully patterned and finished raiment as made-to-order clothes were, a generation since. To-day, thanks to Howe, undergarments cost but very little more than their cloth as delivered by the weaver. A few years ago, a manufacturer in New England sold vast quantities of unlaundered shirts at fifty cents each. His profits, estimated at forty dollars a day, were mainly derived from his cuttings, from which the best paper was manufactured.

Clothing for women is seldom of the plainness of these cheap shirts. A century ago it may have required a month to sew a lady's outfit for a year's wear. To-day that lady's great-granddaughter may want a seamstress at a swift machine to keep busy for that same month, as one elaborate garment is added to another. Where wiser counsels prevail, the plain sewing of a family becomes, with an electric motor, little else than a recreation. In some towns and cities of the United States and Canada, electricity costs only one-quarter of a cent for a horse-power running one hour. Suppose that the current to drive a machine is one-eighth of a horse-power: at that price a sewing machine may be impelled thirty-two hours for a single cent. In his early days, the cost of a machine was so high that Howe hardly expected its adoption by families. It was usually imagined, too, that operation was difficult to master. And yet, by 1867, the price of a good machine had fallen to $55, and in one hour an intelligent woman could learn to work it rapidly. To-day one-half the sewing machines are busy in households, and the other half in factories.

It was the fate of Elias Howe, who bestowed so great a gift upon the world, to enjoy its rewards only a few years. The hardships of his protracted struggle undermined a constitution never robust, even in his youth. In the summer of 1867 he developed Bright's disease at his daughter's house in Brooklyn, and there, after a short illness, he passed away on October 3d, at the early age of forty-eight years. This daughter, Mrs. Jane R. Caldwell, died in New York in August, 1912. Her mother, Elizabeth Ames, died when Mrs. Caldwell was but seven years of age. In 1859 her father had his portrait painted by Joseph Eliot, of Albany: it had the place of honor in Mrs. Caldwell's home in the Borough of the Bronx, ten miles from the City Hall of New York. By her courtesy this portrait has been reproduced for these pages. Mrs. Caldwell remembered how her father was wont to go about his house all day with a shuttle in his hand, thinking about new tension devices and the like. It is certain that, had he lived to the allotted span of human life, he and nobody else would have created for his machine many an improvement now bearing the names of men whom he instructed and inspired.

B. C. Tilghman.

[From Photograph by F. Gutekunst, Philadelphia.]

BENJAMIN C. TILGHMAN

A SMALL group of inventors, high in rank, have been educated men who have pioneered new paths in response to an instinct, rather than as a matter of professional quest with gain as its goal. A thoroughly equipped amateur of this type was General Benjamin Chew Tilghman, of Philadelphia. His independence and vigor of mind brought him to ideas wholly original, and his competency of fortune enabled him to develop these ideas with unflagging ardor throughout a long life. He had the prime impulse indispensable to any great success whatever—an intense interest in his work. Hobby riding by ordinary men adds no little cheer and refreshment to their lives. When a man of General Tilghman's ability chooses invention not as a hobby, but as his career, the toil of research and construction is a joy to him, and a joy which is heightened as his work confers boons and benefits upon his fellow men. General Tilghman was a reserved and quiet gentleman of the old school, so averse from publicity that his achievements have never attracted the attention they richly merit.

His high breeding and personal dignity were the heritage of centuries. He traced his descent from Richard Tilghman, a man of Danish blood, who died in 1463 on his English estate, Holloway Court, near Rochester. Sixth from him in the direct line was another Richard Tilghman, a surgeon, who entered the British Navy under Admiral Blake, to become, like his commander, an ardent follower of Cromwell. This Tilghman signed the famous petition asking that justice be done to one Charles Stuart. From the moment when this " justice " led Charles I. to the scaffold, the grasp of Cromwell upon England became insecure. The strength of the Royalists grew steadily, and Tilghman and his party were openly flouted as regicides, worthy of the gallows. Eleven years after the beheading of the king, and just before his son Charles II. came to the throne, Richard Tilghman and his family emigrated to Lord Baltimore's colony of Maryland, where he acquired lands on Charles River in what is now Queen Anne County, and where he built the Hermitage as his manor-house. His descendants usually chose the bar as their profession, rising to its highest rank. One of them, Matthew Tilghman, a great-granduncle of General Tilghman, came within an ace of signing the Declaration of Independence. He was a delegate from Maryland when Independence was under consideration. When all was settled, he was summoned from his seat in Congress to preside at the State Convention in Annapolis. There the Constitution for Maryland was formulated, and went into effect on August 14, 1776. In his absence his alternate, Charles Carroll of Carrollton, signed the Declaration. He died in 1832, in his ninety-sixth year, the last survivor of the men who signed the great document. James, Matthew, Edward, and William Tilghman were jurists of the foremost mark, William becoming Chief Justice of Pennsylvania, and holding for many years the presidency of the American Philosophical Society. Fifth in line from Richard Tilghman, the sturdy immigrant, was Benjamin Tilghman, an eminent lawyer of Philadelphia, who, in 1808, espoused Anna Maria McMurtrie. On October 26, 1821, was born their third son, Benjamin Chew Tilghman, who was to win fame as an inventor and discoverer. Even as a toddler he was remarkable. When he was three years old his family lived in Chestnut Street, opposite Independence Hall. One day his mother, while out shopping, lost him in a thoroughfare nearby. She became frantic as she sought him in vain, fearing his death from a passing cart, or maiming at the least. When at last she came home, there stood her boy, utterly perplexed at her agitation and tears. As soon as he had missed his mother, he entered a druggist's at the corner, gave the shopman his father's name, told where he lived, and asked to be taken home. Nothing in all this seemed to him out of the way.

When nine years old he took typhoid fever; in his delirium he sang his school ditties and repeated his school verses without dropping a word. Anon he imagined himself in command of soldiers to whom he gave orders in imperative tones, with unconscious prophecy of the orders he was to give thirty years later on the field of war. As a boy he loved fiction and, seated at an entry window upstairs, he would read the Waverley romances with delight. His brother Dick gave warning if Mother approached. Her traditions were Presbyterian, and she frowned upon youths of tender years who read novels. In other respects, too, her views were austere. Her little sons were never permitted to wear overcoats. When Benjamin's school days were at an end, he proceeded to Bristol College in his native State, and thence to the University of Pennsylvania, where he was duly graduated. To please his father, and to sustain the legal traditions of his family, he studied law and was admitted to the bar, but he never practised law. Indeed, he always regarded law with disrelish. From youth he was more at home in a workshop than in a courtroom or a law library. When at his furnace or still he put a question to nature, her responses were not subject to reversal. In the vast, unexplored fields of physics and chemistry which stretched themselves before his imagination, there was abundant scope for the keenest analysis, the utmost sifting of evidence, the most astute cross-examination. Here, he was assured, law and truth were one, and never looked askance at each other.

In every research he toiled hand in hand with his brother, Richard Albert Tilghman, two years his junior, to whom he was devotedly attached. Together, as young men, they journeyed throughout Europe, visiting a succession of chemical works and physical laboratories, factories and mills, so that they became familiar, as few Americans then were, with the best European practice in both manufacture and investigation. On their return home, Richard took up the study of chrome ores; these he treated by new methods, disposing of his patents to a leading firm in Baltimore for a goodly sum. He then experimented with steam at high temperatures, discovering that it parted fats into fatty acids and glycerine.

Benjamin, for his part, gradually perfected the production of steel shot, chilled to surpassing hardness, and extensively used for sawing, polishing, and grinding stone. This shot, placed beneath a saw blade, cuts granite twice as effectively as sand, because so tough as to resist a wear that would rapidly crush sand, and even emery, to powder. In one experiment General Tilghman found his metallic granules tenfold as efficient as sand, while the wear on his blade was reduced to one-fourth its percentage with sand. The best sizes of shot run from 1-100 to 1-20 of an inch in diameter. As important as the economy of this shot is the accuracy of its cuts. A piece of marble or granite may have veins of unusual hardness; these are divided with precision, as if the stone were of uniform resistance throughout.

At the end of an exhaustive round of experiments, General Tilghman said: " A particle of sand is effective in sawing only when it embeds itself in a blade, to stand there as a small sharp tooth. This tooth removes from the stone below it one grain at a time, and no more. Contrast this with the action of shot: they roll over and over between the blade and the stone, and as the point of contact is very small, the pressure there concentrated crushes the hardest stone to splinters of appreciable size so that the pulverization, imposed upon sand, is avoided. Shot cannot be bruised or crushed by the heaviest pressure, so that, strange to say, for all the cheapness of sand, it is dearer than shot, task for task. As a rule, work is trebled in pace by the adoption of shot. At first, to cut a given stone the inventor used shot of one size. He soon found it better to employ shot of different sizes. In the course of a single sweep of the blade the largest shot tend to escape under the blade first, then the next in size, and so on to the end of the cut, so that the blade always has shot under it while the stone is being divided. Almost incredible is the durability of shot, for all the severity of its exposure. A gang of five to seven blades on Connecticut brown stone will consume but 200 pounds in a month. A rip-saw, on the same stone, but 60 pounds per month. A gang on marble uses up about 30 pounds per blade per month. In sawing a square foot of Quincy granite only two pounds are consumed."

Shot, under a ring drill, is used for driving wells, in prospecting for mines, quarries, and veins of oil. It is not so fast as a diamond drill, but in many cases it is equally satisfactory, while much cheaper. In sinking foundations for the Terminal Building, Church and Cortlandt Streets, New York, cores six to eight inches in diameter were taken out of solid rock, much more economically than was feasible by any other method. Not only in cutting stone, but in giving it a surface, this chilled iron shot opens a profitable field. Granite and other hard stones were formerly rubbed smooth by sand or emery. At least nine-tenths of this work may be committed to chilled iron shot, which proceeds twice to thrice as fast as emery. The use of shot demands no machinery whatever. The simplest and cheapest hand-saw may be used, even if but a strip of sheet iron 1-16 of an inch thick, 12 to 14 inches long, with " V " notches half an inch broad and deep, about two inches apart. With no other appliance an ordinary workman has cut a groove

30 inches long, and about ¼ of an inch deep in Quincy granite in twenty minutes; in soft stone his output was proportionately more. When this process was first adopted, rust was a constant annoyance. This rust is due to the trifle of carbon dioxide which water usually contains. A little quick-lime added to the water greedily absorbs this dioxide, and at once rusting is impossible. In pure water, iron may be immersed for weeks and never show the slightest trace of rust.

Benjamin Tilghman had been quietly conducting his factory for some years when, in 1860, the threat of Civil War was unmistakable. His passionate love of the Union was aroused, and when Fort Sumter was bombarded, he at once enlisted as Captain of the Twenty-sixth Regiment of United States Volunteers. This regiment, on its way to the front, in common with other Union troops, was mobbed in passing through Baltimore, and Captain Tilghman deemed himself fortunate to escape with his life. In the field he speedily earned distinction, and was soon advanced to a lieutenant-colonelcy, and then to a colonelcy. In 1862 he was stricken with the Chickahominy fever, from drinking infected water, and for weeks he hovered 'twixt life and death. But he recovered in time to bear a doughty part in the battle of Chancellorsville, where he received a severe wound in a thigh. A slight deflection of the bullet would have laid him in his grave. He went home to Philadelphia, where, as soon as he was able to hobble about on crutches, he was offered the command of a colored regiment. This he promptly accepted. His family believed that his death knell rang out as the train bore him southward once again. Their fears were groundless; he survived the war in vigorous health, while his original regiment, the Twenty-sixth, was cut to pieces not long after his reënlistment. The close of the war found him a general by brevet, in command of a brigade in Florida. His interest in military art and science remained keen as long as he lived; and no veteran of the war, whether white or black, ever appealed to him in vain for friendly aid. His experience in the field confirmed for life his love of fresh air. He had seen many a soldier, desperately wounded, recover health and strength in a breezy tent. So he was wont to say: " Houses are tombs, carpets are shrouds, curtains are grave-clothes."

One morning, not long after peace had followed war, General Tilghman came to a turning-point in his career, and simply by keeping his eyes open and thinking about what he observed. Among the compounds with which he had been experimenting was a little sulphurous acid dissolved in water. Aimlessly enough, he bruised a burnt match stick into this liquid, and next day noticed that the wood had become mucilaginous, so as to look like paper pulp. At once he asked: Can this solution convert wood into material for paper? He put his surmise to a test, and proved it to be sound. What gave particular point to his quest was the fact that common paper for printers' use had then risen to twenty-eight cents in currency per pound, a price almost prohibitory. It was then usual for grocers and butchers to buy old newspapers at half price, and use them for wrapping their parcels. During the Civil War cotton at one time reached $1.98 per pound; linen, used as a substitute, was almost as dear. As these, and their rags, had been the main sources of paper stock, there was an earnest quest, in many fields, for substances from which paper might be produced.

Straw had been employed as an admixture for the coarsest brands, and though their sheets were yellow and brittle, their preparation by alkalis had taught the manufacturers how to attack a vastly better material—wood fiber. Therefore, when General Tilghman began following up the fate of his burnt match stick, with his brother's aid, he did not enter upon vacant territory.

In their chemical production of paper, the Tilghmans had many forerunners at home and abroad. As early as 1821 paper was made from straw by Judge Henry Pettibone, of Meadville, Pennsylvania. One day he observed a tub which had just been emptied of lye. On the ground lay a handful of straw which had served as a strainer for the liquid. The Judge examined a pinch of it in his hand; it seemed just such a strong fiber as might produce paper. He took some of this fiber and a little clean straw to a paper-maker, who soon turned out from the straw a sheet of fairly good paper. Of course, the sheet was straw-colored, and so brittle that it was suitable only for wrapping, but when manufactured by the ton it met a wide and profitable demand. In 1854, Alfred C. Mellier patented in France a method of deriving paper pulp from poplar wood by boiling the fibers in caustic soda, under pressure, at 310° Fahrenheit, and then treating the product with a solution of chloride of lime. His boiler was rotary, so as to keep its contents from matting together. Heat was applied by a steam jacket. In 1855, Hugh Burgess, of Roger's Ford, Pennsylvania, patented a similar process. He was followed by other inventors until, in 1866, the Tilghmans carried through a round of experiments which, chemically, exhausted the field, and left little or nothing to be discovered by their successors, except in one particular. As this affected the material chosen for digesters, it was so vital that its lack caused a long delay in the financial success of the Tilghman process. For the first digesters, in the Tilghman mill at Manayunk, near Philadelphia, lead was the lining; this was so rapidly corroded by its acid contents that repairs and renewals entailed a net loss to the patentees of about $40,000, leading them to abandon their enterprise. It was only in 1883, seventeen years after General Tilghman was granted his patent, that digesters were built of concrete so as to resist corrosion as lead cannot. As usual with a patent of promise, the Tilghman method excited the cupidity of infringers, who would fain hide their theft by mutilating the property stolen. But their every departure, however slight, from the Tilghman rules of procedure, opened the door to utter failure, no matter what substance was molded into digesters. No better evidence can be adduced as to General Tilghman's thorough mastery of the principles involved in bringing forests under tribute to the printing press.

It is worth while to recall his method as originally outlined by his own hand: " Let the whitest parts of wood be chosen, and cut across the grain into slices one-eighth to one-fourth of an inch in length. A strong vessel, of any convenient size and shape, lined with lead, duly furnished with pipes and other accessories, is to be filled about two-thirds with water. A solution of sulphurous acid and lime sulphite in water, having a specific gravity of 1.08 or so, is then introduced until the wood is completely covered and the vessel is nearly full. Then the vessel is tightly closed, and, by means of a steam jacket, its temperature is brought to 260° Fahrenheit, to be there maintained for six to eight hours. The steam is then shut off; fresh water is forced into the top of the vessel; and the acid solution escapes from below into a lead-lined tub, where it is boiled until the sulphurous acid is expelled. This gas, piped to a condenser, is absorbed by cold water for repeated use in future operations. The lime sulphite, usually deposited in the heated vessel, may also be used over and over again. The woody fiber is thoroughly washed and drained, when it is fit to be worked into paper by suitable machinery."

By removing samples of his product every twenty minutes, the inventor ascertained just how the process went on from stage to stage. At first the wood was loosened into coarse fibers: these slowly became separated into threads finer and finer, until perfect pulp appeared. All the cement which had bound together the fibers was dissolved into the boiling liquid. Of course, cane, bamboo, and palmetto required longer cooking than flax, esparto, and similar grasses, reeds, and other annual plants of comparatively weak structure. Intermediate in toughness, and therefore in time of boiling, came the poplars, spruces, and balsams which are to-day the staple of the pulp industry. When a modified treatment was bestowed upon straw and grass, osiers and saplings, used for hats, hoops, baskets, and mats, they soon acquired a pliability which facilitated and improved their manufacture.

For a round of uses steadily growing wider, paper may be of any hue whatever, as when employed for wrapping or box-making. Here no lime sulphite need enter the boiling liquor, and the process may be much abridged, especially in washing and cleansing the produced fiber. General Tilghman early came to the discovery that good results are attained at 210° Fahrenheit, two degrees or so below the ordinary boiling-point of water; and, further, that digestion requires no artificial pressure, although pressure greatly hastens the process. To-day digesters which may be 17 feet wide, and 60 feet high, are constructed with a double course of masonry laid in cement mortar upon an iron shell. The course next to the shell is composed of very hard porous bricks laid in mortar of equal parts of sand and Portland cement; the next, or inside course, is built of vitrified, non-porous bricks laid in mortar compounded of Portland cement, litharge, sand, and glycerine. The lack of this one link in the Tilghman chain held back for years a process which now yields in the United States more than a million tons of paper pulp every year.

Since General Tilghman's time, striking improvements have been effected in apparatus for burning sulphur, and for speedily absorbing the resulting sulphurous acid gas. Much, too, has been accomplished in utilizing by-products formerly thrown away. But most noteworthy of all are advances in the mechanism which builds all kinds of paper from pulp, with swiftness and economy, and of uniformly sound quality.

Spruce, the chief material for pulp, is becoming scarce, so that experiments with other and cheaper woods have been conducted at the Forest Products Laboratory, Wausau, Wisconsin, directed by the United States Department of Agriculture. The chemical engineer in charge, Mr. J. H. Thickens, reported in December, 1911:—"Not only have very promising sheets of pulp been obtained from both the hemlock and jack pine, but paper has been made from them on commercial machines, operating at high speed, and under all other conditions of actual commercial practice, which has the strength, finish, and appearance of standard news paper. The production per grinder, the horse-power consumption per ton, and the yield per cord approximate the averages which obtain in the grinding of spruce."

General Tilghman gave his sulphite process a thorough and costly test, but, balked as he was by the corrosion of his digesters, he abandoned a manufacture from which he had expected great things, and which to-day far exceeds his most sanguine hopes. Without repining or hesitation he turned from chemistry to mechanics, to strike a target much more important than at first attracted his eye. His experiments, ending in the sand blast, brought him to one of the few underived inventions of all time. Nobody disputes his title, or claims a share in his victory. And yet, for ages Nature has been giving Art broad hints in this very field. As long ago as 1838, to cite one record among many, Professor W. P. Blake, of Yale College, traveling through the Pass of San Bernardino, California, noticed granite deeply channeled by sweeping sand. Said he: "Even quartz was cut away and polished; garnets and tourmalines were also cut and left with polished surfaces. Where a garnet or a lump of quartz was embedded in compact feldspar, and favorably presented for the action of the sand, the feldspar was cut away around the hard mineral, which was thus left in relief above the general surface. In Monument Park, Colorado, is a narrow valley where rounded columns ten to forty feet high stand here and there: in many cases they are surmounted with grotesque cap-like coverings balanced upon frail pinnacles. They were carved out by the sand, whirling about in eddies of air and water, so as to act like the chisels of a lathe. Where the depressions were deepest, the rock strata were soft and yielding, and readily cut away. Where the opposing surface was hard, as in the case of the cap-pieces, the action was less rapid. Glancing off from these, the whole force of the sand was directed against the strata below, reducing them in size, until there was hardly enough stem to sustain the weight above."

All this is repeated in Wellington Bay, New Zealand, and wherever else rocks of varying resistance are assaulted by storms of sand. Often, doubtless, this has suggested imitation by art. In most cases it is likely that the impulse to experiment has been checked by the fear that an artificial sand storm would be too slow to have commercial value. Centuries have been required to do the work described by Professor Blake and his fellow explorers. General Tilghman was the first to follow up suggestion by actual trial, and find, as many another inquirer has found, that Nature often holds in her hands prizes easier to pluck than they seem to be.

General Tilghman was a gentleman of unusual reserve and reticence: and a quest as to how the sand blast suggested itself to him has unearthed nothing less than a myth in the making. Surviving friends of his are wont to say that, late in the sixties, he traveled to Egypt, and paid a customary visit to the Sphinx, remarking a deep groove across the back of its neck, which he referred to the sand which had, for centuries, assailed the prone figure. There and then, say the mythmakers, it occurred to him that an artificial gale, laden with sharp sand, would exert a cutting effect of the same kind, at a pace which only experiment could ascertain. To experiment accordingly he appealed, with the result that he gave the world his sand blast. This plausible story is untrue. General Tilghman was never in the land of the Pharaohs. How, then, arose this Egyptian tale? Simply enough. In 1873 Professor John Tyndall was shown the sand blast in Boston, and compared its work with that of the sand which had slowly carved the Sphinx of the desert. Here lay the sole foundation for a stubborn, because widely published, table. Another tradition is that General Tilghman observed how the masonry of Saint Paul's Cathedral in London had its corners rounded by exposure to blasts laden with dust and dirt. Another and more probable story is that, while a soldier in the Southern States, he observed rocks whose softer layers had been deeply eroded by wind-blown sand. Indeed, all along the Atlantic Coast, at Nausett, Massachusetts, and many another lighthouse, one may see the panes of lower windows dulled to opacity by a bombardment of sand. Yet another supposition, lacking evidence, is that General Tilghman remarked the cutting action of solids ejected from muskets and cannon as part of their explosives.

The present writer, in striving to hunt down how General Tilghman was first impelled to experiment with his sand blast, came at last to the Franklin Institute, in Seventh Street, Philadelphia, that most venerable storehouse of science in America. There, in the Journal of the Institute for 1871, was a record by Mr. Coleman Sellers, an eminent engineer, of an early exhibit of the sand blast. Mr. Sellers says that General Tilghman saw a jet of sand impelled by steam escaping at high pressure, and its remarkable effect

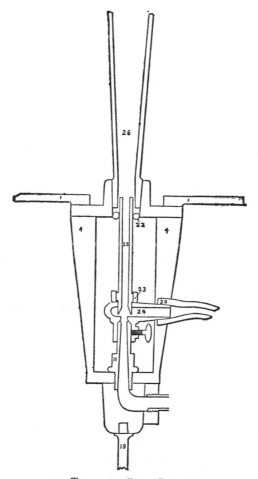

TILGHMAN SAND BLAST

Working parts of upright machine: 1, Main frame. 4, Blast frame. 11, Blast jet. 19, Sand-feed hopper. 20, Sand pipe. 22, Round rubber ring. 23, Round rubber ring. 24, Sand jet. 25, Chilled tube, in which sand and steam mix. 26, Cone.

induced him to repeat as an experiment what he first beheld as an accident. He soon discovered that a blast of sharp sand wrought as deep an incision in one minute as wind-blown sand in a year. In an early test he cut a hole one and one-half inches wide in a slab of corundum one and one-half inches thick, in 25 minutes. His steam was at a pressure of 300 pounds to the square inch, which he soon remarked to be excessive; in ordinary practice he found 10 to

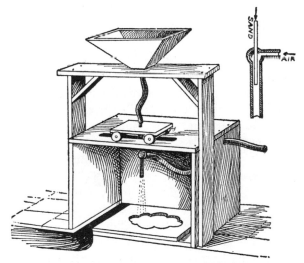

THE TILGHMAN SAND-BLAST MACHINE

20 pounds to be enough. In economy his first apparatus has never been surpassed. A small annular jet of steam escaped into a wide tube, inducing a current of air through a narrow central tube. This air carried sand as it fell from a hopper, which became thoroughly mixed with the steam jet. Appliances of this simple kind were used to inscribe no fewer than 274,000 tombstones of soldiers in the national cemeteries at Arlington, Virginia, and elsewhere. The cost, but $3.35 each, was much less than would have

been paid for chiseled lettering. This apparatus, effective as it was, had faults so serious that it was soon discarded. The sand became damp from admixture with the steam, so that it clogged its feed pipes unless it was carefully dried before use. Glass was apt to be cracked by the heat of the sand; iron and steel were rusted. To avoid these troubles there was recourse to compressed air, faultless in its work, but much more costly than a direct steam blast.

In 1884 Jeremiah E. Mathewson perfected what General Tilghman had begun, retaining the advantage of steam impulsion, while avoiding its drawbacks. In the machine which he devised, sand receives momentum from a steam jet, as in the first Tilghman design. But now, before the mingled sand and steam hit their target, they meet a counterblast of cool air, which condenses and sweeps aside the steam, while it allows the sand to proceed unchecked to do its work in a dry and cool condition. This Mathewson apparatus, entirely self-contained, has no moving parts whatever. It is started by simply attaching a steam pipe, and providing an exhaust flue for the spent steam.*

Thanks to General Tilghman, many amateurs have executed capital work with an inexpensive sand stream, dispensing with a blast altogether. They have filled a hopper with sharp, dry sand, and placed it about ten feet above a table. From the hopper to within two inches of the table runs a vertical pipe, through which the sand falls upon panes of glass or other objects to be treated. Beneath the table a second hopper receives the sand after its work is done; as soon as the first hopper is empty, this second hopper takes its place. As a rule a blast is delivered from a

---

*A Giffard injector, with equal simplicity, employs a steam jet to drive water into a boiler. As the steam condenses, it imparts its momentum to the feed water, so that with no moving part whatever, an injector does all the work of an elaborate pump.

simple tube; in some cases it is preferable to employ a tube with a long, narrow orifice.

How does sand, whether falling by gravity or impelled by a steam jet, exert so rapid an effect? First of all, we must choose sharp, unworn sand, such as abounds in long stretches of the Atlantic seashore. Sand of this sort, in well-planned manufacture, is sifted into sizes each suited to a specific task. A decorator of tumblers selects the

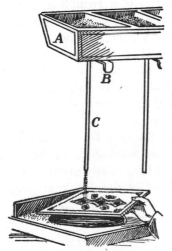

ETCHING WITH SAND FROM A HOPPER

finest grains he can get. A foundryman, who wishes to scour stove-castings, takes the coarsest grains to be had. Whatever its size, sand in a blast neither cuts, grinds, nor abrades the surface it strikes. To compare small things with large, the grains act much as artillery projectiles smash a wall of masonry, each shot striking independently of every other. In this action the sand blast differs from all other processes, and stands alone. A grain of sand has many angles, and the sharpest of these comes to the front, arrow fashion, as the particle flies through the air. The momentum of the particle, small as it is, strikes from a mere point, so that even granite gives way before it, and, indeed, everything else, however hard, excepting only the diamond. At first an observer is astonished as he sees corundum swiftly perforated by sand grains much less hard and tough.

Of course, the sand blast works fastest when directed upon glass, china, porcelain, or other brittle substances. These are depolished in a twinkling, and, strange to say, by a blast which the hand can bear without injury or even discomfort. Rubber, paper, leather, and other elastic materials repel the sand so that its blows are almost without effect. This opens the door to a simple means of decoration. A lamp shade, let us suppose, is to be ornamented with an arabesque or a floral design. This, executed in paper, is laid upon the glass, when the shade is quickly moved in front of the sand blast. All the uncovered parts of the glass are fast depolished, so that in a moment they look as if they had been neatly ground by an emery-wheel; all the parts covered by the design are unaffected, so that, when the paper is washed off, clear glass is uncovered.

Quite different is the effect of this blast upon wrought iron; at first its surface is merely indented; after a few minutes the uppermost particles of iron, being repeatedly bent, break down and crumble. A powerful blast soon cleans a forging or a casting from scale and dirt, while the metal beneath resists the gale, and emerges bright and unworn, unless the bombardment is prolonged of set purpose.

When iron is pickled in an acid solution as a means of cleansing, or glass in like manner is corroded to take a pattern, there is attack not only in front, but from the sides, and this is often harmful. Here the sand blast has a notable advantage, because its blows are delivered directly

in the face and nowhere else. Yet these blows are never so
rude as to break the most delicate ware, although, when
continued long enough, they pierce the toughest granites,
and even corundum itself. When glass is manufactured in
layers of different hues, the sand blast produces cameo effects of great beauty. It may then swiftly turn out labels
for measures, and for the large glass bottles used by chemists and druggists. It removes a scale from forgings and
castings as a preparation for gilding and enameling, tinning
or nickeling. It scours the outside of a bank-safe, and
then smooths the armor plates of warships. It incises marble, limestone, or granite with letters and ornaments. It
takes off dirt and discolorations from buildings of brick
and stone. It removes rust and scale from tubes, tanks,
and boilers, so as greatly to promote their efficiency. It
cleanses the exteriors of boats and ships so as to quicken
their pace through water. Not only iron, but glass, takes
a firmer grasp of paint when subjected for a moment to
a sand stream. The same simple agent refaces wheels of
emery and corundum, and then mildly granulates the cel-
luloid films for cameras. Delivered upon wood, it brings
out its grain with a relief and beauty denied to any other
method. It may yet replace chisels as wielded in stone-
carving and sculpture.

In manufacturing tanks, reservoirs, and boilers to be used
under high pressures, only perfect joints are permissible.
In the production of such joints, the sand blast has immense value. It takes off every particle of scale before
riveting begins, so that two applied surfaces of iron or
steel may be in the closest possible contact. In ordinary
practice rust and dirt may separate these surfaces, so that
leaks follow upon extreme pressures, to be cured only by
excessive and harmful calking. A sand blast, in like
manner, prepares steel rails and girders for welding, so as
to insure perfect union. But it is in foundries that a

sand blast finds its widest utility. A time-honored method of producing a clean surface on an iron or steel casting is by immersion in an acid bath. This may weaken the metal as much as seven per cent. Furthermore, a casting thus treated must be laid aside to dry for a day or two before it can be used. A sand blast does not impair the strength of a casting one whit, and leaves it not only clean, but dry, so that it may be used immediately. An operator wielding a sand blast consuming, every minute, 120 cubic feet of air, compressed to 60 pounds per square inch, will clean as many castings, and remove as many cores, as six men with chisels, hammers, and brushes. And the blast will leave a finish on its work that manual labor cannot approach. When such a casting goes to a milling cutter, or other machine tool, a further saving ensues from the absence of all resisting scale and rust. At Sheffield, where a blast was directed upon armor plate, it proceeded at one square foot per minute, its chilled iron sand being flung at 20 pounds pressure per square inch.

As to this iron sand a word may be said. It is derived from just such shot as General Tilghman manufactured at the outset of his career. It is made up of minute spheroidal pellets of hard, chilled iron, produced by letting molten metal fall through fine holes in a plate of fire clay. Below this colander, in an atmosphere deprived of oxygen, the drops are atomized by jets of superheated steam. The red-hot globules then fall into the water, which chills them into intense hardness. When cool, they are sifted into sizes which vary from 1-40,000 to 1-16 of an inch in diameter. This iron sand cuts stone better than does common sand or emery. When granite is cut with a chisel and mallet, the stone is apt to be bruised or fractured beyond the line of cutting, so that, after a hand dressing, there may be one-sixth to one-fourth of an inch to grind away. This waste and loss are wholly avoided by using a sand blast.

Sand in water does work which dry sand cannot do. When, for example, globes and shades for lamps are to be treated, sand and water, duly mixed, yield effects much more delicate than are otherwise feasible. Usually the sand is mingled with three times its weight of water, the mixture being thoroughly stirred, and cast as a quick jet against the glass, which is rotated in a suitable holder. A seven-inch globe is well ground in thirty seconds. This excellent plan was anticipated as far back as 1846 by George Escol Sellers, at the factory of Miles Greenwood, in Cincinnati, where he built a machine to scour pots and kettles with sand and water. After the surfaces were thus scoured they passed into a zinc chloride solution, and thence into molten metal for their final surfacing. For some unknown reason this ingenious plan was discontinued without having been patented, or in any way made public. In 1871, twenty-five years later, in commenting upon the sand blast, Coleman Sellers, of Philadelphia, drew attention to his brother's old and discarded mixture of sand and water, which, indeed, may have been exemplified by many a housewife as she cleansed her kitchen ware with sand from a neighboring beach.

Whether a sand blast be wet or dry, it is an excellent aid in finishing files and rasps as first manufactured, or in restoring their points after wear. The old method of renewal was to grind out the remains of the teeth, recut and reharden their points, entailing a good deal of cost and trouble, while reducing the thickness of every blank. A worn-down file is quickly resharpened when slowly drawn several times from tang to point between two convergent streams of fine sand, striking the metal at 90 degrees. For this work the best sand is that which has been used to grind plate glass. Two or three minutes' exposure will resharpen a 14-inch rough file. Second-cut or smooth files are treated even more rapidly. It is amazing to pick up an old file, so dull as to be almost worthless, and find that a sand blast restores its keenness in a few seconds. And a new file is improved when held under a sand blast, especially if its teeth curl over slightly. Repeated tests have proved that files thus treated have been increased in their cutting quality as much as one-eighth on both steel and cast iron, and on gun metal almost double. Many manufacturers subject all their files to sand blasts at frequent intervals, so as to keep them up to the highest notch of efficiency, by preventing their teeth from flattening down.

Tools of great importance, and exposed to severe strains, are the cutters of milling machines. In an approved method of production they are hardened and tempered in the usual manner, then dipped in oil, and finally sandblasted. If there has been any overheating in the furnace, though not enough to do apparent harm, says Mr. J. V. Woodworth, cracks will appear on the surfaces of the teeth. These cracks, which are best seen immediately after sandblasting, are frequently so small that they cannot be detected by ordinary means.

To clean castings is one of the principal uses of the sand blast. Here a capital aid was devised by Mr. J. E. Mathewson,—a tumbling barrel in which the castings are placed, with apertures through each axis for a sand blast. Through its perforated sides the abraded powders slowly drop. As the barrel turns but thrice in a minute, no harm befalls its contents.

Much more stubborn than rust or scale on a casting are the layers of paint successively laid upon a ship. Yet even these disappear under a prolonged attack from a heavy sand blast. The steamship *Austrian,* of the Allan Line, had, 'tween decks, coat upon coat of sea paint, until it stood not less than one-eighth of an inch thick. It was removed down to the bright metal, at the rate of 12 square feet per hour, by applying 60 cubic feet of sand-laden air per minute, compressed to 50 pounds per square inch. A reservoir holding 15 cubic feet supplied a nozzle 7-16 of an inch in diameter. In angles and around bolts the removal of paint was absolute,—a feat impossible to hammers, chisels, and scrapers. If paint can be detached by an air blast carrying sand, an air blast laden with paint far outspeeds brush work. A simple Redman spraying machine was thus employed to paint the buildings of the Columbian Exposition at Chicago, in 1893. It covered 300 square feet per hour, and drove its pigment deeply into the walls and ceilings.

While always exploring new territory for the sand blast, General Tilghman felt a keen interest in the new weapons of war, especially in the torpedoes constantly being designed and tested. In association with his brother, he planned a torpedo to be propelled rocket fashion, by a slow-burning powder. For its excursions they sank on their grounds a trough 80 feet long, which they filled with water. They found it impossible to avoid premature explosions of the powder, so that repeatedly their models were suddenly burst into splinters, which crashed into the surrounding walls and rafters. General Tilghman, inured as he had been to shot and shell in actual warfare, bore these explosions with equanimity. His nephew and assistant, Benjamin C. Tilghman, II., had never been under fire, so that at first he displayed much agility as he dodged the flying missiles. It was a good while before he came to his uncle's indifference to unlooked for bombardments. He was heartily glad when these experiments, acknowledged to be a failure, were abandoned for good and all.

Thus closed the active work of General Tilghman. As he approached his eightieth year his step became halting and his pulse feeble. In February, 1901, he was stricken by paralysis; five months later, on July 3d, he passed away at his residence, 1114 Girard Street. He was unmarried. The establishment which he founded, and where his scientific library is preserved, flourishes, as during his lifetime, at 1126 South Eleventh Street, Philadelphia.

Ott. Mergenthaler

OTTMAR MERGENTHALER

On the morning of October 26, 1872, the steamer *Berlin* from Bremen reached its dock at Locust Point, in Baltimore. Its five hundred steerage passengers were mainly immigrants bound for the West, with here and there an artisan who hoped to earn good wages without going far from his landing-place. Among these was a lithe and comely young fellow of eighteen, about five feet seven in height, his large, well-shaped head firmly set on broad shoulders. As he strides up-town he turns his calm blue eyes with wonder on the traffic that impedes him at every step. In a round-topped wooden trunk he brings a good stock of clothes for the approaching winter, and thirty dollars in cash. More important still is the silver watch in his vest pocket. He has adjusted its movement daily during the voyage, so that it is now as accurate as the ship's own chronometer. Indeed, our young German could, at a pinch, make such a watch if he liked, for it is as a watchmaker that he registered himself on the *Berlin*. It is this skill in watchmaking that assures Ottmar Mergenthaler that he will devise the best machine to supplant the compositor. To-day in America four out of five automatic typesetters are linotypes created by this German immigrant, who thus stands beside his compatriot, John Gutenberg, in transfiguring the printer's art. One of these great inventors devised types to be moved by hand; the second superseded these types by matrices moved by a keyboard fourfold as rapidly.

To realize the vast stride due to Ottmar Mergenthaler, let us watch an old-time compositor at his wooden case. Before him are 150 compartments or so, varying in size, each filled with a particular letter of the alphabet, large or small, a numeral, a punctuation mark, or other character. In his left hand is a " stick," a flat metal receiver for his type. Its length is regulated by a central slide fastened by a screw. As he sets " America," let us say, he picks up the letters, A-m-e-r-i-c-a, one after another. Next to this word he places a printer's " space "; this is a thin piece of metal, not so high as type, so that, while it separates words from one another, it receives no ink in the printing-press. As our compositor comes near the end of his line, he takes account of a fact on which turned the chief obstacle to setting type by machinery. His types vary much in breadth: " m " is twice as wide as " n "; " w " is twice as wide as " i." More than this. Every line of type must end with a word, a syllable, a numeral, or a punctuation mark. Words vary much more than letters in the spaces they occupy: " a " is a word, and so is " strength," with eight letters in its one syllable. Suppose that a compositor has room for only two " m " letters at the end of a line, and that " strength " is the next word he has to set. What is he to do? He must space out his words with " quads " until his line is full, leaving " strength " for his next line. This task of completing, or justifying, each line requires judgment and skill; it consumes quite one-sixth of a type-setter's day. Again and again did inventors try in vain to perform justification by mechanical means. They devised types with corrugations, or with hollow spaces, so as to be squeezed together at the end of a line. They adopted wedges, only to create bulges which refused to subside. They employed rubber, only to find it cause insufferable annoyance. How justification was at last accomplished we shall duly see; that feat it was which loosened the grasp that typesetters had for four centuries maintained on their art. And what was a typesetter's pace when quick both of eye and touch? He could set in an hour 1,000 " ems " or

breadths of the letter " m," which serves as the compositor's
unit: this was equal to about 350 words. But an old-time
compositor did more than merely compose. When his columns or pages had been duly printed from in a press, he
had to distribute his types; that is, he had to return each
type to its proper compartment in his wooden case, there to
await the next task of composition. To distribute types
demanded about one-fourth as much time as to compose.
An error here, of course, led to an error in composition, as
when " u " appeared instead of " n."

From this setter of type, obliged to stand all day at his
case, we pass to an operator comfortably seated at a Mergenthaler linotype. Before him is spread a keyboard of
ninety characters, much easier to his touch than those of a
typewriter. Each key controls the descent of a matrix, a
slender bar of metal in which is sunk a character to serve
as a mold. To set " America " he lightly presses the key
marked " A "; it sets free a matrix " A " from its box in
a large magazine of similar matrices. This " A," in full
view, glides to an assembling space which supplants the old-
fashioned stick. Next the keys for m-e-r-i-c-a are lowered,
so that in a moment " America " is composed. At the end
of that word and of every other, the operator touches a
key which inserts a spaceband. How this device serves
much better than a space we shall presently understand. As
our operator approaches the end of a line he must exercise
judgment, much as if he were setting type with his fingers.
It will not do for him to begin to compose " strength," for
example, when only two " em " spaces remain vacant before
him. At the proper point he decides that he has matrices
enough for a line, and that instant he moves a lever which
effects justification; how this marvel is wrought will become clear as we proceed. When the line of type is justified, it is automatically carried to a mold where liquid type-
metal is forced against the matrices and spacebands, much

as when types are cast at a foundry.   But instead of a single character as " a " or " o " being cast, we have here a line

MATRIX

of words ready to be printed.   This " slug," as it is called, in a moment is hard and cool enough to pass to a tray,

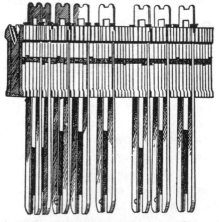

LINE OF MATRICES, WITH JUSTIFIERS BETWEEN THE WORDS

where other slugs are swiftly added, so as to form a page or a column for the printing press.   These slugs present fresh faces to the printed paper, and may be left standing at but nominal cost for interest. A set of matrices often replaces a font of type weighing two hundred times as much.

A LINE O' TYPE (SLUG)

What about distribution, a task which seems to ask for uncommon accuracy of touch and vision, with a faultless

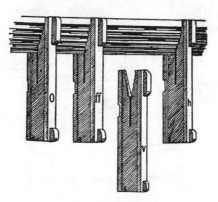

DISTRIBUTOR BAR AND MATRICES

memory? This difficult feat is intrusted to a section of the machine which returns matrices to their boxes as quickly as 270 per minute, and unerringly, unless a matrix is bent by accident, or becomes injured by prolonged use or undue exposure to molten metal. This wonderful linotype, therefore, requires of an operator nothing beyond the touching

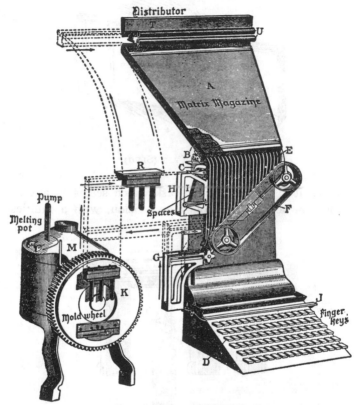

DIAGRAM OF THE MACHINE

of keys through which he produces a page or a column in beautiful new type, with perfect justification, and with all the drudgery of distribution at an end. Can Initiative go further than this? Are not inventors right when they hold that every task of the human hand, however delicate and difficult, may be committed to quicker and stronger fingers of steel and brass?

John Gutenberg, before he invented movable types, was a cutter of gems and a framer of mirrors. In these handicrafts he came to a daintiness of touch and an exactness of eye which prepared him to cut type-molds with strict uniformity. Upon that uniformity turned his revolution of the art of typography. Mergenthaler, who was to recreate

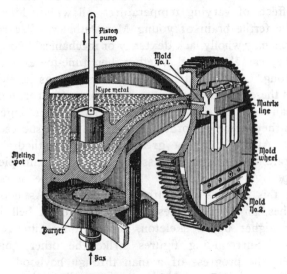

MOLD WHEEL AND MELTING POT

the art of Gutenberg, never learned the compositor's trade. It was as a watchmaker that he came to precision in measurement, to the utmost nicety in tempering a spring, or in blending the ingredients of an alloy. As a lad he was trained to cut teeth and pinions with unfailing accuracy, to drill jewels with a steady and even pressure. He saw that if a watch is to be accurate, its mechanism must be considered as a whole. Every new addition must harmonize with all the other parts to form a unit which is at once refined and intricate. Often the chronometers which came into his hands were highly complex in their design. Some of them, on the release of a detent, rang out the hours and the minutes. Others exhibited the phases of the moon, or every successive constellation of the northern heavens throughout a twelvemonth. In those days of hand-made watches there was an instructive diversity in their escapement and fusees, their devices for neutralizing the effects of varying temperatures, all with golden hints for the fertile brain of young Mergenthaler. Wearers of watches may wholly lack dexterity or mechanical knowledge, but they can always tell whether their time-pieces are right or wrong. And a watchmaker thrives only as he skilfully serves these unrelenting critics. Let us remember, too, that Germany is dotted with tower-clocks of rare ingenuity. Often they chime elaborate tunes as the hours succeed each other. At Strasburg the great clock of the cathedral in its elaborate mechanism surpasses every other time-piece in Europe. A globe displays the courses of the stars, and above this appears the path of the moon. As noon approaches, an angel strikes the quarters on a bell in his hand; higher up, a skeleton, representing Time, strikes twelve. Surrounding figures strike the other quarters, showing the progress of a man through boyhood, youth, manhood, and old age. Under the first gallery, the symbolic deity of the day steps forth,—Apollo on Sunday, Diana on Monday, and so on. In the uppermost niche the twelve apostles move around a figure of the Redeemer, bowing in homage as they pass. On a pinnacle is perched a cock, which flaps its wings, stretches its neck, and crows, awakening echoes from the remotest arches of the cathedral. Schwilgue, who built this clock, Vaucanson, who constructed automata of ingenuity quite as marvelous, contributed not a little to the advancement of invention. They endowed cams with new forms adapted to wholly new tasks. They took, of necessity, noteworthy strides in the art of timing, an art which to-day plays a leading part in engines, looms, and much other machinery, and notably in the linotype.

Germany, the fatherland of John Gutenberg, gave Ottmar Mergenthaler to the world. He was born on May 10, 1854, in Bietigheim, a quaint and picturesque town of four thousand inhabitants, about twenty miles north of Stuttgart. His father, John George Mergenthaler, was a teacher; his mother, Rosina Ackerman, came of a family which for generations had been of the teaching guild. Ottmar, the third of their five children, was instructed at his father's school, where, happily, his lessons included music, to give him cheer and solace as long as he lived. At home he did not eat the bread of idleness. He helped to cook meals, wash dishes, build fires in winter, and till the garden in the summer; one of his tasks the year round was to feed the pigs and cattle, which contributed to the family larder. "It was all work and no play," wrote the inventor many years afterward, "yet the boy submitted willingly to almost any imposition, for he had been accustomed to it from childhood and knew no better." He continues:

"In this way time elapsed until he arrived at fourteen, when he was to leave school to receive his training as a teacher. As the time drew near he gave much thought to the subject of his future and the profession his parents had chosen for him. 'Would I like to be a teacher?' he asked himself. 'No,' was his answer; 'why should I?' In his father's case he had seen nothing but a very small salary with no prospect whatever of further advancement. He had seen his father subjected to many vexations on the part of the State Inspectors of schools. The boy became clear in his mind that he did not want to be a teacher, but what calling should he choose? His father diligently inquired as to the chances of success offered by the various higher trades, as also did the parson of the village, who took a warm interest in what he considered a very promising boy. But the responses were not encouraging. The cabinet-maker thought his business ruined by the competition of the big factories, but said that the carpenter still made a fair living. The carpenter, in his turn, took a gloomy view of his trade, and thought that the locksmith and gunsmith had the best outlook; these, when questioned, believed the machinist to be the man of the future, and so throughout the circle, until the boy and his friends concluded that they must choose among evils, and that the path to be taken was that for which the lad had the best talent. He had for years successfully handled the rather rebellious village clock, he had kept several other clocks in repair, he had cut many models of animals out of wood with his penknife, and a general handiness with tools gave him an idea that machinery was what attracted him most. His special desire was to become a maker of mathematical instruments, but the cost of an apprenticeship to that trade was beyond his father's purse, and, besides, his education was deficient. A college course, he was told, was needed by anybody who aspired to be more than a mere workman. At last the boy compromised between what he wanted and what he could get, by becoming an apprentice to the brother of his step-mother, a maker of watches and clocks in Bietigheim. He was to serve four years without wages, pay a small premium, furnish all his own tools, and receive board and lodging from this uncle, Mr. Hahl.

"In May, 1868, he began work, and soon found himself at home in his new surroundings. A pleasant and kindly spirit pervaded the home of the Hahls, and while the hours of labor were long, they gave opportunity for advancement in learning and for recreation. Hahl usually employed six or eight young men, some as apprentices, others as journey-men. In their cheery company work was a pleasure, and four years passed swiftly and gainfully. Young Mergen-thaler applied himself to mastering the intricacies of his trade, with energy and enthusiasm. With a rare mechan-ical talent he combined skill, which brought him to profi-ciency in every branch of the business almost without in-struction, and with a minimum of opportunity for practice. So well did he succeed that his uncle felt constrained to pay him his wages for a year before his apprenticeship expired. For this liberality Hahl had never had occasion but this once in a business career of more than thirty years.

"Meanwhile the young man tried to advance himself by taking advantage of the neighboring night-schools and Sunday-schools, conducted for the special benefit of young men learning a trade or business. Here he received his first start in mechanical drawing, which later on assisted him so much, particularly in the drafting of his inventions and designs, an advantage over many other inventors which can hardly be overrated. In the summer of 1872, his apprenticeship having expired, the young man commenced to look around for an opportunity to turn his acquirements to better account than was possible in the small town where he had learned his trade. The Franco-German war had closed shortly before this period, and the vast army of Germany had returned home and been disbanded. The workmen thus set free poured into every avenue of business, and in most cases, as a mark of sympathy and as a just reward, they displaced men who had not gone to the front in the service of the Fatherland. To make matters worse, there were no longer any large army contracts to maintain the activity of nearly every field of manufacture. Everything industrial was being readjusted, and heightened taxes, increased military duties, and decreased opportunities for wage-earners, created widespread dissatisfaction, especially in Southern Germany, where the people seriously objected to the yoke of Prussian militarism. Thousands of young men left their homes to avoid military service, and young Mergenthaler was caught in the general discontent, and concluded to emigrate, if possible. Already his two elder brothers had been drafted into the army, and it was high time for him to act if he was to get away at all. In this dilemma he applied for aid to August Hahl, a son of his uncle and employer, who was established as a maker of electrical instruments in the city of Washington, asking for the loan of passage money, to be worked out when he reached the factory. The cash was promptly forwarded, and young Mergenthaler, when he landed in Baltimore in October, 1872, at once proceeded to the Hahl shop in Washington.

"He began work forthwith at fair wages. Electrical instruments were new to him, but soon he was as efficient as any of his fellow-workmen; and within two years he took the leading place in the shop, acting as foreman, and whenever Mr. Hahl was absent, as business manager. Besides the manufacture of electrical clocks and bells, his tasks were chiefly in executing instruments for the United States Signal Service. This Service had been but recently established, and several of its officers were then devising its heliographs, gages for rain and snow, registers for wind velocities, and the like. Nearly all experimental work, and many of the standard instruments, as finally adopted, were carried out at the Hahl shop, usually by Mergenthaler. It was work that he liked, and for which he developed a particular aptitude, both in skill and ease of execution. He readily grasped an inventor's ideas, and improved upon them where he perceived that improvement was possible. Washington was at that time the focus for important inventions, originated not only in the United States, but throughout the world. The law then required that a model should accompany every application for a patent, and as these models were, as a rule, built in Washington, many model-makers in that city were kept busy the year round. Mergenthaler thus came into daily contact with inventors from far and near, and inventions furnished the staple of his thought and conversation. In such surroundings the young man could hardly fail to unfold his own inventive talent, and long before he was of age he left the impress of his ingenuity on many a machine and instrument.

" In the autumn of 1873 occurred the memorable financial panic ushered in by the bankruptcy of Jay Cooke & Company. Business in Washington fell into utter stagnation, involving the Hahl shop with every other in the city. Its employees shrank in number until a mere remnant remained, which, fortunately, included Mergenthaler. Hahl attributed the shrinkage of his business solely to Washington as a place, deeming that Baltimore would afford him a much larger circle of customers. Against Mergenthaler's advice, to Baltimore the Hahl shop was removed, but the expected improvement in business failed to appear. For a little while the shop was busy in providing signal instruments, to be used at the Centennial Exhibition, in Philadelphia. When these were finished, there was almost nothing to do. Hahl was in a sorry plight, in debt as he was to his hands for hundreds of dollars in wages."

At this point of depression in the fortunes of young Mergenthaler let us interrupt his story as we listen to a warm personal friend of his, Henry Thomas, now of Baltimore: " Those formative years in Washington, Mergenthaler was wont to regard as the happiest of his life. He was one of a coterie of young Germans who lived together, sang together, and often took long walks together. Early on Sundays we were wont to stroll to Great Falls or Chain Bridge, halting at the farmhouse of a German friend. At his hospitable board we refreshed ourselves with clabber, potatoes in uniform, black bread, and beer in moderation. Ottmar, reserved and almost silent with strangers, always let himself go in our company. He was a generous comrade, complying and kind, no spoil-sport. His voice, a fine barytone, was often heard in a repertory of German songs and ballads. In those days his health was vigorous and his step elastic. He gave promise of being hale and hearty at fourscore. We were all ambitious, but he brought it farther than any one of us all."

To resume Mergenthaler's own story:

" One day early in August, 1876, we find Hahl at his office, 13 Mercer Street, Baltimore, in conversation with Mr. Charles T. Moore, of White Sulphur Springs, Virginia. Mr. Moore was the inventor of what he called a ' writing machine.' Its failure he attributed to defective workmanship. As his financial sponsors he named James O. Clephane, Louis Clephane, Maurice Pechin, and J. H. Crossman, all of Washington. Hahl the next day went to Washington to secure, if possible, the task of reconstructing this machine. He found the backers of Mr. Moore discouraged and unwilling to advance any more cash unless a satisfactory result was guaranteed. ' No result, no money,' was their verdict. Mergenthaler in the meantime had thoroughly examined the machine, and found that, while its workmanship was faulty, yet this was less a cause of failure than errors of design. He gave the project serious thought, and, after a few days, saw his way clear to remodeling the machine so as to overcome some of its defects and at the same time simplify it greatly. He so informed Hahl, and advised him to undertake the reconstruction at his own risk, as the result, in his opinion, was beyond doubt, provided that he should be free to make such changes as he pleased, and that the compensation should be just. This suggestion went into effect, Hahl guaranteeing that a reconstructed machine should make its letters, including the widest and narrowest, print clear and sharp on a page, each letter duly spaced, so as to produce the effect of printing from regular type. In case of success, $1,600 was to be received by Hahl; in the event of failure, he was to be paid nothing."

On these terms the machine was taken in hand. In its original form it bore upon the successive circles of a cylinder the characters to be printed. By manipulating keys while this cylinder revolved, its characters were printed in lithographic ink on a paper strip. This strip was then cut into lengths of a line each, justified by the due separation of words and syllables, and then transferred to a lithographic stone for printing.*

Crude though this machine was, in Washington, Chicago, and New York it had printed copies of legislative proceedings, court testimony, and other documents. When Hahl handed this apparatus to Mergenthaler to be overhauled and improved, in that simple act he gave the inventor his first impulse toward supplanting the ancient art of typesetting, and ushered in the dawn of a new and

---

*Had Moore used lithographic ink directly on a typewriter, he would have easily won success, always barring the task of justification, with which indeed he might have dispensed, as in all the typewriters of to-day. At present a stencil plate, readily cut in wax on a standard typewriter, enables an operator to print with ink 2,000 or more impressions from an ordinary typewritten sheet.

memorable era. A model, incorporating Mergenthaler's improvements, performed all that was desired. He was

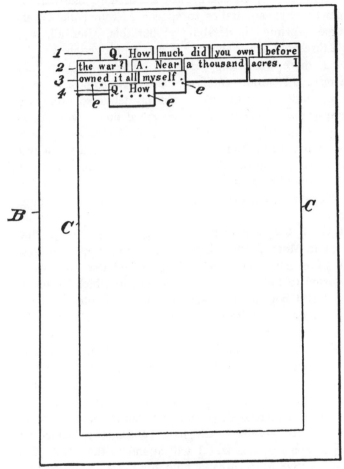

A TRANSFER SHEET
Charles T. Moore. Patented March 19, 1878.

then commissioned to build a machine of full size; this he finished during the summer of 1877. An ordinary stock ticker of to-day has one wheel for letters, another for figures. Mergenthaler paralleled this feature: his keys in their usual descent struck Roman characters; a shift-key, like that of a typewriter, caused italics to appear. From both wheels the type imprinted itself sharply: but this, after all, was only a threshold achievement. When reproduction was attempted, there was disappointment. The stone here and there refused to absorb the finer lines of the imposed script. Too much or too little ink might be delivered from the printing-press, so that blotches presented themselves alongside spaces utterly bare. Not seldom the paper became stained with oil as it ran past the printing cylinder. Worst of all: the inevitable slowness of lithographic printing wholly forbade success. In truth, the scheme was puerile, and no inventor, however resourceful, could make anything of it.

James O. Clephane, who had originally suggested this machine to Moore, saw at last that the difficulties of lithography were insurmountable. He proposed that stereotypy be resorted to instead. The typewriter, in which he felt a keen interest both as an inventor and a promoter, had recently demonstrated its success; he proposed that a typewriter should impress its characters on a strip of papier maché, from which, as a matrix, a stereotype should be produced. Mergenthaler up to this time had never seen a stereotype, and knew nothing of its manufacture. A survey of the process in a printing office nearby made him skeptical as to Clephane's plan, so he said: " Don't hold me responsible for results." Clephane responded: " Give me an impression machine and I will attend to the rest." By the end of 1878 Mergenthaler built for Clephane a machine which clearly impressed on papier maché letters and words duly spaced. But joy at the neatness of this work gave place to dejection when this matrix, forty lines in length, was covered with molten type metal. This metal penetrated every joint, crack, and pore of the papier maché so thoroughly that to separate mold and metal was hardly feasible. Amid many failures, good castings occasionally appeared. These were diligently cleared of burrs. The paper clinging to their surfaces was removed by pens, brushes, and acids. Hours might be spent in making presentable a single page. And there was usually a provoking displacement of material toward the right side of each character. Another besetment arose from having to keep the paper wet during printing. Mergenthaler patiently overcame these obstacles one by one, and brought the process to a point where success seemed near. But success was never close enough to be grasped. Many inventors have essayed this task of designing an impression machine, only to waste their time as Mergenthaler did. He finally became convinced that this phase of stereotypy was impracticable, and told his employers so. Their hopes, nevertheless, were unquenchable. For five years thereafter they kept on stereotyping in a shop of their own in Washington, only to reach at last the conclusion that their endeavor was wholly futile.

As Clephane and his friends discussed their experiments, they felt that, while they had followed a wrong track, their aim was well worthy of renewed pursuit. And who was more competent for that pursuit than the young Baltimore machinist? Accordingly in January, 1883, they engaged him to take up as a whole the problem of devising a machine to supersede typesetting. As Mergenthaler reconsidered the subject, he was certain that he must exclude the annoyances of the papier maché method as at first adopted. To avoid the bulges which arose as one letter after another was impressed upon its surface, he planned to imprint a matrix LINE BY LINE, each line being justified as a unit. This project he had outlined in a drawing toward the close of 1879. Just then his treasury was absolutely empty, and in a fit of rage he had torn his sketch into ribbons. There was now the prospect of funds adequate to the experiments proposed. Clephane had at this time interested in his plans Lemon G. Hine, a leading lawyer of Washington, one of the commissioners who ruled the city, a man of ability and character, and withal a born diplomatist. He brought not only capital to the enterprise, but energy and dash. The associates now opened a printing office in commodious quarters at Seventh Street and Louisiana Avenue, where soon they had seven rotary machines at work. New paging and other auxiliaries were installed, and the staff of operators was considerably augmented. Everything possible to insure success seemed to be present, and yet the only issue was failure.

For a moment let us return to the personal annals of Mergenthaler in Baltimore. In 1881 he married Emma Lachenmayer, to which union four sons and a daughter were born. On New Year's Day, 1883, he dissolved a partnership with Hahl which had existed for two years, and began business for himself in Bank Lane. There he immediately took in hand the revised plans of his friends in Washington. Hine, who assumed all outlays, requested Mergenthaler to proceed at once with his improved design: he began forthwith to construct an experimental model which should print twelve letters at a time. It was built in a hurry and creaked with defects; yet it demonstrated a principle distinctly superior to that of the preceding machine. This new design, expanded to a working scale, was tested in the fall of 1883, with an encouraging measure of success. A persistent difficulty lay in the task of drying the matrix. In ordinary stereotypy the matrix is dried while still on the type. Mergenthaler had to strip off his matrix while wet, and dry it afterward, because production was too rapid to allow a matrix to remain long enough on the type to have its moisture driven off by heat. This impediment brought our inventor to a decisive turning-point. He now plainly saw that papier maché was unsuitable for his work, and must be discarded. He took a leaf out of the practice of typefounders, and proceeded to cast from his matrices in fluid type metal. The experience of four centuries had shown that molten type metal thus cast solidifies almost instantly, without adhering to its mold. In this returning step he dismissed for good and all the trouble with protruding papier maché, and the necessity for driving off moisture from a mixture of water and pulp.

But even with his new resource of casting from metal, the inventor's path was still thorny. As his plans first crystallized in his mind, he required as an outfit no fewer than 4,500 matrices, such as then cost two dollars each. And where was he to find $9,000 for their purchase? For weeks this perplexed his brain. While regarding this difficulty from every point of view, he was called to Washington to consult Clephane and Hine. On board the train there flashed across his mind: Why have separate matrices at all; why not stamp matrices into typebars and cast metal into them in one and the same machine? Here was his first unification of composing and casting, an idea which glowed more and more brightly with promise as he dwelt upon it. He felt sure that type metal would solidify fast enough to permit a quick working of the mechanism he now imagined. He was certain that good and cheap matrices could be punched into type metal, and each line readily justified by springs. On reaching Washington, Mergenthaler sought to persuade his friends to adopt his new and audacious plan. They were at first reluctant. Why had an idea so obvious not been carried out long before? At last they yielded to the inventor's arguments, and bade him embody his novel design in two machines.

These bar-indenting machines carried a series of metal bars, bearing upon their edges printing characters in relief, the bars being provided with springs for justification. The papier maché matrix lines resulting from pressure against the characters were secured upon a backing sheet, over which was laid a gridiron frame containing a series of slots, into which type metal was poured by hand to form slugs bearing the characters from which to print. These machines were promptly succeeded by a machine which cast its slugs automatically from the matrix sheets, one line at a time. As these machines followed one another, their creator rose to new heights of skill and outlook. He was soon designing a band machine which distinctly surpassed its predecessors. In this model the characters required for printing were indented in the edges of a series of narrow brass bands, each band containing a full alphabet, and hanging with its spacers, side by side with other bands in the machine. Each band tapered in thickness from top to bottom. By touching a keyboard the bands dropped successively, bringing the characters required into line at a desired point. A casting mechanism was then brought into contact with this line of characters, and molten metal was forced through a mold of proper dimensions, forming a slug with a perfect printing surface.

The first of these machines, whose creation opened a new chapter in the mechanism of typography, was ready to be tested early in January, 1884, and a day was appointed when a few friends might behold the linotype at work. A dozen spectators were numerous enough to fill the little shop in Bank Lane. They came half an hour too soon, so that the inventor, in their presence, deftly gave his cams and molds their finishing touches. At last all was completed, and Ottmar Mergenthaler stood before his keyboard as calm and collected as at any time for eight years past. He composed a line on the keys, then turned the driving pulley by hand, observing closely every pulse of the mechanism until it had finished a cycle and come to a full stop. All moved easily and with precision. The inventor now asked that

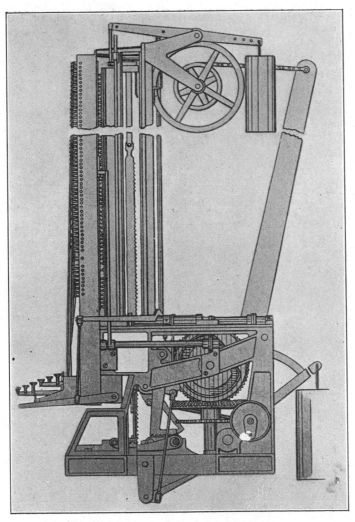

LINOTYPE.   FIRST BAND MACHINE OF 1883

steam power be connected. This was done. He composed a second line, removed the stopper from the metal pump, and touched the line key. Smoothly and silently the matrices slid into their places, were clamped and aligned, and the pump discharged its fused metal. A finished LINOTYPE, shining like silver, dropped from the machine, the while that each matrix, its duty performed, now took its way through the distributing mechanism to its own receptacle. All was accomplished in fifteen seconds. A scene as worthy of monumental commemoration as the first pulling of a proof from movable types by John Gutenberg. A few additional lines followed at the swift touch of Mergenthaler, who then invited Miss Julia Camp, an expert and rapid typewriter, to take his place at the keys. Miss Camp had for years produced better results than any other operator with the lithographic and indenting machines. To-day her work at the keyboard of the linotype was as convincing as that of the inventor himself.

How did the mechanism execute the difficult task of justification? The operator, with the aid of a scale and pointer, could see the length of his line as it grew before him. At the proper moment near the end of a line, he duly enlarged the spaces betwixt words by striking a space-key until his pointer showed the line to be quite full. It was soon decided to substitute graduated wedges for this plan. These wedges Mergenthaler had borne in view for his first band machine of 1883, but their high cost had warned him off. In those days of small things, $400 was as much as he dared expect a printer to pay for a composing machine, and a price so low excluded automatic justification.

At this period in the history of linotypy, the parties financially interested organized themselves as " The National Typographic Company of West Virginia." They established a shop at 201 Camden Street, Baltimore, of which Mergenthaler was given charge. From Bank Lane he brought his tools and machinery, to which the Company added with liberality. A contract was now signed by the Company, Mergenthaler agreeing that all his inventions, past and future, should become the property of the Company. On his producing a practical machine he was to receive as royalty ten per cent. on the cost of all machines manufactured, and a thousand shares of the Company's stock. Now followed two years, during which, day by day, the inventor improved and simplified his linotype, always

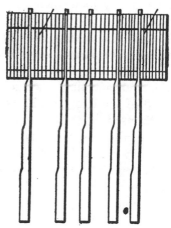

MERGENTHALER'S GRADUATED-WEDGE JUSTIFIER
Patented August 11, 1896.

finding his directors patient and cordial in their support as he abandoned good designs for better. Besides his amazing faculty as an inventor, Mergenthaler had the personality which makes an employer beloved by his hands. His men were proud and fond of him. They rendered him ungrudging service; their good will did much to cushion the jolts of experimental work with its inevitable hitches, its constant balking of the best laid plans. One of his staff at

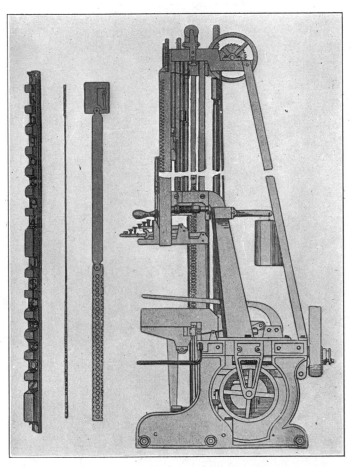

LINOTYPE. FIRST DIRECT CASTING BAND MACHINE OF 1884

that time was William R. Brack, now of New York, who declares: "Ottmar Mergenthaler was the 'whitest' man one could work for. He was good to his employees, and no matter how humble their station, he had always a kind word for them, and a friendly word to say of them. His goodness of heart included dumb animals, horses especially, and he would not permit them to be ill-treated. One evening I was returning home from the linotype factory, and I rode in the horsecar with him. At an unpaved crossing the driver lost his temper and began to whip his horses unmercifully. Mergenthaler sprang to their rescue, and gave the driver such a reprimand as he never heard before. It had the desired effect, too. That man never abused his horses again."

Says Charles R. Wagner, of New York, another machinist, who helped to build the first linotypes: "There never was an employer better liked than Mergenthaler. When rush orders obliged all hands to work overtime, he would walk through the shop and ask us if we had dined. If we answered no, he would order dinner from a neighboring restaurant to be brought in at once. When Mr. Hine resigned as president of the Company, Mergenthaler gave all hands a capital supper at the shop. That night he made a telling speech. When he parted from the Linotype Company, he bought the old Walker Horseshoe Works at Locust Point, Baltimore, where he intended to form a community of his work people. At this factory he built 300 linotypes under contract with the Linotype Company. After these machines were finished, he confined his work, so far as linotypes were concerned, simply to repairs. But he was an inventor through and through, so he had to devise a threshing machine, and improve a basket-making machine, and contrive much else equally ingenious and original. The recreation he enjoyed most was singing. For years he was an active member of the Liederkranz of Baltimore, and became its president. Apart from music, he was a man to stay at home. When he traveled in America or Europe, he took his family with him. At home or abroad, his friends were friends for life."

Thanks, in no small degree, to the capacity and good will of his staff, Mergenthaler, in February, 1885, completed a much improved linotype, with an automatic justifier. This, in the same month, he exhibited at the Chamberlain Hotel in Washington, attracting the attention of printers from all parts of the world, as well as of President Arthur and other national leaders. A banquet was given in honor of the inventor to mark his great achievement. He delivered a capital speech, in which he reviewed the principal steps of his invention, with a forecast of its coming success, since more than fulfilled.

While this latest linotype was much more effective and smooth in working than its immediate forerunners, its inventor soon divined how he could make a much better machine. His matrix bands were not precise in their dimensions, and if an operator fell into a single error, all that preceded that error on a line had to be thrown away. Another fault was more serious: as the movements of the machine were hidden, the operator could not see what he was doing. Mergenthaler felt that he must redesign his machine throughout, so as to confer visibility on its motions. He intended, also, that his lines of type should afford an opportunity to correct an error as work proceeded, just as in manual typesetting.

At this critical stage of his progress our inventor seems to have taken a glance at what other inventors were doing, as they sought to supplant manual composition. One of their noteworthy attempts was to release individual types from their several boxes by a keyboard, these types sliding together to form a long line, duly divided into short lines and justified by a second operator. This may have

prompted the next idea which arose in Mergenthaler's mind,
—the adoption of single matrices, instead of bands, each
impressed with all the characters of a font. This new
project he sketched in a few masterly strokes, and showed
to Clephane, Hine, and his other financial backers. It was a
recurrent shock to these men that Good was constantly
ousted by Better, only to have Better make way for Better
Still, with Best ever below the horizon.

> " As if machinery were invented
> For only this—to be amended."

Mergenthaler's present design was wholly new from base
to crest, and new machines had become odious to the men
who had to pay for them. When were experiments to end,
so that dividends might begin? Hine, the faithful friend
of Mergenthaler, said : " Not many stockholders can stand
being told that they have the best machine in the world,
but that they should make another still better." These men
were not conducting a bureau of mechanical research, but a
machine shop meant to earn and pay a profit as soon as possible. In truth, Mergenthaler, in the successive phases of
his linotype, realized advances which usually require successive generations of inventors, or a cohort of designers
banded for attack by a powerful syndicate or trust. On
this occasion Mergenthaler's fellow share-holders were patient once again, acknowledging that if his latest model
were practicable, it would be well worth its cost in dollars
and delay.

Mergenthaler, thus indorsed, now devoted his days and
nights to developing his single-matrix machine. Its details
were immeasurably more troublesome than those of any
earlier linotype, rising, as they did, to a new and higher
plane of invention. A cathedral clock, such as that we
have noticed at Strasburg, has thousands of parts which

present a simple drama as its hours are ticked off, demanding in its constructor rare ingenuity. But, after all, its labyrinth of wheels and pinions, levers and cams, are bound together rigidly, and must move onward with inevitable precision when once the weights are wound up, and every working surface is clean and bright. But Mergenthaler had for the essential parts of his linotype a procession of matrices at times rigidly held in their mechanism, at other times wholly free as they moved from their magazines, and were freely restored to those magazines for their next excursion. There must be no sticking at any point, from undue friction or other cause. More than a score of movements must follow each other with swiftness and precision, at temperatures, too, varying as much as 480° Fahrenheit.

Indeed, the linotype is supreme among the modern machines which integrate a comprehensive round of operations and turn out a complete article. Typesetting, typefounding, and stereotyping had been executed by hand, and, in part, by machinery, before Mergenthaler began to build his linotype. He united all three processes in one machine, so that an operator, with little more labor than in working a typewriter, now produced lines of type ready for printing. Had Mergenthaler in his machine dealt with types, these small and weak pieces of metal would have been liable to break in passing through an intricate distributor. His matrices could easily be made much stronger than types, and, because much larger, they easily received the numerous slots and nicks required for distribution. There was genius, too, in choosing a line instead of a type as his unit, greatly reducing the cost and labor of handling composed matter, while lessening the hazard of pi-ing, so much dreaded by printers. These are the points of excellence which keep the creation of Mergenthaler far in advance of its rivals.

At this period the success of the linotype was assured, so as to draw around it a circle of leading newspaper publishers. Foremost of these came Stilson Hutchins, proprietor of the *Washington Post,* who one day brought with him his friend Whitelaw Reid, of the *New York Tribune,* an introduction big with fate for the linotype, as we shall duly see. Another member of the group was Melville E. Stone, of the *Chicago News,* who was chosen president of the Company in the place of Mr. Hine, who resigned. Mr. Stone wished the factory to be removed to Chicago, that it might receive his personal supervision. Mergenthaler declined to leave Baltimore, so in Baltimore the factory remained. There work proceeded with energy never for a moment relaxed, Mergenthaler engaging Sumter Black, a capital draftsman, as his assistant. In the summer of 1885 the independent matrix machine was brought to a triumphant test. In every particular it displayed an advance on previous designs. The matrices were stored in vertical copper tubes, each matrix descending at the touch of a finger key, to be caught by its ears as it dropped on a tiny railroad. Thence it was blown by an air blast to the assembling-point. As each matrix was in full view during its journey, an operator could correct errors in a moment. He could as easily insert italics or other unusual characters. Wedge spacers came in between words to justify each line, and then the line of matrices was borne to the front of a mold where casting was effected.

Hard work, long protracted, had been needed to score this great mechanical triumph. A task every whit as hard was to induce printers to employ the linotype so skilfully created. Manual composition was to them quite satisfactory, for it yielded them a fair profit. It was all very well to watch a model machine as it responded to the touch of its inventor, or one of his trained assistants, but what would befall its intricate levers and cams under the fingers

of an everyday operator? Then came the query: " How do
we know that Mergenthaler has come to the end of his
improvements? Where will we be if next year he super-
sedes his costly machine of to-day?" Listening to these
objections, and to the answers which they elicited, a syndicate of newspaper publishers resolved to give the linotype a fair trial in their offices. These leaders deserve
mention: Whitelaw Reid, of the *New York Tribune;* Melville E. Stone, of the *Chicago News,* to whom succeeded
Victor E. Lawson; Henry Smith, of the *Chicago Inter-
Ocean,* and Walter N. Haldeman, of the *Louisville Courier-
Journal.*

To their composing rooms the linotype went forthwith.
Mr. Reid, who gave the linotype its name, was the first to
set its mechanism in motion. In July, 1886, it began work
on the daily edition of the *Tribune,* and also composed " The
Tribune Book of Open Air Sports," issued that year as a
premium. Other machines followed in quick succession,
until, at the close of 1886, a dozen of them were busy in the
Tribune office. They gave fair satisfaction, but they disclosed weaknesses and defects under the severe strain of
newspaper production. Trouble, too, arose from the employment of operators wholly unused to machinery. In the
meantime, despite Mergenthaler's protest, he was ordered
to build one hundred additional machines. He plainly saw
how he could banish difficulties which stood in the way of
easy and accurate working. But his board of directors
decided that the *Tribune* model was good enough, and en-
joined him from modifying its design, for the present at
least. Indeed, the Board went the length of ordering him
to manufacture a second lot of one hundred machines, making a total of two hundred, although the inventor prophesied danger and loss from this precipitancy. To Mergenthaler each of his successive models was but a milestone to
be passed in an onward march. To the Linotype Company

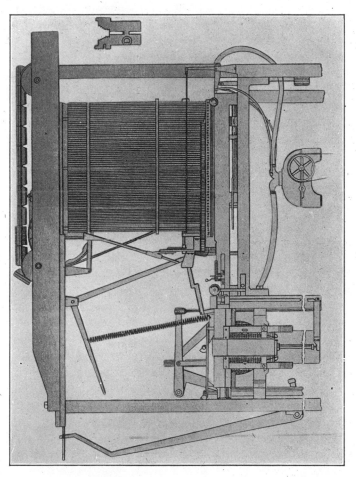

LINOTYPE. FIRST MACHINE WITH INDEPENDENT OR FREE MATRICES
OF 1885

this *Tribune* machine marked a winning-post, which it was idle to overpass.

With undisguised reluctance Mergenthaler proceeded to execute the behest of his directors. The plant in Camden Street was enlarged, and its staff was increased from forty to one hundred and sixty. In Preston Street a building was hired where one hundred hands were kept busy producing matrices and assembling linotypes. Contracts were let for the framework of the machines, and for some of their larger parts, so as to confine the Company's own manufacture to matrices, to the more delicate mechanism, and to assembling. Mergenthaler had now to cover a vast and diversified field. First of all, he had to design many special tools: he had to educate raw recruits into proficiency: and all the while he was under constant pressure from his stockholders for quick and ample dividends.

A prime need was to produce matrices at low cost. An attempt to have them furnished by contractors ended in total failure. To supply an adequate plant for matrices demanded no fewer than thirty special machines, all to be provided with skilled attendants. With these at command, Mergenthaler was able to turn out matrices at a cost within the estimates of his principals. His initial task was to prepare and maintain the stamps which indented these matrices. The Benton & Waldo engraving machine, when it appeared, was just what he needed, but it came so late that it found Mergenthaler far advanced in devising a similar machine. In the meantime vexations sprang up on every side. Contractors were tardy with deliveries; and their supplies were often of inferior quality. From the *Tribune* office were returned faulty matrices which testified to careless manufacture. Mergenthaler did all that mortal could in training his staff. He printed instructions in detail, such as are issued to-day by " efficiency experts." He remained with his men from dawn to dusk—and later. When he saw a mistake, he corrected it with his own hands; but, nevertheless, work proceeded with provoking slowness, especially in the assembling-room. Thus always must a pioneer suffer from the absence of formed habits and aptitudes in his working force, from their utter lack of the inherited and contagious skill which abounds in every long established trade and industry.

From the *Tribune* office Mergenthaler received golden hints from two trusty lieutenants, Ferdinand J. Wich and Ernest Girod. At first the cams which ejected the slugs were of cast iron, so as to wear rapidly. They suggested hardened steel instead. Cams which bore grooves were liable to choking by splashes of molten metal. These grooves should be omitted in future designs. The ejector lever was feebly bolted to its frame, so that it soon worked loose. Strength here was called for. Minor improvements in the lifting and distributing mechanism were also proposed by these faithful allies of the inventor. His new machines always embodied the improvements thus suggested to him.

It was the task of assembling his machines that most exasperated the forbearing spirit of Mergenthaler. As a spur he offered a bonus of ten dollars for every machine assembled within a reasonable, appointed cost. One of his men was soon assembling two machines a week, adding twenty dollars to his wages every Saturday night. Including his handsome bonus, this dexterous worker's machines cost less to assemble than any others produced in the shop, repeating the familiar experience that the highest priced labor is cheapest in the end, because the most efficient. Mergenthaler now extended his bonuses from the assembling-room to the manufacturing department, where they stimulated output in the like cheering fashion. By February, 1888, fifty machines had been delivered to newspaper offices within the subscribing circle. During this period of hard work, largely experimental, Mergenthaler

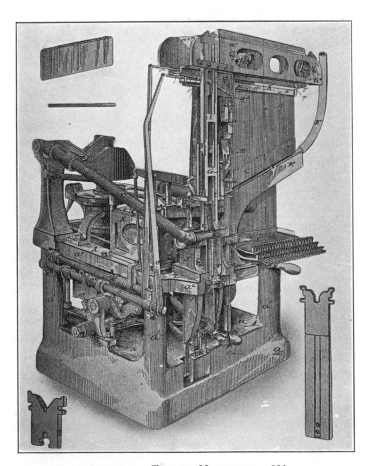

LINOTYPE. TRIBUNE MACHINE OF 1886

and his directors gradually drifted apart. Their quarrel culminated on March 15, 1888, when, in a mood of just anger, the inventor resigned from the Company's service. Mergenthaler was a sensitive man, of highly strung nerves, and unrelenting criticism from a standpoint purely financial chafed him beyond endurance. The Company now removed its factory from Baltimore to Brooklyn, where its vast structure on Ryerson Street forms one of the landmarks of Greater New York. In 1889, the next year, immense profits began to be reaped from linotypes. In that twelvemonth the *New York Tribune* saved $80,000 by the use of its machines. Other offices netted a proportionate gain. And yet the inventor's royalty was now only fifty dollars per machine, to which figure, in a moment of weakness, he had been induced to lower his compensation. In thus modifying his original agreement, which gave him $120, Mergenthaler committed what he regarded as the chief mistake of his life.

Mergenthaler's pride and passion was the machine which he had created, and, notwithstanding his rupture with the Linotype Company, he continued to add to the value of their property by further improvement of his designs. As his assistant he engaged Alfred Peterson, a talented draftsman. Surveying the results of actual work for months together, Mergenthaler proceeded to dismiss one difficulty and defect after another. First of all, he attacked the keyboard touch, which was hard and variable, so that only a deft operator could keep the matrices from occasionally flying out of their channels. The distributor lacked strength: this part and other parts were not easy of access to a repairer. Matrices were no longer borne by an air blast, but fell by gravity to the assembling-space from magazines diagonally placed. The distributing elevator was replaced by the familiar arm which, after the casting process, now lifted the lines of matrices to the top of the machine, where they automatically dropped into their individual boxes. The column base was introduced, the justifying and locking devices were improved, the channel plate was provided with hinged ends, double channels were furnished for " e " and " n," the two-line letter was devised so as greatly to facilitate the composition of advertisements in newspapers. This machine, says Mr. Frederick J. Warburton, treasurer of the Mergenthaler Linotype Company, marks the milestone between linotypes ancient and modern.

Severe toil and unending anxiety told at last on the rugged frame of Mergenthaler. In September, 1888, he was attacked by pleurisy, and for weeks his life trembled in the balance. He recovered, thanks to the nursing of his devoted wife, but with health so impaired that he afterward fell a victim to consumption. As he regained strength he resumed work on his linotype, and by the close of 1888 he brought its mechanism to the form which it substantially retained until his death, eleven years later. His designs, sketched with his wonted clearness, were laid before his friends, with the information that the inventor had not the means to give them effect. Again James Ogilvie Clephane stepped into the breach; he collected ten checks, each for $200, and remitting the $2,000 to Mergenthaler, enabled him to build what proved to be his last and best machine. In the course of 1889 this model was brought to a test which stamped it as an unqualified success. It was not only swifter than its forerunners, but it did better work. As a structure it had gained both strength and steadiness. But its weight was still excessive, a fault chargeable to its draftsman, whose frames were apt to be unduly massive. It was determined to lighten the patterns judiciously, and then build a second machine to serve as a model in manufacturing. This machine was finished in February, 1890, and forthwith exhibited in the *Judge* Building, New York, by James Clephane and Abner Greenleaf, the friends tried and true of its inventor. This exhibition had a telling result: within a few months several hundred orders were received. All doubt and hesitation on the part of printers was now at an end. Firms of limited capital, or who wished to avoid risks of supersedure, could lease machines instead of buying them. The Company established a school for linotypers, in which expertness rapidly passed from seniors to juniors. The machine of 1888 was an acknowledged money-maker. Its successor of 1890 was quicker, easier to handle, and much less liable to get out of order.

While the linotype had been quietly passing from practicability to excellence, it had won over the publishers at first by scores, and then by hundreds. But what of the working printers, especially those enlisted in the Typographical Unions? It was a memorable day for the manufacturing company when its machines were adopted by the *Standard-Union* office in Brooklyn, a few blocks away. This large office was under the jurisdiction of Typographical Union No. 6, the largest and most powerful in America. This acceptance of the linotype by organized labor came about mainly through the diplomacy of Mr. Hine, a man of tact, sympathy, and candor. In December, 1891, Mr. Hine resigned from the presidency of the Company, and was succeeded by Mr. Philip T. Dodge, who, as patent attorney and legal adviser, had rendered inestimable services to the concern.

While financiers were at last reaping golden harvests from the linotype, there was tragedy not far away. Mergenthaler's invention came to its victory at a time of profound depression in business. This, on one hand, stimulated sales of the machine, the while that many a compositor past his prime was thrown out of work. Operators at the new keyboard were for the most part dexterous young fellows, who soon outpaced hand typesetters four to five times. Then, more than now, a good deal of work had to be done at

cases, in setting books, in composing display advertisements, and the like.   This kept a few veterans on payrolls;
but at first hundreds, and then thousands, were cut adrift.
To-day there are more compositors proportionately than
ever before.   Newspapers are leafier, books more numerous.
This expansion, to be credited as much to cheap paper as to
cheap composition, came only in the course of years; and in
the meantime there was acute and widespread suffering.
Over and over again appeared characteristic aid from within
the ranks of printers themselves.   In one large New York
office the operators for years worked but five days in the
week, so that they might be employed in sevens instead of
fives.   During that time of bitter stress many a poor old
printer, unfit to face the new rivalry of keys and cams, took
his life.   One morning a Union almoner entered a printer's
wretched quarters near Brooklyn Bridge, where a baby had
two hours before been born.   Every stick of furniture but
a bed and a chair had been sold for bread or burned for
fuel.   This almoner was a story-writer for weekly journals.
A friend to whom he recited this visit asked him why he
did not describe it in his next tale?   Said he: " I would as
lief make ' copy ' out of my mother's deathbed! "

When other revolutionary inventions threaten similar
woe, may not Property be just and merciful enough to
bestow a part of its enormous gains on the men, and women,
from whom otherwise the new machinery would tear the
little that they have?   During 1910 the Mergenthaler
Linotype Company earned $2,733,000, having built to the
close of that year in America no fewer than 16,000 machines.   In foreign lands the production to the same date
was about 10,000 machines.

While shadows closed around many an old-time compositor, they fell also upon Mergenthaler, the innocent cause
of pain and loss as well as the creator of vast new wealth
through his marvelous mechanism.   Toward the end of

1894 the inventor's health underwent a marked change for the worse. He was informed by his physician that tuberculosis had begun its ravages. Mergenthaler at once removed to the Blue Mountains of Maryland, and afterward took up his residence at Saranac Lake, New York, in the Baker cottage, occupied seven years prior by Robert Louis Stevenson. Although he sometimes enjoyed days which promised a restoration of strength, these days became fewer and fewer. Dreading the rigors of the North, he concluded to take up his abode in Arizona. Thither he went from Baltimore in June, 1896. Near Prescott he built a pavilion where he lived for six months with a guide as his companion. Thence he sought a more favorable climate in Deming, New Mexico, where, in November of the next year, his house, with its contents, was destroyed by fire. He had occupied himself for months in writing his autobiography, based upon many records, legal and personal, and hundreds of letters. All went up in flame. In April, 1898, he returned from Deming to Baltimore, where he wrote an autobiography much briefer in compass than the volume burned in New Mexico. In Baltimore his strength steadily failed, and he expired on Saturday, October 28, 1899, at his house, 159 West Lanvale Street. Three days later his burial took place in Loudon Park Cemetery. Long before the closing scene his heart was cheered by recognition of his great talents: he was awarded a medal by Cooper Institute, New York; the John Scott medal by the City of Philadelphia; and the Elliott Cresson gold medal by the Franklin Institute, Philadelphia.

Let us return to 1899, and watch a linotype as its inventor left it, that we may have a just impression of his extraordinary gifts as an inventor. At the top of the machine is a magazine, divided into 90 parts, containing about 1,500 matrices, which respond to an operator's touch on a keyboard. Each matrix is a small, flat plate of brass, having on one edge an incised letter, and in the upper end a series of teeth for distributing purposes. There are several matrices for each character, and for spaces and " quads " of definite thicknesses. Used in connection with these matrices are spacers shaped as double-wedges, inserted between words.

As the keyboard is manipulated, the matrices descend to an inclined traveling belt, which carries them into the assembler. This task continues until the assembler contains characters enough for one line of print. It then moves to a mold extended through the mold wheel, the mold being of the size required for a slug. The assembled matrix line now closes the front of this mold, and the faces of the matrices are brought into line with it. At this point the wedge-shaped spacers are pushed through the line, effecting justification. Behind the mold is a pot, heated by gas, containing molten type metal. This pot has a mouthpiece arranged to close the rear of the mold, and is provided with a pump. While the matrix line is in position, this pump forces its metal into the mold, so as to fill the incised characters of the matrices. The type metal solidifies instantly. The mold wheel then makes part of a revolution, bringing the mold in front of an ejector blade, which pushes the slug out of the mold into a receiving galley, ready for printing. To insure absolute accuracy in the thickness and height of slugs, knives act upon them during their travel to the galley. The line of matrices is then lifted from the mold to the distributor bar at the top of the machine, the wedge-shaped spacers being left behind and taken to their own receptacle.

Automatic distribution, perfected in this machine, deserves a moment's pause. It began with a French inventor, Robert Etienne Gaubert, in 1840. His mechanism was much improved by Soreson and other ingenious mechanics. To an observer unfamiliar with contrivances of this kind, the effect is puzzling. How do the " a's " find their way

THE LINOTYPE MACHINE, 1899

into box " a," the " b's " into box " b," and so on? Let us take the simplest case possible, and suppose that the " a's " have an ear at each upper end, by which they ride on a rail along which they are impelled by a rapid screw. Let that rail end just above the " a " box, and all the " a's " will drop into that box. But in a linotype there are 90 characters, and it is impossible to give each a pair of rails to itself. What then? Suppose you give the " b's " two pairs of ears, one pair above the other, with four rails for them to ride upon. The " b's " will fall only at a place where both pairs of rails come to an end, and at that point they will find the " b " box. Each matrix in the whole array of 90 is thus provided with ears peculiar to itself,

TWO WEDGES IN CONTACT, THEIR OUTER SIDES PARALLEL

and with a box into which it drops when those ears find their rails interrupted.

Justification, every whit as difficult as distribution, was accomplished by Mergenthaler in his step-by-step wedges. These were forced between each pair of words until a line, effectually tightened, was cast. The spacers patented by Jacob William Schuckers, in 1885, are a preferable because a continuous device. He placed two long thin wedges together so that their boundaries were parallel. When such pairs of wedges are driven into a line as far as they will go, perfect justification is the result. In its original form, dating from the dawn of human wit, a wedge has had boundaries inclined to each other. There was long ago a heightening of the value of wedges by using them in pairs, the sharp edge of one wedge being laid against the thick back of another, so that their outer boundaries were parallel. Wedges thus united, and slidden upon one another, serve to lift great weights. In small sizes they are the taper-parallels and taper-wedges of machinists. In a few small printing offices there still linger wedges in pairs used to secure type in its iron frame, called a chase. One

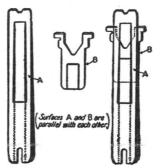

J. W. SCHUCKERS' DOUBLE-WEDGE JUSTIFIER

series of wedges is cast on the inner side of this chase; between these cast wedges and the type wooden wedges, or quoins, are driven by a shooting stick and a mallet. Here, indeed, Schuckers may have received a suggestion for double-wedges so refined as to conquer a field incomparably more important than any other to which wedges had ever before been applied.*

* Jacob William Schuckers was born in Philadelphia on March 18, 1831, of a German father and a Irish mother. In 1832 his parents removed to Wooster, Ohio, which became their permanent home. Jacob attended public schools until 1846, when he entered the composing room of the Wooster *Republican*, and learned the printer's trade. He remained there until 1859, when he went to Cleveland, Ohio, and worked as a printer on the *Leader* of that city. During the summer of 1860 he became a clerk in the United States Treasury at Washington. Next year, when the Hon. Salmon P. Chase, of Ohio, was appointed Secretary of the Treasury, he engaged Schuckers as his private secretary, always regarding him with im-

We note that in a linotype three distinct operations go forward together,—composing one line, casting a second, and distributing a third, so that the machine has a pace exceeding that at which an expert operator can finger his keys. This high speed of circulation renders it unnecessary to have more than a few matrices of any uncommon sort, such as accented or mathematical characters. A linotype usually turns out 5,000 ems of solid, justified, and perfectly spaced matter per hour, in the hands of a single operator; this is four to five times faster than manual composition. As each line is composed in plain sight, corrections may be effected before a line is cast, as easily as in typesetting by hand. As errors in distribution are impossible, machine proofs are much less faulty than matter set by hand. By a change of matrices and molds, easily and quickly effected, a machine produces any face, from agate to small pica, and any length of line not exceeding five inches. Each magazine contains channels for a font of matrices: these may be of any face desired, and each machine may have two, three, or four magazines.

A machine requires about one-third of a horse-power

plicit confidence and high esteem. When Mr. Chase became Chief Justice of the United States Supreme Court, Schuckers proceeded to Albany, New York, where he studied law, but he developed a dislike of law, and never completed his studies. He now wrote a Life of Mr. Chase, and for years contributed to the *Sun* and other New York papers, as well as to the press of Philadelphia. In that city he speculated in real estate with profit, but the panic of 1873 swept away his little fortune. He then began to devise a typesetting machine, producing a succession of ingenious designs. In his latest model he used a typewriter keyboard, and introduced his double-wedge spacer. During the closing years of his life he resided in Newark.

In 1901 he was secretary for the New Jersey Commission at the Pan-American Exhibition in Buffalo. In October he was taken seriously ill. On November 19 he died: four days afterward his remains were laid at rest in Rock Creek Cemetery, Washington.

to drive it; this can be most satisfactorily supplied by an electric motor. It is important that the metal for the melting pot be of good quality, and maintained in excellence. Its temperature should not exceed 550° Fahrenheit. This metal, in the latest machines, is heated by electricity.

Since Mergenthaler's day his linotype has been adapted to composing books of the most exacting kind, mathematical treatises and the like. The book in the reader's hands was composed on a Number One model. Both for the composition of books and newspapers new facilities are constantly being created by the Mergenthaler Linotype Company, whose staff of inventors is directed by Mr. John R. Rogers. In the latest model four magazines of matrices are at an operator's command. As each of these magazines gives him a choice of either of two letters for every one of his 90 keys, he has no fewer than 720 different characters at his fingers' ends. Mr. Rogers has devised a simple mode of casting slugs with deep recesses, into which brass rules may be readily inserted for tabular work such as reports of banks, boards of trade, and the like. A device equally ingenious casts letters twice as long as ordinary type: these serve to print an initial word in an advertising or other announcement. To-day letters are cast in many languages, and in sizes large enough for newspaper headings. Manual composition in newspaper and job offices has, therefore, a narrower field than ever, with a prospect of total supersedure at no distant day. In its earlier models, the linotype offered but one font for a single task. To-day a No. 9 machine permits the union, in one line, of eight or more diverse alphabets. Metal for slugs may now be hard enough to print 100,000 impressions before showing perceptible wear. It may be recalled that Mergenthaler, at the outset of his project for single matrices, estimated their cost at two dollars each. To-day a matrix bearing a single letter costs but three cents.

INDEX

INDEX

A

Accidental discoveries, 192

Air engines, their shortcomings, 227

Allston, Washington, teacher of S. F. B. Morse, 123; on Morse's theory of colors, 136; letter from Morse on photography, 155; portrait and *Jeremiah* presented by Morse to Yale, 173

Alphabet, dot-and-dash, Morse, 149; its precursors, 150; its universal applicability, 152

Appleby, John F., knotter, 305

Ardrey, Robert L., "American Agricultural Implements" on Ogle reaper, 282; on early McCormick reaper, 299; on Appleby self-binder, 307

Armor and guns, their duel, 31, 53; a forecast in Fulton's "Torpedo War," 53

Artists in their imagination akin to inventors, 128

B

Bacon, Francis, telegraphic code, 149

Banks, Nathaniel P., cousin and shopmate of Elias Howe, 344

Barlow, Joel, host of Robert Fulton, 47; death, 47; letter from Fulton to, 64

Beach, Alfred E., writing machine, 323, 326

Bell, Patrick, describes his reaper, 284; Slight's account, 290; picture of reaper, 291; testimonial to Bell, 293

Bernard, Charles, on John Ericsson as draftsman, 243

Bird, tailor, of India, 346

Blakey, William, devises tubular boiler, 12

Blanchard, Thomas, birth and early life, 107; copied busts on lathe in National Capitol, 104; details of design, 106; builds a forge, 107; makes an apple-parer, 108; makes tacks and a tack machine, 109; its details, 110, 111; designs a lathe guided by a cam, 112; invents copying lathe, 113; its uses and modifications, 115; advocates a railroad for Massachusetts, 115; builds the *Vermont, Massachusetts,* and other steamers, 116; designs a machine for bending timber, 116, 117; becomes an expert in patent cases, 118

Bloodgood, Abraham, revolving turret, 255

Blower, centrifugal, Ericsson, 221

Blunt, Colonel S. E., modern rifle Springfield Armory compared with Whitney musket, 100

Boiler, water-tube, Stevens, advantages, 13; used by Fulton, 58

Boyce, Joseph, cutters for reapers, 281

Brack, William R., on Ottmar Mergenthaler, 415

Braithwaite, John, partner of John Ericsson, 221

Bramah, Joseph, revolving cutters, 106

British inventors beginning 19th century, 280

Brown, Thomas and Joseph, build Ogle reaper, 282

Bushnell, David, torpedoes, 47

436 INDEX

h